Math into LaTeX

Third Edition

George Grätzer

Math into $\LaTeX$

Third Edition

BIRKHÄUSER • SPRINGER
BOSTON NEW YORK

George Grätzer
Department of Mathematics
University of Manitoba
Winnipeg, MB R3T 2N2
Canada

Library of Congress Cataloging-in-Publication Data
Grätzer, George A.
Math into LaTeX / George Grätzer.–3rd ed.
p. cm.
Includes bibliographical references and index.
ISBN 0-8176-4131-9 (alk. paper) — ISBN 3-7643-4131-9 (alk. paper)
1. LaTeX (Computer file) 2. AMS-LaTeX. 3. Mathematics printing—Computer programs. 4. Computerized typesetting. I. Title

Z253.4.L38 G745 2000
686.2'2544536—dc21 00-036088
CIP

ISBN 0-8176-4131-9 Printed on acid-free paper.

Birkhäuser ®

Printed in the United States of America. (HP)

9 8 7 6 5 4 3 SPIN 11318521

Birkhäuser is part of *Springer Science+Business Media*

www.birkhauser.com

Short contents

Contents

List of tables

List of figures

Quick Finder

Preface to the third edition

Why a new edition?

The Internet

Just a few years ago, the Internet consisted of little more than e-mail, USENET, and FTP sites. The state-of-the-art in information technology was Gopher, a text-based system using hierarchical menus to organize documents. Today the World Wide Web dominates the headlines in major magazines and newspapers. Many journals now have electronic editions, and new journals published solely on the Internet are beginning to appear. E-books and e-learning have started to establish themselves. The popularity and ease of use of the World Wide Web make it one of the best ways to share LaTeX articles, reports, and books with a wider audience.

Part VI discusses the interaction between LaTeX and the Internet:

- Chapter 13 examines the role of the Internet as the main source for information about using and customizing LaTeX.
- Chapter 14 explains how to publish your own LaTeX articles, reports, and books on the World Wide Web.

New focus

This edition focuses on the "standard LaTeX." The first edition of this book (published in 1993) described AMS-LaTeX, version 1.1, and the `amsart` document style. AMS-LaTeX, version 1.1, was a stand-alone product that was incompatible with the standard LaTeX of the time, LaTeX 2.09. The second edition (in 1996) reported on the new LaTeX (then called LaTeX 2_ε) and the new LaTeX-compatible

AMS packages that replaced $\mathcal{A}_{\mathcal{M}}\mathcal{S}$-LaTeX, version 1.1, but the book still had an $\mathcal{A}_{\mathcal{M}}\mathcal{S}$-LaTeX–centric view.

This third edition is about LaTeX. Where necessary, I recommend that you use packages to extend LaTeX's capabilities. For typesetting mathematics, I strongly recommend that you use the AMS packages.

AMS packages, version 2.0

The American Mathematical Society released version 2.0 of the AMS packages in 1999. This third edition covers the changes made in this release.

Books

The first and second editions of this book dealt primarily with the tasks involved in writing articles. In Part V, the third edition addresses the issues that arise when creating longer documents. In addition to chapters on BIBTeX and *MakeIndex*, I have added a new chapter on writing books. Appendix F illustrates the importance of choosing a well-designed book document class.

Other changes

LaTeX LaTeX 2_{ε} has been remarkably stable since its release in 1996, becoming the standard LaTeX (see Section C.1.2). Changes have been minor except for advances in using LaTeX with non-English languages (see the new Appendix E) and the widespread use of the PostScript CM and AMS fonts (see the new Section D.1).

Reorganization and additions Due to the new emphasis on writing books, a number of sections and subsections have moved from Chapter 2 and Chapters 6–8 to the new Chapter 12.

I have carefully revised the content to cover the changes made in LaTeX and the AMS packages. I have added new material based on my own experiences (since 1996, I have typeset roughly 1500 pages—including two books—using LaTeX) and in response to e-mail queries from readers of previous editions (as an example, see the revised Section 5.6.2 on the `split` subsidiary math environment). Most of the text has been rewritten and there are many minor corrections.

In 1999, my introductory book, *First Steps in LaTeX*, [30] was published; it is based on Part I of the second edition of this book. Part I of this third edition takes into account the rewriting and editing that was done for *First Steps*.

Illustrations I believe that a visual illustration of a complicated construct substantially cuts the learning curve. So I have almost doubled the number of illustrations. See, for example, the illustrations of aligned formulas in Section 1.6.2;

the new Section 5.1, a visual guide to multiline math formulas; and the two-page spread of bibliographic styles in Chapter 10.

Web enhanced In the introduction, I explain how I plan to keep you, the reader, up-to-date on changes to come via the Web.

Two recurring questions

When I hear from readers, there are two questions that come up again and again:

1. I do not have much time to spend learning the technical aspects of writing articles. Do I really need a book as large as this one?
2. Can you help me to get started from scratch, covering everything from installing a working LaTeX system to the rudiments of text editing?

My answer to the first question is no. You do not need to read the entire book to get started. If you only read Part I (the short course), the few pages discussing the top matter of an AMS document (Section 8.1), and those parts of the book that cover the types of mathematical expressions your work uses, you will be able to write a basic article. *Math into LaTeX* is as large as it is because it addresses the use of LaTeX for a wide range of users. You can be very selective about what you choose to read at first, and come back later for more detail as needed.

The second question is addressed in a very small way by a section in the introduction, *Setting the stage*. There are dozens of different LaTeX implementations and hundreds of text editors. Your environment will be based on the kind of computer you have (or have access to), what you need your LaTeX system to do, how much work you are willing to do to maintain the system, and how much money you are willing to spend. Sections 13.2 and 13.3 will help you select a LaTeX system that meets your needs.

Because of the complex choices involved, no one book can possibly cover all of the possible combinations. I assume that you have a working and up-to-date LaTeX system, that you know how to use some text-editing application (even Word will do), and that you know the basics of working with your computer's operating system.

George Grätzer

Introduction

Is this book for you?

This book is for the mathematician, physicist, engineer, scientist, or technical typist who has to learn how to typeset articles containing mathematical formulas.

Part I provides a quick introduction to LaTeX, so that you will be ready to type your first article (such as the sample article on pages 44–45) in a very short time. That is followed, in Parts II–IV, by a detailed exposition that provides you with a solid foundation in LaTeX, so that typing mathematical documents will become second nature.

You can find specific topics in the short table of contents, in the detailed table of contents, in the Quick Finder, or in the index. While the index is LaTeX-oriented, the Quick Finder lists the main topics mainly using the terminology utilized by word processing applications. For example, to find out how to italicize text, look under "italics" in the Quick Finder, and under `\emph` in the index.

Setting the stage

Watch someone type a mathematical article in LaTeX. You will see that

- *A text editor* is used to create a LaTeX *source file*. A source file (we will call it `first.tex`) might look like the following:

```
\documentclass{article}
\begin{document}
The hypotenuse: $\sqrt{a^{2} + b^{2}}$.  I can type math!
\end{document}
```

  Note that the source file `first.tex` is different from a typical word-processor file: All characters are displayed at the same size and in the same font.

- *Typeset the source file and view the result on their monitor* (the two corners indicate material that is shown as typeset by LaTeX):

The hypotenuse: $\sqrt{a^2 + b^2}$. I can type math!

- *Continue the editing cycle.* You will go back and forth between the source file and the typeset version, making changes and observing the results of those changes.
- *Print the file.* Once you are satisfied with the typeset version, you can print the document, creating a paper version of the typeset article.

Unfortunately, I cannot tell you exactly how your particular text editor works, or how typesetting and printing is done on your system. Just as there are many text editors (ranging from the ancient `vi` to modern editors with graphical user interfaces), there are many LaTeX setups, each with its own unique installation and a different way of typesetting and printing. However, the following two examples should give you some idea of the process.

Example 1: UNIX

UNIX commands are typed at a *shell prompt* (such as `unix$`). The following command starts a text editor:

```
unix$ vi first.tex
```

Once the editor starts, you type the text of your article. When you are ready to typeset the article, save the file and quit the editor. Back at the shell prompt, typing

```
unix$ latex first
```

results in a series of messages scrolling up the screen as the file is typeset.

When this process is complete, you will have a DVI file, `first.dvi`, that may be viewed (in an X Window environment) by typing

```
unix$ xdvi first
```

If changes must be made, you can return to the editor and make them, save and quit, then typeset and preview the file again. To print the DVI file, type a command such as the following at the shell prompt:

```
unix$ dvips first | lpr
```

Example 2: TEXTURES *on a Macintosh*

When you start the TEXTURES application on a Macintosh computer, a blank text-editing window appears. Type the text of your document in the window and save it as `first.tex`. When you are ready to typeset the document, make sure that the `LaTeX` format is selected in the `Typeset` menu, and then choose `Typeset` from the same menu.

A second window (titled `first.tex typeset`) appears, displaying the typeset version of your document:

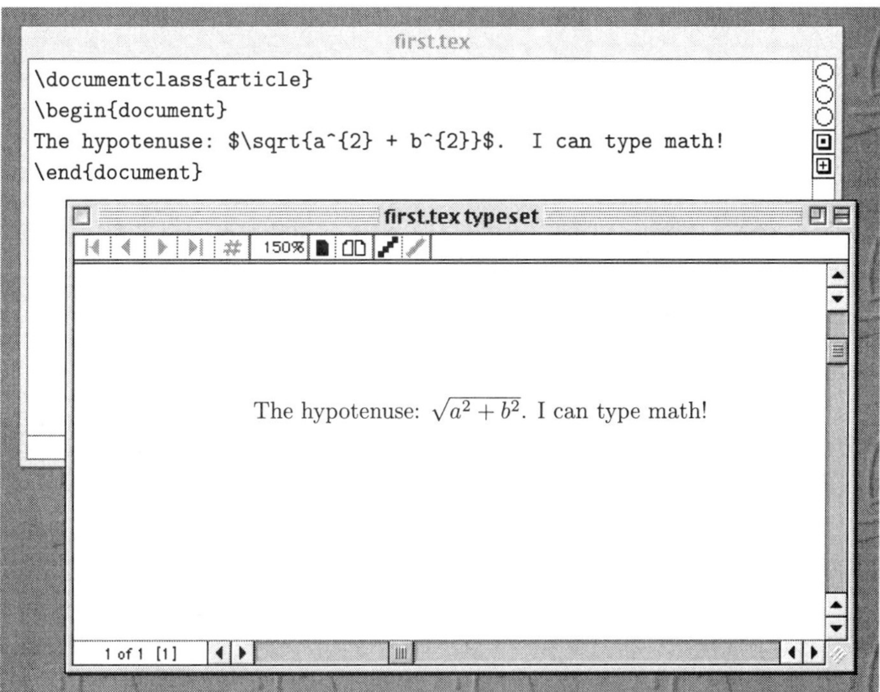

To print your document, choose `Print...` from the `File` menu. To continue editing your document, simply click the mouse in the text-editing window to bring it to the front, and type. Depending on how you have set the options, the changes in the LaTeX source file may automatically appear in the window displaying the typeset version.

Choosing a LaTeX setup

In Sections 13.2 and 13.3, I briefly review a few of the most popular LaTeX setups. My best advice is to get the same LaTeX setup as that of a friend or colleague so they can help you get started. Many LaTeX implementations come on a CD-ROM or are downloadable from the Internet, and installation is often no more complicated than double-clicking on an icon. Learning the fundamentals of using a text editor (typing text and simple editing) is easy—if you know how to use a word processor, you already know how to use a text editor. And it is just as easy to become familiar with a few basic commands for tasks such as typesetting and printing.

Now that you have some idea of the basic requirements for typing a mathematical article in LaTeX, you are ready for the rest of the introduction.

What is document markup?

When you work with a word processor, you see your document on the computer monitor more or less as it will look when printed, with different fonts, font sizes, font shapes (e.g., roman, italic) and weights (e.g., normal, boldface), interline spacing (leading), indentation, and so on.

Working with a *markup language*[1] is different. Since all characters appear in the same font in your text editor, to indicate changes in the typeset text, you must *mark up* the source file, that is, add commands to format the text. For instance, to emphasize the phrase `detailed description` in a LaTeX source file, type

```
\emph{detailed description}
```

The `\emph` command is a markup command; the marked-up text will yield the typeset output

detailed description

In this book, I will introduce you to LaTeX, a markup language designed and implemented by Leslie Lamport, based on Donald E. Knuth's typesetting language TeX (see Donald E. Knuth's *The TeXbook* [34] and Leslie Lamport's *LaTeX: A Document Preparation System* [39]). I believe that you will find that it is actually quite easy to learn how to mark up text.

On pages 290–297, I juxtapose the source file for an AMS sample article with the typeset version. The markup in the source file may appear somewhat challenging at first, but I think you will agree that the typeset article is a pleasing rendering of the marked-up material.

[1]Markup languages have always dominated typographic work of high quality. Communications on the World Wide Web are also customarily written in a markup language called HTML (HyperText Markup Language). More about markup languages in Section 14.1.1.

TeX

The TeX composition language was designed for typesetting mathematical and scientific articles and books, and can handle complex mathematical formulas as well as text: To get the formula $\int_{0}^{\pi} \sqrt{\alpha^{2} + x^{2}}\,dx$, type

```
$\int_{0}^{\pi} \sqrt{\alpha^{2} + x^{2}}\,dx$
```

You do not have to worry about determining the size of the integral symbol or how to construct the square root symbol that covers $\alpha^2 + x^2$ because TeX does this for you!

A tremendous part of the appeal of the TeX language is that a source file is *plain text* (ASCII text), which is easy to transmit *electronically* to colleagues, coauthors, journals, editors, and publishers.

TeX is also *platform independent*. You may type the first version of a source file on a Macintosh computer; your coauthor may make improvements to the same file on a PC (a computer running Microsoft Windows); and the journal publishing the article may use a UNIX machine (a computer running a UNIX variant such as Solaris or Linux) to prepare the manuscript for printing.[2]

LaTeX

LaTeX was built on TeX's foundation, and has commands that are easier to use, a set of structural elements, and a larger set of diagnostic messages.

LaTeX provides the following additional features:

- A document is divided into *logical units,* including an abstract, various sections and subsections, theorems, and a bibliography. The logical units are typed independently of one another. Once all the units have been typed, LaTeX controls the *placement* and *formatting* of these elements.
- Line 4 of the sample article `intrart.tex` (on page 39) reads

  ```
  \documentclass{article}
  ```

  This line tells LaTeX to load the *document class* `article`, which causes LaTeX to format the document as a generic article. When submitting your article to a journal that is equipped to handle LaTeX manuscripts (the number of such journals is increasing rapidly), the editor can simply substitute the name of the journal's document class to make the body of your article conform to the journal's design. (Depending on the journal, you may need to use the AMS article document class, `amsart`, in order to ensure that the front matter of your article also adapts.) Many journals make their own document classes available to prospective authors to use while preparing their articles.

[2]You may take this sentence as a definition of the three major computing platforms. We will only discuss tools that are available in some form on all three platforms.

- LaTeX's automatic numbering relieves you of tedious bookkeeping chores. Imagine that you have finished writing an article, with all of your theorems and equations numbered and properly cross-referenced. After a final reading, you must make some changes: Section 4 needs to be moved after Section 7, and some new theorems have to be inserted somewhere in the middle. Such minor changes used to be a major headache! But with LaTeX, it almost becomes a pleasure to make such changes: LaTeX automatically renumbers the sections, theorems, and equations in your article, and rebuilds the cross-references.
- With LaTeX you may use BIBTeX , an application that helps you create and maintain bibliographic databases, so references do not have to be retyped for each article. BIBTeX will select and format the needed references from your database.
- Compiling a large index is a big job. LaTeX users are assisted by *MakeIndex,* an application which makes this job easier.

The AMS packages

The AMS packages distill the American Mathematical Society's (AMS) years of experience in publishing mathematical journals and books; they add a host of features related to mathematical typesetting, especially the typesetting of multiline formulas and the production of finely tuned printed output. The AMS packages enhance LaTeX's capabilities in three different areas:

1. **Math.** The amsmath package adds a wide variety of tools for typesetting math, including

   - Powerful tools to deal with multiline math formulas. For instance, in the following formula, the equal signs ($=$) and the explanatory comments are vertically aligned:

$$\begin{aligned} x &= (x+y)(x+z) && \text{(by distributivity)}\\ &= x+yz && \text{(by Condition (M))}\\ &= yz. \end{aligned}$$

   - Numerous constructs for typesetting mathematical formulas, exemplified by the following:

$$f(x) = \begin{cases} -x^2, & \text{if } x < 0;\\ \alpha + x, & \text{if } 0 \leq x \leq 1;\\ x^2, & \text{otherwise.} \end{cases}$$

   - Special spacing rules for dozens of formula types; for example,

$$a \equiv b \pmod{\Theta}$$

typed inline becomes $a \equiv b \pmod{\Theta}$.

- Multiline subscripts, as in

$$\sum_{\substack{i^2+j^2=50\\ i,\, j\leq 10}} \sum \frac{x^i + y^j}{(i+j)!}$$

- User-defined symbols for typesetting math, such as

$$\operatorname{Trunc} f(x), \quad \hat{\hat{A}}, \quad {}^*\!\sum\nolimits^*$$

- Formulas numbered in a variety of ways:
  - Automatically (with numbers)
  - Manually (with tags)
  - By groups, with a group number such as (2) and individual formulas numbered as (2a), (2b), and so on

2. **Document classes.** The AMS packages provide a number of document classes; the most important of which is the AMS article document class, `amsart`; it allows the input of title page information (e.g., author, address, e-mail address) as separate entities. As a result, a journal can typeset even the title page of an article according to its own specifications without having to retype any information.

   The AMS document classes provide the `proof` environment and three theorem styles: plain, definition, and remark. (See the `sampart.tex` sample article on pages 286–288: Theorem 1 uses the plain style, Definition 1 uses the definition style, and the Notation uses the remark style.)

   Many users also prefer the visual design of the `amsart` document class to the simpler design of the classic LaTeX `article` document class.

3. **Fonts.** The AMS packages provide hundreds of symbols for binary operations, binary relations, negated binary relations, arrows, extensible arrows, and so on (see the tables in Appendix A); there are also additional math alphabets such as blackboard bold, Euler Fraktur, Euler Script, and math bold and math bold italic. Here are just a few examples:

$$\leftleftarrows, \quad \blacktriangle, \quad \nexists, \quad \supsetneqq, \quad \mathbb{A}, \quad \mathfrak{p}, \quad \mathscr{E}$$

The AMS calls these enhancements $\mathcal{A}\kern-.1667em\lower.5ex\hbox{$\mathcal{M}$}\kern-.125em\mathcal{S}$-LaTeX (consisting of the math packages and the document classes) and AMSFonts (consisting of the font-related packages and the fonts themselves). In this book, to simplify the terminology, I refer to all these enhancements collectively as AMS *packages;* I use AMS *distribution* and AMS *enhancements* as synonyms.

Ⓐ I will point out in the text which commands are LaTeX commands and which are defined by AMS packages. References to AMS commands will also be indicated by the use of a symbol in the margin (such as the one shown here). A smaller version, Ⓐ, is used in the tables of Appendixes A and B and in the index.

What's in the book?

Just before this introduction is the **Quick Finder**, a brief index using mainly non-LaTeX terms.

Part I (**Chapter 1**) will help you get started quickly with LaTeX; if you read it carefully, you will be ready to type your own first article and to tackle LaTeX in more depth.

Part I guides you through

- Text markup, which is quite easy
- Math markup, which is not so straightforward; several sections ease you into mathematical typesetting, including
  - The basic building blocks of math formulas
  - How to build up a complex formula in simple steps
  - A formula gallery
  - Equations and multiline formulas
- The anatomy of an article
- How to set up an article template
- Typing your first article

Part II introduces the two most basic skills for writing with LaTeX in depth: *typing text* and *typing math.*

Chapters 2 and **3** introduce *text* and *displayed text.* Chapter 2 is especially important because when you type a LaTeX document, most of your time is spent typing text. The topics covered include special characters and accents, hyphenation, fonts, and spacing. Chapter 3 covers displayed text, including *lists* and *tables,* and for the mathematician, proclamations (theorem-like structures) and proofs.

Chapters 4 and **5** discuss *inline* and *displayed math.* Typing math is the heart of any mathematical typesetting system. Chapter 4 discusses this topic in detail, including basic constructs, operators, delimiters, building new symbols, fonts, and grouping equations. Chapter 5 presents one of the major contributions of the AMS packages: aligned multiline formulas. This chapter also discusses other forms of multiline formulas.

Part III discusses the parts of a LaTeX document. In **Chapter 6**, you learn about the structure of a LaTeX document. The most important topics are sectioning and cross-referencing. In **Chapter 7**, the most commonly used standard LaTeX document classes are presented: `article`, `report`, and `letter` (the `book` class is discussed in Chapter 12), along with a description of the standard LaTeX distribution.

In **Chapter 8**, we discuss the AMS document classes. In particular, I present the title page information for the AMS article document class and provide a description of the standard AMS distribution.

Chapter 8 also features the AMS sample article, `sampart.tex`, first in typeset form (pages 286–288), then in mixed form, juxtaposing the source file and the typeset article (pages 290–297). You can learn a lot about LaTeX and the AMS packages just by reading the source file one paragraph at a time and seeing how that paragraph is typeset by LaTeX.

Part IV (**Chapter 9**) introduces techniques to *customize* LaTeX to speed up the typing of source files and the typesetting of documents: user-defined commands, user-defined environments, and custom formats. You will learn how parameters that affect LaTeX's behavior are stored in *counters* and *length commands,* how to change them, and how to design your own custom lists.

Chapter 9 also contains a version of the AMS sample article utilizing the user-defined commands collected in `lattice.sty`.

In **Part V** (**Chapters 10** and **11**), we will discuss longer documents, which have special needs. Two applications, contained in the standard LaTeX distribution, BIBTeX and *MakeIndex* make compiling large bibliographies and indexes much easier.

I present the LaTeX and the AMS book document classes in **Chapter 12** along with the *dos and don'ts* of book writing in LaTeX.

Part VI deals with LaTeX and the Internet. **Chapter 13** discusses where to find useful LaTeX-related information on the Internet. The main topics are:

- Obtaining files from the Internet
- CTAN, the Comprehensive TeX Archive Network
- Obtaining the LaTeX distribution and the AMS packages
- Getting the sample files for this book
- Some commercial TeX implementations
- Freeware and shareware TeX implementations
- TeX user groups and the AMS
- Important LaTeX-related FTP and Web sites

You can share your LaTeX articles, reports, and books by putting them on the Web so that others can view, read, download, and print them. **Chapter 14** tells you how.

You will probably find yourself referring to **Appendices A** and **B** time and again: They contain the math and text symbol tables.

Appendix C relates some historical background material on LaTeX: how it developed and how it works. **Appendix D** is a brief introduction to the use of PostScript fonts in a LaTeX document.

Appendix E briefly describes the use of LaTeX for languages other than American English. **Appendix F** shows a few pages from a book typeset with a Springer-Verlag book document class along with excerpts from the source document.

Appendix G will help orient those people who have previously worked with

(Plain) TEX, LATEX, version 2.09, AMS-TEX, or AMS-LATEX, version 1.x. Some tips are given to smooth your transition to using the current standard LATEX and the AMS packages. Finally, **Appendix H** points you towards some areas for further study.

Mission statement

This book is a guide for typesetting mathematical documents within the constraints imposed by LATEX, an elaborate system with hundreds of rules. LATEX allows you to perform almost any mathematical typesetting task through the appropriate application of its rules. You can customize LATEX (as it was designed to be modified) by introducing user-defined commands and environments and by changing LATEX parameters.

You can also extend LATEX by invoking packages that accomplish special tasks: One such set of packages from the AMS plays an important role in this book—as it should in any book dealing with mathematical typesetting.

It is not my goal to teach you

- How to modify LATEX code to change LATEX's behavior
- How to write TEX code to create your own packages (LATEX extensions)
- How to design beautiful documents (writing document classes)

The definitive book on the first topic is Michel Goossens, Frank Mittelbach, and Alexander Samarin's *The LATEX Companion* [17]. The second and third topics still await authoritative books.

A recommendation

I strongly recommend that you use the amsart document class for all your articles. 
Begin each article with the lines

```
\documentclass{amsart}
\usepackage{amssymb,latexsym}
\begin{document}
```

and you can ignore all of the discussions in this book about LATEX commands versus AMS commands, and LATEX fonts and the latexsym package versus AMS fonts and the amssymb package.

Some of you may not be able to follow this recommendation, including those who work with older installations whose system managers cannot or will not install a newer version of LATEX or the AMS packages, and those who are forced to use a publisher's document class file that is not compatible with the AMS packages. But most users of LATEX who typeset documents with significant amounts of math will find that using the amsart document class and loading amssymb and latexsym make their work easier.

Keeping up-to-date

Like most computer-related subjects, the material in this book is subject to change over time. While LaTeX itself may not change much until the advent of LaTeX3, there is a new version of the amsmath package on the horizon, introducing a variant of the `equation` environment that will automatically break long formulas into shorter lines. Chapter 13 deals with the Internet, which is in a state of constant flux. To keep you up-to-date, I am maintaining a Web page to track these changes for you. To find this page, go to my home page,
`http://www.maths.umanitoba.ca/homepages/gratzer/`
and follow the links `LaTeX books` and `MiL Update`. Or go directly to
`http://www.maths.umanitoba.ca/homepages/gratzer/LaTeXBooks/milupdate.html`

Conventions

To make this book easy to read, I use some simple conventions:

- Explanatory text is set in this typeface: Galliard.
- `Computer Modern typewriter is used to show what you should type (as well as messages from LaTeX). All the characters in this typeface have the same width, making it easy to recognize.`
- I also use Computer Modern typewriter to indicate
  - Commands (`\parbox`)
  - Environments (`align`)
  - Documents (`intrart.tex`)
  - Document classes (`article`)
  - Document class options (`draft`)
  - Directories or folders (`work`)
- The names of *packages,* which are extensions of LaTeX, are set in a sans-serif typeface (amsmath).
- When I show you how something looks when typeset, I use Computer Modern, TeX's standard typeface:

I think you will find this typeface sufficiently different from the other typefaces I have used (the strokes are much lighter) so that you should not have much difficulty recognizing typeset LaTeX material. When the typeset material is a separate paragraph (or paragraphs), corner brackets in the margin set it off from the rest of the text—unless it is a single displayed formula.

- For explanations in the text, such as

  Compare iff with iff, typed as `iff` and `if{f}`, respectively.

the same typefaces are used. Because they are not set off spatially, it may be a little more difficult to see that iff is set in Computer Modern roman, whereas `iff` is set in the Computer Modern typewriter typeface.

- I usually introduce commands with examples, such as

  ```
  \\[22pt]
  ```

  However, it is sometimes necessary to define the syntax of a command more formally. For instance,

  ```
  \\[length]
  ```

  where *`length`* is a *placeholder* representing the value you have to supply. I use the Computer Modern typewriter italic font for placeholders.
- I use the term *directory* to mean both directory and folder.

Acknowledgments

This book is based, of course, on its previous editions. I would like to thank the many people, too numerous to list here again, who read and reread those earlier manuscripts.

I received professional reports on the manuscript from Barbara Beeton, Nandor Sieben, and Ferenc Wettl. Arthur Ogawa commented on Part I. The chapter on BIBTEX has been carefully reviewed—again—by Oren Patashnik (the author of BIBTEX); the chapter on the Web was read by Sebastian Rahtz (the author of the hyperref package and coauthor of the *The LATEX Web Companion* [19]); the chapter on books was read by Fred Bartlett (Electronic Publishing, Springer-Verlag New York).

Claire M. Connelly did an outstanding job editing the manuscript, far and beyond the call of duty; in addition to editing the text and making suggestions for improvements, she redesigned the tables and updated the index. Melissa O'Neill provided two ingenious Perl scripts for cleaning up the index. Ann Kostant demonstrated that publishers care; this complex project greatly benefited from her guidance and editorial advice. Elizabeth Loew carefully guided the manuscript to publication.

George Grätzer
E-mail: `gratzer@cc.umanitoba.ca`
Home page: `http://www.maths.umanitoba.ca/homepages/gratzer/`

omplete-s
ust lattice

Georg in*
Compute
Winnebag
menuhin@co

Mar

In th ributiv
tices, th
complete

1 Intro

he following

e exists an infin
t complete congruence re s.

e Π^* construction

e following cons tion is crucia our proof of our Theorem:

efinition 1 *Let* D_i*, i* $\in$ *I, be c ete distributive lattices satisfying condi- n (J). Their* Π^* *produ defi s follows:*

$$= \Pi(D_i^- \mid i \in I) + 1;$$

that is, $\Pi^*(D \mid i \in I)$ *I) with a new unit element.*

Notation 1 *If* $i \in I$ *a then*

$$\langle \ldots, 0, \ldots, \overset{i}{d}, \ldots, 0, \ldots \rangle$$

is the element of $\Pi^*(D_i \mid i \in I)$ *whose th component is d and all the other components are 0.*

esearch supported by the NSF under grant number 3466.

PART I

A short course

CHAPTER

1

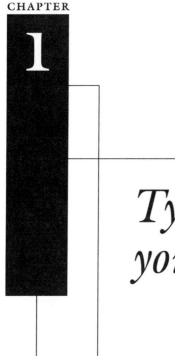

Typing your first article

In this chapter, you will write your first article. All you have to do is to type the (electronic) *source file*; LaTeX does the rest. I will introduce you to the most important commands for typesetting text and math by working through examples. More details are provided in the rest of the book.

A source file is made up of *text, math* (e.g., $\sqrt{5}$), and *instructions to LaTeX.* You would type the last sentence as follows:

```
A source file is made up of \emph{text,} \emph{math} (e.g.,
$\sqrt{5}$), and \emph{instructions to \LaTeX.}
```

In that sentence,

```
The source file is made up of \emph{text,} \emph{math} (e.g.,
```

is text,

```
$\sqrt{5}$
```

is math, and

```
\emph{instructions to \LaTeX.}
```

is an instruction (a command with an argument). Commands, as a rule, start with a backslash (\) and tell LaTeX to do something special. In this case, the command `\emph` emphasizes its *argument* (the text between the braces). Another kind of instruction is called an *environment*.

For instance, the commands

```
\begin{flushright}
```

and

```
\end{flushright}
```

enclose a `flushright` environment—text that is typed between these two commands is right justified (lined up against the right margin) when typeset. (The `flushleft` environment creates left-justified text; the `center` environment creates text that is centered on the page.)

In practice, text, math, and instructions are usually mixed. For example,

```
\emph{My first integral:} $\int \zeta^{2}(x) \, dx$.
```

produces

My first integral: $\int \zeta^{2}(x) \, dx$.

which is a mixture of all three. Nevertheless, I will introduce the three topics (typing text, typing math, and giving instructions to LaTeX) as if they were independent in order to make the discussion clearer.

We will be working with a number of sample documents; you can type the documents from the examples in the text; alternatively, you can download them from the Internet (see Section 13.1). I suggest you create a directory on your computer named `samples` to store the sample files, and another directory called `work` where you can keep your working files. Whenever you want to use one of these documents, copy it from your `samples` directory into your `work` directory, so that the original remains unchanged. *In this book, the* `samples` *and* `work` *directories will refer to the directories you have created.*

1.1 Typing text

We start with the keyboard, proceed to type a short text-only note, and learn some simple rules for typing text in LaTeX.

1.1.1 The keyboard

The following keys are used to type text in a LaTeX source file:

```
a-z   A-Z   0-9
+ = * / ( ) [ ]
```

You may also use the following punctuation marks:

, ; . ? ! : ' ' -

and the spacebar, the Tab key (which—unlike in a word processor—has the same effect as the spacebar), and the Return (or Enter) key.

Since TEX source files are "pure text" (ASCII[1] files), they are very portable. There is one possible problem[2] limiting this portability: The line endings used. When you press the Return (or Enter) key, your text editor writes an invisible code into your source file that indicates where the line ends. Because this code is different on each of the major platforms (Macintosh, PC,[3] and UNIX[4]), you may have problems reading a source file created on a different platform. Luckily, many text editors include the ability to switch end-of-line codes; some even do so automatically.

Finally, there are twelve special keys that are mostly used in LATEX instructions:

$ % & ~ _ ^ \ { } " |

There are commands available so that you can typeset most of these special characters (as well as composite characters, such as accented characters) if you need to use them in your document. For instance, $ is typed as `\$`; the underscore, _, is typed as `\_`; and % is typed as `\%`; whereas ä is typed as `\"{a}`. See Section 2.4 for a complete discussion of symbols not available directly from the keyboard and Appendix B for the text symbol tables.

LATEX prohibits the use of other keys on your keyboard (unless you are using a version of LATEX that is set up to work with non-English languages—see Appendix E). When trying to typeset a source file that contains a prohibited character, LATEX will display an error message similar to the following:

```
! Text line contains an invalid character.
l.222 completely irreducible^^?
                                ^^?
```

In this message, `l.222` means line 222 of your source file. You must edit that line to remove the character that TEX cannot understand. The log file (see Section C.2.4) will also contain this message.

[1]ASCII stands for American Standard Code for Information Interchange.

[2]Actually, there is another problem, directory structure, that we will discuss in Section 9.1.1.

[3]A computer running Microsoft Windows.

[4]A computer running a UNIX variant such as Solaris or Linux.

1.1.2 Your first note

We start our discussion on how to type a note in LaTeX with a simple example. Suppose you want to use LaTeX to produce the following:

It is of some concern to me that the terminology used in multi-section math courses is not uniform.

In several sections of the course on matrix theory, the term "hamiltonian-reduced" is used. I, personally, would rather call these "hyper-simple." I invite others to comment on this problem.

Of special concern to me is the terminology in the course by Prof. Rudi Hochschwabauer. Since his field is new, there is no accepted terminology. It is imperative that we arrive at a satisfactory solution.

Create a new file in your `work` directory with the name `note1.tex` and type the following, including the spacing and linebreaks shown, but not the line numbers (or copy the `note1.tex` file from the `samples` directory; see page 4):

```
% Sample file: note1.tex
% Typeset with LaTeX format
\documentclass{article}

\begin{document}
It is of some concern to me   that
the terminology used in  multi-section
 math courses is not uniform.

In several sections of the course on
matrix theory, the  term
 ``hamiltonian-reduced'' is used.
 I, personally, would rather call these ``hyper-simple.'' I
invite others to comment on this  problem.

Of special concern to me is the terminology in the course
by Prof.~Rudi Hochschwabauer.
  Since his field is new, there is
 no accepted
terminology.   It is imperative
that we arrive at a satisfactory solution.
\end{document}
```

The first two lines start with `%`. These lines are called *comments* and are ignored by LaTeX. The `%` character is very useful. For example, if you want to add some notes to your source files, and you do not want those notes to appear in the typeset version of your article, you can begin those lines with a `%` , and TEX will ignore everything on them when typesetting your source file. You can also comment out part of a line:

```
simply put, we believe % Actually it is not so simple.
```

Everything on the line after the `%` character will be ignored.

Line 3 specifies the *document class* (in our case, `article`), which controls how the document will be formatted.

The text of the note is typed within the `document` environment; that is, between the lines

```
\begin{document}
```

and

```
\end{document}
```

Now typeset `note1.tex`; you should get the same document shown on page 6. As you can see from this example, LATEX is different from a word processor. It disregards the way you input and position the text, and follows only the formatting instructions given by the markup commands. LATEX notices when you put a space in the text, but it ignores *how many spaces* have been inserted. Similarly, one or more blank lines mark the end of a paragraph.

LATEX, by default, fully justifies the text by placing space between words—the *interword space*—and a somewhat larger space between sentences—the *intersentence space*. If you have to force an interword space, you can use the \␣ command (the symbol ␣ means a blank space).

The `~` (tilde) command also forces an interword space, but with a difference: It keeps the words together on the same line. This command is called a *tie* or *nonbreakable space*—see Section 2.4.3.

Note that on lines 12 and 13, the left double quotes are typed as `` (two left single quotes) and the right double quotes are typed as '' (two right single quotes). The left single quote key is not always easy to find; it is usually hidden in the upper-left or upper-right corner of the keyboard, and shares a key with the tilde (`~`).

1.1.3 *Lines too wide*

LATEX reads the text in the source file one line at a time; when the end of a paragraph is reached, LATEX typesets the entire paragraph. Most of the time, there is no need for corrective action. Occasionally, however, LATEX gets into trouble when trying to split the paragraph into typeset lines. To illustrate this situation, modify `note1.tex`: In the second sentence, replace `term` by `strange term`; in the fourth sentence, delete Rudi␣ (including the blank space following Rudi). Now save this modified file in your work directory using the name note1b.tex. (If you downloaded the sample files, you can find note1b.tex in the samples directory—see page 4.)

When you typeset note1b.tex, you should obtain the following:

It is of some concern to me that the terminology used in multi-section math courses is not uniform.

In several sections of the course on matrix theory, the strange term "hamiltonian-reduced" is used. I, personally, would rather call these "hyper-simple." I invite others to comment on this problem.

Of special concern to me is the terminology in the course by Prof. Hochschwabauer. Since his field is new, there is no accepted terminology. It is imperative that we arrive at a satisfactory solution.

The first line of paragraph two is about 1/4 inch too wide. The first line of paragraph three is even wider. On your monitor, LaTeX displays the following messages:

```
Overfull \hbox (15.38948pt too wide) in paragraph at lines 10--15
[]\OT1/cmr/m/n/10 In sev-eral sec-tions of the course on ma-trix
the-ory, the strange term ‘‘hamiltonian-
 []
Overfull \hbox (23.27834pt too wide) in paragraph at lines 16--22
[]\OT1/cmr/m/n/10 Of spe-cial con-cern to me is the ter-mi-nol-ogy
in the course by Prof. Hochschwabauer.
 []
```

You will find the same messages in the log file, note1b.log (see Section 1.13).

The first message,

```
Overfull \hbox (15.38948pt too wide) in paragraph at lines 10--15
```

refers to paragraph two (lines 10–15 in the source file—its location in the typeset document is not specified). The typeset version of this paragraph has a line that is 15.38948 points too wide. LaTeX uses *points* (pt) to measure distances; there are about 72 points in 1 inch (or about 28 points in 1 cm); thus 15.38948 points is about this long: ⌴.

The next two lines,

```
[]\OT1/cmr/m/n/10 In sev-eral sec-tions of the course on ma-trix
the-ory, the strange term ‘‘hamiltonian-
```

identify the source of the problem: LaTeX did not hyphenate the word

```
hamiltonian-reduced
```

because it (automatically) hyphenates a hyphenated word *only at the hyphen.*

The second reference,

```
Overfull \hbox (23.27834pt too wide) in paragraph at lines 16--22
```

is to paragraph three (lines 16–22 of the source file). There is a problem with the word `Hochschwabauer`, which LaTeX's standard hyphenation routine cannot handle. (A German hyphenation routine would have no difficulty hyphenating `Hochschwabauer`; see Appendix E.) If you encounter such a problem, you can either try to reword the sentence or insert one or more optional hyphen commands (`\-`), which tell LaTeX where it may hyphenate the word. In this case, you can rewrite `Hochschwabauer` as `Hoch\-schwabauer` and the second hyphenation problem will disappear.

Sometimes a small horizontal overflow can be difficult to spot. The `draft` document class option may help (see Sections 7.1.1, 8.5, and 12.1 for more about document class options): LaTeX will put a black box (or *slug*) in the margin to mark an overfull line. You can invoke this option by changing the `\documentclass` line to

```
\documentclass[draft]{article}
```

A version of `note1b.tex` with this option can be found in the `samples` directory under the name `noteslug.tex`.

1.1.4 *More text features*

Next, you will produce the following note:

March 12, 2000

From the desk of George Grätzer

February 7–21 *please* use my temporary e-mail address:

`George_Gratzer@umanitoba.ca`

Type in the following source file and save it as `note2.tex` in your `work` directory, without the line numbers (`note2.tex` can also be found in the `samples` directory—see page 4):

```
1  % Sample file: note2.tex
2  % Typeset with LaTeX format
3  \documentclass{article}
4
5  \begin{document}
6  \begin{flushright}
7     \today
8  \end{flushright}
9  \textbf{From the desk of George Gr\"{a}tzer}\\[22pt]
10 February~7--21 \emph{please} use my temporary e-mail address:
11 \begin{center}
12    \texttt{George\_Gratzer@umanitoba.ca}
13 \end{center}
14 \end{document}
```

This note introduces several additional features of LaTeX:

- The `\today` command (in line 7) displays the date on which the document is being typeset.
- The use of environments to *right justify* (lines 6–8) or *center* (lines 11-13) text.
- The use of text style commands, including the `\emph` command (line 10) to *emphasize* text, the `\textbf` command (line 9) to **embolden** text, and the `\texttt` command (line 12) to produce `typewriter-style` text.

  These are *commands with arguments.* In each case, the argument of the command follows the name of the command and is typed between braces; that is, between `{` and `}`.
- Almost all LaTeX commands start with a backslash (`\`) followed by the command name; for instance, `\textbf`. The command name is terminated by the first *non-alphabetic character* (i.e., by any character other than a–z or A–Z). Note that command names are *case sensitive:* Typing `\Textbf` or `\TEXTBF` will generate an error message.
- The use of double hyphens for number ranges (*en dash*): `7--21` (in line 10) typesets as 7–21. Use triple hyphens for the *em dash* punctuation mark—such as the one in this sentence.
- Forcing a line break with the `\\` command. To create additional space between lines (as in the last note, under the line **From the desk...**), you can use the `\\` command and specify an appropriate amount of vertical space: `\\[22pt]` (see also Formula 20 in Section 1.5). Note that this command uses *square brackets* rather than braces because the argument is *optional.* The distance may be given in points (`pt`), centimeters (`cm`), or inches (`in`).

  To force a page break, use `\newpage`.
- Special rules for special characters (see Section 1.1.1), for *accented characters,* and for some *European characters.* For instance, the special character underscore (_) is

typed as _, and the accented character ä is typed as \"{a}. Accents are explained in Section 2.4.7 (see also the tables in Appendix B).

You will seldom need to know more than we have discussed here about typing text. When you do, however, see Chapters 2 and 3. See also Appendix B, where all text symbols are organized into tables.

1.2 Typing math

Now we will start mixing text with math formulas.

1.2.1 A note with math

In addition to the regular text keys and the twelve special keys discussed in Section 1.1.1, three more keys are needed to type mathematical formulas:

$$| \quad < \quad >$$

($|$ is the shifted \ key on many keyboards.) The formula $2 < |x| > y$ uses all three.

You will begin typesetting math with the following note:

In first-year calculus, we define intervals such as (u, v) and (u, ∞). Such an interval is a *neighborhood* of a if a is in the interval. Students should realize that ∞ is only a symbol, not a number. This is important since we soon introduce concepts such as $\lim_{x \to \infty} f(x)$.

When we introduce the derivative

$$\lim_{x \to a} \frac{f(x) - f(a)}{x - a},$$

we assume that the function is defined and continuous in a neighborhood of a.

To create the source file for this mixed text and math note, create a new document with your text editor. Name it math.tex, place it in the work directory, and type in the following source file—without the line numbers (or simply copy math.tex from the samples directory; see page 4):

```
% Sample file: math.tex
% Typeset with LaTeX format
\documentclass{article}

\begin{document}
In first-year calculus, we   define intervals  such as
$(u, v)$ and $(u, \infty)$.  Such an interval is a
\emph{neighborhood} of  $a$
```

```
if  $a$ is in the interval.  Students should
realize that  $\infty$ is only a
symbol, not a number.  This is important since
we soon introduce concepts
 such as $\lim_{x \to \infty} f(x)$.

When we introduce the derivative
\[
   \lim_{x \to a} \frac{f(x) - f(a)}{x - a},
\]
we assume that the function is defined and continuous
in a neighborhood of  $a$.
\end{document}
```

This note introduces several basic concepts of math in LaTeX:

- There are two kinds of math formulas and environments:
  - *Inline* math environments can open and close with `$` (as seen throughout this book) or open with `\(` and close with `\)`.
  - *Displayed* math environments open with `\[` and close with `\]`.
- Within math environments, LaTeX uses its own spacing rules and completely ignores the white space you type with two exceptions:
  1. Spaces that delimit commands (so in `$\infty a$` the space is not ignored; in fact, `$\inftya$` is an error)
  2. Spaces in the arguments of commands that temporarily revert to text mode (`\mbox` is such a command; see Sections 1.3 and 4.5)

  The white space that you add when typing math is important only for the readability of the source file. To summarize:

Rule ■ Spacing in text and math
In text mode, many spaces equal one space, whereas in math mode, your spacing is ignored (unless the space terminates a command).

- The same formula may be typeset differently depending on whether it is inline or displayed. The expression $x \to a$ is set as a *subscript* to lim in the inline formula $\lim_{x \to a} f(x)$, typed as `$\lim_{x \to a} f(x)$`, but it is set *below* lim in the displayed version,

$$\lim_{x \to a} f(x)$$

  typed as

```
\[
   \lim_{x \to a} f(x)
\]
```

- A math symbol is invoked by a command. For example, the command for ∞ is `\infty` and the command for $\to$ is `\to`. The math symbols are organized into tables in Appendix A.

  To access all LaTeX symbols, use the latexsym package; in other words, begin your article with

```
\documentclass{article}
\usepackage{latexsym}
```

Ⓐ Many of the symbols listed in Appendix A require the amssymb package. To use all of the LaTeX and AMS symbols, load both packages:[5]

```
\documentclass{article}
\usepackage{latexsym,amssymb}
```

Ⓐ The amssymb package loads the amsfonts package, which contains the commands for using the AMSFonts (see Section 4.13.2).

- Some commands, such as `\sqrt`, need *arguments* enclosed in { and }. To typeset $\sqrt{5}$, type `$\sqrt{5}$`, where `\sqrt` is the command and `5` is the argument. Some commands need more than one argument. To get

$$\frac{3+x}{5}$$

type

```
\[
   \frac{3+x}{5}
\]
```

`\frac` is the command, `3+x` and `5` are the arguments.

1.2.2 *Errors in math*

Even in such a simple note there are many opportunities for errors. To help familiarize yourself with some of the most commonly seen LaTeX errors and their causes, we will deliberately introduce mistakes into `math.tex`. The version of `math.tex` with mistakes is `mathb.tex`. By inserting and deleting `%` signs, you will make the mistakes visible to LaTeX one at a time. (Recall that lines starting with `%` are ignored by LaTeX.) Type the following source file, and save it under the name `mathb.tex` in the `work` directory (or copy the file `mathb.tex` from the `samples` directory—see page 4). As usual, do not type the line numbers! They are shown here to help you with the exercises.

[5] Recall my recommendation from page xxxvi.

```
1   % Sample file: mathb.tex
2   % Typeset with LaTeX format
3   \documentclass{article}
4
5   \begin{document}
6   In first-year calculus, we  define intervals  such as
7   %$(u, v)$ and $(u, \infty)$.  Such an interval is a
8    $(u, v)$ and  (u, \infty)$.  Such an interval is a
9   \emph{neighborhood} of $a$
10  if $a$ is in the interval.  Students should
11  realize that  $\infty$ is only a
12  symbol, not a number.  This is important since
13  we soon introduce concepts
14   such as  $\lim_{x \to \infty} f(x)$.
15  %such as $\lim_{x \to \infty  f(x)$.
16
17  When we introduce the derivative
18  \[
19      \lim_{x \to a} \frac{f(x) - f(a)}{x - a}
20  %   \lim_{x \to a} \frac{f(x) - f(a)  x - a}
21  \]
22  we assume that the function is defined and continuous
23  in a neighborhood of  $a$.
24  \end{document}
```

Exercise 1 Note that on line 8, the third `$` is missing. When you typeset the `mathb.tex` file, LaTeX generates the following error message:

```
! Missing $ inserted.
<inserted text>
                $
l.8 ..., v)$ and    (u, \infty
                                        )$.  Such an interval is a
?
```

Since the `$` was omitted, LaTeX reads `(u, \infty)` as text; but the `\infty` command instructs LaTeX to typeset a math symbol, which can only be done in math mode. So LaTeX offers to put a `$` in front of `\infty`. LaTeX attempts a cure, but in this example it comes too late, because math mode *should* start just before `(u`.

Whenever you see the `?` prompt, you may press Return to ignore the error and continue typesetting the document (see Section 1.13.2 for other options and other prompts).

Exercise 2 Delete the `%` at the beginning of line 7 and insert a `%` at the beginning of line 8 (this eliminates the previous error); then delete the `%` at the beginning of line 15 and insert a % at the beginning of line 14, introducing a new error (the closing brace of the subscript is missing). Now typeset the note. You will get the error message

```
! Missing } inserted.
<inserted text>
                }
l.15 ...im_{x \to \infty f(x)$

?
```

LaTeX is telling you that a closing brace (}) is missing, but it is not sure where the brace should be. LaTeX noticed that the subscript started with {, but reached the end of the math formula before finding the matching }. You must look in the formula for a { that is not balanced, and insert the missing }.

Exercise 3 Now delete the % at the beginning of line 14, and insert a % at the beginning of line 15, removing the previous error. Delete the % at the beginning of line 20 and insert a % at the beginning of line 19, introducing our final error (omitting the closing brace of the first argument and the opening brace of the second argument of `\frac`). Save and typeset the file. You will get the error message

```
! LaTeX Error: Bad math environment delimiter.

l.21 \]
```

This error message says that LaTeX believes that there is a bad math environment delimiter on line 21 of your source file, specifically, the `\]`. When we look at the source file, we can see that this delimiter is correct, which means that the problem must lie within the displayed formula preceding the delimiter, which is the case: LaTeX was trying to typeset

```
\lim_{x \to a} \frac{f(x) - f(a)  x - a}
```

but `\frac` requires *two* arguments: LaTeX found `f(x) - f(a) x - a` as the first argument, then found the `\]`, closing the displayed math environment before a second argument was found.

See Section 1.10 for more information about finding and fixing problems in your LaTeX source files.

1.3 *Building blocks of a formula*

A formula is built from a large collection of components. We group them as follows:

- Arithmetic
  - Subscripts and superscripts
- Binomial coefficients
- Congruences
- Delimiters
- Ellipses
- Integrals
- Math accents
- Matrices
- Operators
  - Large operators
- Roots
- Text

In this section, I will describe each of these groups, and provide examples illustrating their use.

Some of the commands in the following examples are defined by the amsmath package; in other words, to typeset these examples with the LaTeX `article` document class, your file must begin with Ⓐ

```
\documentclass{article}
\usepackage{amssymb,latexsym,amsmath}
```

But recall my recommendation from page xxxvi: You may begin your articles with

```
\documentclass{amsart}
\usepackage{amssymb,latexsym}
```

and ignore all of the discussions about packages and fonts. (The amsmath package is automatically loaded by the `amsart` document class.)

Arithmetic The arithmetic operations $a + b$, $a - b$, $-a$, a/b, and ab are typed as you might expect:

```
$a + b$, $a - b$, $-a$, $a / b$, $a b$
```

If you wish to use $\cdot$ or $\times$ for multiplication, as in $a \cdot b$ or $a \times b$, use `\cdot` or `\times`, respectively. The expressions $a \cdot b$ and $a \times b$ are typed as follows:

```
$a \cdot b$  $a \times b$
```

Displayed fractions, such as

$$\frac{1 + 2x}{x + y + xy}$$

are typed with `\frac`:

```
\[
   \frac{1 + 2x}{x + y + xy}
\]
```

The `\frac` command is seldom used inline because it can disrupt the interline spacing of the paragraph; see the comment on page 318 for another example of this problem.

Subscripts and superscripts Subscripts are typed with _ (underscore) and superscripts with ^ (caret). Subscripts and superscripts should be enclosed in braces; that is, typed between { and }. To get a_1, type the following characters:

Begin inline math mode:	`$`
Type the letter a:	`a`
Subscript command:	`_`
Put the subscripted 1 in braces:	`{1}`
Exit inline math mode:	`$`

that is, type `$a_{1}$`. Omitting the braces in this example causes no harm, but to get a_{10}, you *must* type `$a_{10}$`; indeed, `$a_10$` is typeset as $a_1 0$. Further examples: a_{i_1}, a^2, a^{i_1}, a_n^2 are typed as

```
$a_{i_{1}}$, $a^{2}$, $a^{i_{1}}$, $a_{n}^{2}$
```

Binomial coefficients For binomial coefficients, LaTeX offers the `\choose` command. For example, $\binom{a}{b+c}$ is typed inline as

```
$a \choose {b + c}$
```

whereas a displayed version,

$$\binom{\frac{n^2-1}{2}}{n+1}$$

is typed as

```
\[
  \frac{n^{2} - 1}{2} \choose {n + 1}
\]
```

Ⓐ The amsmath package provides the `\binom` command for typesetting binomial coefficients. The examples shown above are typed as

```
$\binom{a}{b + c}$
```

and

```
\[
   \binom{ \frac{n^{2} - 1}{2} }{n + 1}
\]
```

The amsmath package considers \choose to be an obsolete command. If you use \choose when you have amsmath loaded, you will see the following warning: (A)

```
Package amsmath Warning: Foreign command \atopwithdelims;
\frac or \genfrac should be used instead.
```

Congruences The two most important forms are

$a \equiv v \pmod{\theta}$	typed as	`$a \equiv v \pmod{\theta}$`
$a \equiv v \pod{\theta}$	typed as	`$a \equiv v \pod{\theta}$`

The second form requires the amsmath package. The command \pmod behaves differently when the amsmath package is used: Its inline and displayed forms use different spacing (see Section 4.7.3). (A)

Delimiters Parentheses and square brackets are examples of delimiters; they are used to delimit some subformulas, as in `$[(a*b)+(c*d)]^2$`, which typesets as $[(a * b) + (c * d)]^2$. They can expand vertically to enclose a formula:

$$\left(\frac{1 + x}{2 + y^{2}} \right)^{2}$$

is typed as

```
\[
   \left( \frac{1 + x}{2 + y^{2}} \right)^{2}
\]
```

The `\left(` and `\right)` commands tell LaTeX to size the parentheses correctly (relative to the size of the symbols inside the parentheses). Two further examples,

$$\left| \frac{a + b}{2} \right|, \quad \left\| A^{2} \right\|$$

would be typed as

```
\[
  \left| \frac{a + b}{2} \right|,
      \quad \left\| A^{2} \right\|
\]
```

where `\quad` is a spacing command (see Sections 4.11 and A.9).

Additional delimiters are listed in Sections 4.6 and A.6.

Ellipses The *ellipsis* (...) in text is provided by the `\ldots` command:

A...Z is typed as `A \ldots Z`

In formulas, the ellipsis can be printed either as *low* (or *on-the-line*) *dots* with the `\ldots` command:

$F(x_1, x_2, \ldots, x_n)$ is typed as `$F(x_{1}, x_{2}, \ldots, x_{n})$`

or as centered dots with the `\cdots` command:

$x_1 + x_2 + \cdots + x_n$ is typed as `$x_{1} + x_{2} + \cdots + x_{n}$`

If you use the amsmath package, the command `\dots` will typeset the correct ellipsis (with the correct spacing) in most cases; if it does not, see Section 4.4.3 on how to specify the appropriate ellipsis from the four types available.

Integrals The command for an integral is `\int`; the lower limit is specified as a subscript and the upper limit is specified as a superscript. For example, the integral $\int_0^\pi \sin x \, dx = 2$ is typed as

```
$\int_{0}^{\pi} \sin x \, dx = 2$
```

`\,` is a spacing command (see Sections 4.11 and A.9).

Math accents The four most frequently used math accents are:

$\bar{a}$ typed as `$\bar{a}$`

$\hat{a}$ typed as `$\hat{a}$`

$\tilde{a}$ typed as `$\tilde{a}$`

$\vec{a}$ typed as `$\vec{a}$`

See Section 4.9 for a complete list.

Matrices LaTeX provides the `array` environment to typeset matrices.

`array` is a *subsidiary math environment:* It must be used inside a displayed math environment or within an `equation` environment (see Section 1.6).

For example,

$$\begin{array}{cccc} a+b+c & uv & x-y & 27 \\ a+b & u+v & z & 134 \end{array}$$

is typed as

```
\[
  \begin{array}{cccc}
    a + b + c & uv    & x - y & 27\\
    a + b     & u + v & z     & 134
  \end{array}
\]
```

The required argument consists of a character `l`, `r`, or `c` (meaning left, right, or center alignment) for each column. All the columns in this example are centered, so the argument is `cccc`.

The amsmath package provides the `matrix` subsidiary math environment; using this environment, you would type the previous example as follows: Ⓐ

```
\[
  \begin{matrix}
    a + b + c & uv    & x - y & 27\\
    a + b & u + v & z & 134
  \end{matrix}
\]
```

Both environments separate adjacent matrix elements within a row with ampersands (`&`); rows are separated by linebreak commands (`\\`). No linebreak command is needed on the last row.

The basic form of the AMS `matrix` environment does not include delimiters. Several additional subsidiary math environments do, including `pmatrix` and `vmatrix`. For example, Ⓐ

$$\mathbf{A} = \begin{pmatrix} a+b+c & uv \\ a+b & u+v \end{pmatrix} \begin{vmatrix} 30 & 7 \\ 3 & 17 \end{vmatrix}$$

is typed as follows:

```
\[
  \mathbf{A} =
  \begin{pmatrix}
    a + b + c & uv\\
    a + b & u + v
  \end{pmatrix}
  \begin{vmatrix}
    30 & 7\\
    3 & 17
  \end{vmatrix}
\]
```

As you can see, `pmatrix` typesets as a `matrix` between a pair of `\left(` and `\right)` commands, while `vmatrix` typesets as a `matrix` between a pair of `\left|` and `\right|` commands. See Section 5.7.1 for a listing of all the matrix variants.

Operators To typeset the sine function, $\sin x$, type: `$\sin x$`.

Note that `$sin x$` would be typeset as $sinx$ because LaTeX interprets this expression as the product of four variables.

LaTeX calls `\sin` an *operator;* there are a number of operators listed in Sections 4.7.1 and A.7 (see Section 4.7.2 for user-defined operators). Some are just like `\sin`; others produce a more complex display:

$$\lim_{x \to 0} f(x) = 0$$

which is typed as

```
\[
  \lim_{x \to 0} f(x) = 0
\]
```

Large operators The command for *sum* is `\sum` and for *product* is `\prod`. The following examples,

$$\sum_{i=1}^{n} x_{i}^{2} \qquad \prod_{i=1}^{n} x_{i}^{2}$$

are typed as

```
\[
  \sum_{i=1}^{n} x_{i}^{2} \qquad
   \prod_{i=1}^{n} x_{i}^{2}
\]
```

`\qquad` is a spacing command (see Sections 4.11 and A.9) used to separate the two formulas.

Sums and products are examples of *large operators;* these are listed in Section A.7.3. They appear in a different style and size when used in an inline formula: $\sum_{i=1}^{n} x_{i}^{2} \quad \prod_{i=1}^{n} x_{i}^{2}$.

Roots `\sqrt` produces the square root; for instance, $\sqrt{a + 2b}$ is typed as

```
$\sqrt{a + 2b}$
```

The n-th root, $\sqrt[n]{5}$, requires the use of an *optional argument,* which is specified using brackets (`[ ]`, see Section 2.3.1): `$\sqrt[n]{5}$`.

Text You can include text in a formula with an `\mbox` command. For instance,

$$a = b, \qquad \mbox{by assumption}$$

is typed as

```
\[
   a = b, \mbox{\qquad by assumption}
\]
```

Note the spacing command `\qquad` (equivalent to `\quad\quad`) in the argument of `\mbox`. You could also have typed

```
\[
   a = b, \qquad \mbox{by assumption}
\]
```

because `\qquad` works in math mode as well as in text mode (see Sections 4.11 and A.9).

If you use the amsmath package, the `\text` command is available as a replacement for the `\mbox` command. It works just like `\mbox` except that `\text` automatically changes the size of its argument when necessary, as in a^{power}, typed as

```
$a^{\text{power}}$
```

1.4 *Building a formula step-by-step*

It is easy to build up complex formulas from the components described in Section 1.3. Try the following formula:

$$\sum_{i=1}^{\left[\frac{n}{2}\right]} \binom{x_{i,i+1}^{i^2}}{\left[\frac{i+3}{3}\right]} \frac{\sqrt{\mu(i)^{\frac{3}{2}}(i^2-1)}}{\sqrt[3]{\rho(i)-2}+\sqrt[3]{\rho(i)-1}}$$

(I have used the AMS `\binom` command; if you want to stick with LaTeX, you could use the `\choose` command instead.)

You should build this formula up in several steps. Create a new file in your work directory. Name it `formula.tex`, type in the following lines, and save it:

```
% File: formula.tex
% Typeset with LaTeX format
\documentclass{article}
\usepackage{amssymb,latexsym,amsmath}
\begin{document}
\end{document}
```

(Using standard LaTeX, the fourth line should be \usepackage{latexsym}.)

At present, the file has an empty document environment. Type each part of the formula as an inline or displayed formula within this environment so that you can typeset the document and check for errors. (You can find these formulas in the file gallery.tex in the samples directory.)

Step 1 We will start with $\left[\frac{n}{2} \right]$:

```
$\left[ \frac{n}{2} \right]$
```

Type the previous line into formula.tex and test it by typesetting the document.

Step 2 Now you can do the sum:

$$\sum_{i=1}^{\left[\frac{n}{2} \right]}$$

For the superscript, you can copy and paste the formula created in Step 1 (without the dollar signs), so that you have the following:

```
\[
  \sum_{i = 1}^{ \left[ \frac{n}{2} \right] }
\]
```

Step 3 Next, do the two formulas in the binomial:

$$x_{i,i+1}^{i^{2}} \qquad \left[\frac{i+3}{3} \right]$$

Type them as separate formulas in formula.tex:

```
\[
  x_{i, i + 1}^{i^{2}} \qquad \left[ \frac{i + 3}{3} \right]
\]
```

Step 4 Now it is easy to do the binomial. Piece together the following formula by copying and pasting the previous formulas (dropping the \qquad command):

```
\[
  \binom{ x_{i,i + 1}^{i^{2}} }{ \left[ \frac{i + 3}{3} \right] }
\]
```

which typesets as

$$\binom{ x_{i,i+1}^{i^{2}} }{ \left[\frac{i+3}{3} \right] }$$

Step 5 Next, type the formula under the square root, $\mu(i)^{\frac{3}{2}}(i^2 - 1)$:

```
$\mu(i)^{ \frac{3}{2} } (i^{2} - 1)$
```

and then the square root, $\sqrt{\mu(i)^{\frac{3}{2}}(i^2 - 1)}$:

```
$\sqrt{ \mu(i)^{ \frac{3}{2} } (i^{2} - 1) }$
```

Step 6 The two cube roots, $\sqrt[3]{\rho(i) - 2}$ and $\sqrt[3]{\rho(i) - 1}$, are easy to type:

```
$\sqrt[3]{ \rho(i) - 2 }$  $\sqrt[3]{ \rho(i) - 1 }$
```

Step 7 Now the fraction

$$\frac{\sqrt{\mu(i)^{\frac{3}{2}}(i^2 - 1)}}{\sqrt[3]{\rho(i) - 2} + \sqrt[3]{\rho(i) - 1}}$$

which is typed, copied, and pasted together as

```
\[
   \frac{ \sqrt{ \mu(i)^{ \frac{3}{2}} (i^{2} -1) } }
        { \sqrt[3]{\rho(i) - 2} + \sqrt[3]{\rho(i) - 1} }
\]
```

Step 8 Finally, the whole formula,

$$\sum_{i=1}^{\left[\frac{n}{2}\right]} \binom{x_{i,i+1}^{i^2}}{\left[\frac{i+3}{3}\right]} \frac{\sqrt{\mu(i)^{\frac{3}{2}}(i^2 - 1)}}{\sqrt[3]{\rho(i) - 2} + \sqrt[3]{\rho(i) - 1}}$$

is formed by copying and pasting the pieces together, leaving only one pair of displayed math delimiters:

```
\[
   \sum_{i = 1}^{ \left[ \frac{n}{2} \right] }
      \binom{ x_{i, i + 1}^{i^{2}} }
            { \left[ \frac{i + 3}{3} \right] }
      \frac{ \sqrt{ \mu(i)^{ \frac{3}{2}} (i^{2} - 1) } }
           { \sqrt[3]{\rho(i) - 2} + \sqrt[3]{\rho(i) - 1} }
\]
```

Note the use of

- Hierarchical indentation, to keep track of the structure of the formula
- Spacing to help distinguish the braces (some text editors will help you balance braces)
- Separate lines for the various pieces of the formula

It is to your advantage to *keep your source file readable.* LaTeX does not care how its input is formatted, and would happily accept the following:

```
\[\sum_{i=1}^{\left[\frac{n}{2}\right]}\binom{x_{i,i+1}^{i^{2}}}
{\left[\frac{i+3}{3}\right]}\frac{\sqrt{\mu(i)^{\frac{3}
{2}}(i^{2}-1)}}{\sqrt[3]{\rho(i)-2}+\sqrt[3]{\rho(i)-1}}\]
```

But this haphazard style will not only make it more difficult for your coauthors or editor to work with your source file, it will make finding mistakes difficult. Try to find the error in the next version:

```
\[\sum_{i=1}^{\left[\frac{n}{2}\right]}\binom{x_{i,i+1}^{i^{2}}}
{\left[\frac{i+3}{3}\right]}\frac{\sqrt{\mu(i)^{\frac{3}
{2}}}(i^{2}-1)}}{\sqrt[3]{\rho(i)-2}+\sqrt[3]{\rho(i)-1}}\]
```

(Answer: `\frac{3}{2` should be followed by `}}` and not by `}}}`.)

1.5 Formula gallery

In this section, I present the formula gallery, a collection of formulas—some simple, some complex—that illustrate the power of LaTeX and the AMS packages. (You can find these examples in the file `gallery.tex` in the `samples` directory.) Some of the commands in these examples have not been discussed previously, but you should be able to answer most of your questions about how they work by comparing the source with the typeset result or by looking up these commands in the later parts of this book. Occasionally, I will give you a helping hand with some comments.

Many of these formulas are taken from textbooks and research articles. The last six are reproduced from the document `testart.tex`, which was distributed by the AMS some years ago.

Ⓐ Some of these examples require the amssymb and amsmath packages; be sure to include the line

```
\usepackage{amssymb,latexsym,amsmath}
```

following the `documentclass` line of any article using such constructs; or follow my recommendation on page xxxvi and ignore this warning. I will point out what additional packages (if any) are required for each formula.

Formula 1 A set-valued function:

$$x \mapsto \{\, c \in C \mid c \leq x \,\}$$

```
\[
  x \mapsto \{\, c \in C \mid c \leq x \,\}
\]
```

Note that both | and \mid are typeset as $|$. Use | for absolute value signs. In this formula, \mid is used because it provides extra spacing (see Section 4.6.4). To equalize the spacing around $c \in C$ and $c \leq x$, a thin space (\,) was added inside each brace (see Section 4.11). The same technique is used in several other formulas in this section.

Formula 2

$$\left| \bigcup (\, I_{j} \mid j \in J \,) \right| < \mathfrak{m}$$

is typed as

```
\[
   \left| \bigcup (\, I_{j} \mid j \in J \,) \right|
    < \mathfrak{m}
\]
```

The \left| and \right| commands are delimiters; they create vertical bars whose size adjusts to the size of the formula. The \mathfrak command provides access to the *Fraktur math alphabet* (which requires either the amsfonts or the eufrak package). 

Formula 3 Note that you have to add spacing both before and after the text fragment for some in the following example. The argument of \mbox is typeset in text mode, so the space is recognized.

$$A = \{\, x \in X \mid x \in X_{i},\ \mbox{ for some $i \in I$} \,\}$$

```
\[
   A = \{\, x \in X \mid x \in X_{i},
            \mbox{ for some $i \in I$} \,\}
\]
```

Formula 4 Space to show logical structure:

$$\langle a_{1},a_{2} \rangle \leq \langle a'_{1},a'_{2}\rangle \qquad \mbox{iff} \qquad a_{1} < a'_{1} \quad \mbox{or} \quad a_{1} = a'_{1} \mbox{ and } a_{2} \leq a'_{2}$$

```
\[
   \langle a_{1},a_{2} \rangle \leq \langle a'_{1},a'_{2}\rangle
    \qquad \mbox{if{f}} \qquad a_{1} < a'_{1} \quad  \mbox{or}
    \quad a_{1} = a'_{1} \mbox{ and } a_{2} \leq a'_{2}
\]
```

Note that in if{f} (in the argument of the first \mbox) the second f is enclosed in braces to avoid the use of the ligature—the merging of the two fs. For the proper way of typesetting iff without a ligature, see Section 2.4.6.

Formula 5 Here are some examples of Greek letters:

$$\Gamma_{u'} = \{\, \gamma \mid \gamma < 2\chi, \ B_{\alpha} \nsubseteq u', \ B_{\gamma} \subseteq u' \,\}$$

```
\[
  \Gamma_{u'} = \{\, \gamma \mid \gamma < 2\chi,
   \ B_{\alpha} \nsubseteq u', \ B_{\gamma} \subseteq u' \,\}
\]
```

Ⓐ See Section A.1.2 for a complete listing of Greek letters. The `\nsubseteq` command requires the amssymb package.

Ⓐ **Formula 6** `\mathbb` allows you to use the blackboard bold math alphabet (which only provides capital letters):

$$A = B^{2} \times \mathbb{Z}$$

```
\[
  A = B^{2} \times \mathbb{Z}
\]
```

Ⓐ Blackboard bold requires the amssymb package.

Formula 7 The `\left[` and `\right]` delimiters set square brackets whose size is proportional to the height of the symbols delimited by them:

$$y^C \equiv z \vee \bigvee_{ i \in C } \left[s_{i}^{C} \right] \pmod{ \Phi }$$

```
\[
  y^C \equiv z \vee \bigvee_{ i \in C } \left[ s_{i}^{C} \right]
   \pmod{ \Phi }
\]
```

Notice how the superscript is set directly above the subscript in s_{i}^{C}.

Formula 8

$$y \vee \bigvee (\, [B_{\gamma}] \mid \gamma \in \Gamma \,) \equiv z \vee \bigvee (\, [B_{\gamma}] \mid \gamma \in \Gamma \,) \pmod{ \Phi^{x} }$$

```
\[
  y \vee \bigvee (\, [B_{\gamma}] \mid \gamma \in \Gamma \,)
   \equiv z \vee \bigvee (\, [B_{\gamma}]
   \mid \gamma \in \Gamma \,) \pmod{ \Phi^{x} }
\]
```

Ⓐ The spacing shown was created by the amsmath package.

Formula 9 Use \nolimits to force the "limit" of the large operator to display as a subscript:

$$f(\mathbf{x}) = \bigvee\nolimits_{\!\mathfrak{m}} \left(\, \bigwedge\nolimits_{\mathfrak{m}} (\, x_{j} \mid j \in I_{i} \,) \mid i < \aleph_{\alpha} \,\right)$$

```
\[
   f(\mathbf{x}) = \bigvee\nolimits_{\!\mathfrak{m}}
    \left(\,
       \bigwedge\nolimits_{\mathfrak{m}}
        (\, x_{j} \mid j \in I_{i} \,) \mid i < \aleph_{\alpha}
    \,\right)
\]
```

Notice that a negative space (\!) was inserted to bring the $\mathfrak{m}$ a little closer to the big join symbol $\bigvee$.

The \mathfrak command requires either the amsfonts or eufrak package. Ⓐ

Formula 10 The \left. command gives a blank left delimiter, which is needed to balance the \right| command (if the \left and \right commands are not balanced, you will get an error message):

$$\left. \widehat{F}(x) \right|_{a}^{b} = \widehat{F}(b) - \widehat{F}(a)$$

```
\[
  \left. \widehat{F}(x) \right|_{a}^{b}
   = \widehat{F}(b) - \widehat{F}(a)
\]
```

Formula 11

$$u \underset{\alpha}{+} v \overset{1}{\thicksim} w \overset{2}{\thicksim} z$$

```
\[
  u \underset{\alpha}{+} v \overset{1}{\thicksim} w
   \overset{2}{\thicksim} z
\]
```

The \underset and \overset commands require the amsmath package. A special case, placing a symbol above a binary relation, can be done in LaTeX with the \stackrel command. Ⓐ

Formula 12 In this formula, \mbox would not work properly because the overset text would be too large, so we use \text, which requires the amsmath package: Ⓐ

$$f(x) \overset{\text{def}}{=} x^{2} - 1$$

```
\[
  f(x) \overset{ \text{def} }{ = } x^{2} - 1
\]
```

Formula 13

$$\overbrace{a + b + \cdots + z}^{n}$$

```
\[
  \overbrace{a + b + \cdots + z}^{n}
\]
```

Ⓐ The symbol typed as the exponent is attached to the horizontal curly brace. Note that if you use the amsmath package, `\dots` will do.

Formula 14

$$\begin{vmatrix} a + b + c & uv\\ a + b & c + d \end{vmatrix} = 7$$

```
\[
  \begin{vmatrix}
    a + b + c & uv\\
    a + b & c + d
  \end{vmatrix}
  = 7
\]
```

$$\begin{Vmatrix} a + b + c & uv\\ a + b & c + d \end{Vmatrix} = 7$$

```
\[
  \begin{Vmatrix}
    a + b + c & uv\\
    a + b & c + d
  \end{Vmatrix}
  = 7
\]
```

Ⓐ The `vmatrix` and `Vmatrix` environments require the amsmath package. In LaTeX, the second matrix would be typed as

```
\[
  \left\|\begin{array}{cc}
     a + b + c & uv\\
     a + b & c + d
  \end{array}\right\|
  = 7
\]
```

which produces the typeset formula

$$\left\|\begin{array}{cc} a + b + c & uv\\ a + b & c + d \end{array}\right\| = 7$$

Note, again, that the LaTeX spacing is different.

Formula 15

$$\sum_{j \in \mathbf{N}} b_{ij} \hat{y}_{j} = \sum_{j \in \mathbf{N}} b^{(\lambda)}_{ij} \hat{y}_{j} + (b_{ii} - \lambda_{i}) \hat{y}_{i} \hat{y}$$

is typed as

```
\[
  \sum_{j \in \mathbf{N}} b_{ij} \hat{y}_{j}
   = \sum_{j \in \mathbf{N}} b^{(\lambda)}_{ij} \hat{y}_{j}
   + (b_{ii} - \lambda_{i}) \hat{y}_{i} \hat{y}
\]
```

The `\mathbf{N}` command makes a bold **N**. Since the `\mathbf` command cannot be used to produce a bold math symbol (in math mode), the amsmath package offers the `\boldsymbol` command: `\boldsymbol{\alpha}` produces $\boldsymbol{\alpha}$. Ⓐ

Formula 16 To produce the formula

$$\biggl(\prod^n_{\, j = 1} \hat x_{j} \biggr) H_{c} = \frac{1}{2} \hat{k}_{ij} \det \widehat{ \mathbf{K} }(i|i)$$

try typing

```
\[
  \left( \prod^n_{\, j = 1} \hat x_{j} \right) H_{c}
   = \frac{1}{2} \hat k_{ij} \det \hat{ \mathbf{K} }(i|i)
\]
```

which typesets as

$$\left(\prod^n_{\, j = 1} \hat x_{j} \right) H_{c} = \frac{1}{2} \hat k_{ij} \det \hat{ \mathbf{K} }(i|i)$$

This is not quite right. You can correct the overly large parentheses by using the `\biggl` and `\biggr` commands in place of `\left(` and `\right)`, respectively (see Section 4.6.2). Adjust the small hat over **K** by using `\widehat`:

```
\[
  \biggl( \prod^n_{\, j = 1} \hat x_{j} \biggr) H_{c}
   = \frac{1}{2} \hat{k}_{ij} \det \widehat{ \mathbf{K} }(i|i)
\]
```

which will give you the original formula.

Formula 17 In this formula, I have used `\overline{I}` to get $\overline{I}$ (you could also use `\bar{I}`, which is typeset as $\bar{I}$):

$$\det \mathbf{K}(t = 1, t_{1}, \dots, t_{n}) = \sum_{I \in \mathbf{n}} (-1)^{|I|} \prod_{i \in I} t_{i} \prod_{j \in I} (D_{j} + \lambda_{j} t_{j}) \det \mathbf{A}^{(\lambda)} (\overline{I} | \overline{I}) = 0$$

```
\[
  \det \mathbf{K} (t = 1, t_{1}, \ldots, t_{n})
    = \sum_{I \in \mathbf{n} }(-1)^{|I|} \prod_{i \in I} t_{i}
    \prod_{j \in I} (D_{j} + \lambda_{j} t_{j})
    \det \mathbf{A}^{(\lambda)}(\,\overline{I} | \overline{I}\,)
    = 0
\]
```

Ⓐ Note that if you use the amsmath package, \dots will do.

Formula 18 The command \| provides the $\|$ math symbol in this formula:

$$\lim_{(v, v') \to (0, 0)} \frac{H(z + v) - H(z + v') - BH(z)(v - v')}{\| v - v' \|} = 0$$

```
\[
   \lim_{(v, v') \to (0, 0)}
    \frac{H(z + v) - H(z + v') - BH(z)(v - v')}
         {\| v - v' \|} = 0
\]
```

Formula 19 This formula uses the calligraphic math alphabet:

$$\int_{\mathcal{D}} | \overline{\partial u} |^{2} \Phi_{0}(z) e^{\alpha |z|^2} \geq c_{4} \alpha \int_{\mathcal{D}} |u|^{2} \Phi_{0} e^{\alpha |z|^{2}} + c_{5} \delta^{-2} \int_{A} |u|^{2} \Phi_{0} e^{\alpha |z|^{2}}$$

```
\[
   \int_{\mathcal{D}} | \overline{\partial u} |^{2}
    \Phi_{0}(z) e^{\alpha |z|^2}
    \geq c_{4} \alpha \int_{\mathcal{D}} |u|^{2} \Phi_{0}
    e^{\alpha |z|^{2}}
    + c_{5} \delta^{-2} \int_{A} |u|^{2}
    \Phi_{0} e^{\alpha |z|^{2}}
\]
```

Ⓐ **Formula 20** The \hdotsfor command sets dots that span multiple columns in a matrix. The \dfrac command is the displayed variant of the \frac command (see Section 4.4.1).

$$\mathbf{A} = \begin{pmatrix} \dfrac{\varphi \cdot X_{n,1}}{\varphi_{1} \times \varepsilon_{1}} & (x + \varepsilon_{2})^{2} & \cdots & (x + \varepsilon_{n-1})^{n-1} & (x + \varepsilon_{n})^{n} \\ \dfrac{\varphi \cdot X_{n,1}}{\varphi_{2} \times \varepsilon_{1}} & \dfrac{\varphi \cdot X_{n,2}}{\varphi_{2} \times \varepsilon_{2}} & \cdots & (x + \varepsilon_{n-1})^{n-1} & (x + \varepsilon_{n})^{n} \\ \hdotsfor{5} \\ \dfrac{\varphi \cdot X_{n,1}}{\varphi_{n} \times \varepsilon_{1}} & \dfrac{\varphi \cdot X_{n,2}}{\varphi_{n} \times \varepsilon_{2}} & \cdots & \dfrac{\varphi \cdot X_{n,n-1}}{\varphi_{n} \times \varepsilon_{n-1}} & \dfrac{\varphi \cdot X_{n,n}}{\varphi_{n} \times \varepsilon_{n}} \end{pmatrix} + \mathbf{I}_{n}$$

```
\[
  \mathbf{A} =
  \begin{pmatrix}
    \dfrac{\varphi \cdot X_{n, 1}} {\varphi_{1} \times
      \varepsilon_{1}} & (x + \varepsilon_{2})^{2} & \cdots
      & (x + \varepsilon_{n - 1})^{n - 1}
      & (x + \varepsilon_{n})^{n}\\[10pt]
    \dfrac{\varphi \cdot X_{n, 1}} {\varphi_{2} \times
      \varepsilon_{1}} & \dfrac{\varphi \cdot X_{n, 2}}
      {\varphi_{2} \times \varepsilon_{2}} & \cdots &
      (x + \varepsilon_{n - 1})^{n - 1}
      & (x + \varepsilon_{n})^{n}\\
    \hdotsfor{5}\\
    \dfrac{\varphi \cdot X_{n, 1}} {\varphi_{n} \times
      \varepsilon_{1}} & \dfrac{\varphi \cdot X_{n, 2}}
      {\varphi_{n} \times \varepsilon_{2}} & \cdots
      & \dfrac{\varphi \cdot X_{n, n - 1}} {\varphi_{n}
      \times \varepsilon_{n - 1}} &
      \dfrac{\varphi\cdot X_{n, n}}
            {\varphi_{n} \times \varepsilon_{n}}
  \end{pmatrix}
   + \mathbf{I}_{n}
\]
```

Note the use of the command `\\[10pt]`; if you only use `\\`, the first and second lines of the matrix will be set too close.

This formula requires the amsmath and amssymb packages. I will show you how to rewrite the formula to make it shorter and more readable in Section 9.1.2. Ⓐ

1.6 *Displayed formulas*

1.6.1 *Equations*

The `equation` environment creates a displayed math formula and automatically generates an equation number. The equation

$$\int_{0}^{\pi} \sin x \, dx = 2 \tag{1}$$

is typed as

```
\begin{equation}\label{E:firstInt}
  \int_{0}^{\pi} \sin x \, dx = 2
\end{equation}
```

The equation number (which is automatically generated) depends on how many other equations occur before the given equation. The placement and style of the equation number is dependent on the document class and packages loaded by your document. (In this book, you will find equation numbers on the left—which is the AMS default—except for the sample LaTeX article on pages 44–45.)

To refer to this formula without having to remember a number (which may change if you edit your document), you can assign a *name* to the equation in the argument of a `\label` command. In this example, I have called the first equation `firstInt` (first integral), and used the convention that the label of an equation starts with `E:`, so that the complete `\label` command is

```
\label{E:firstInt}
```

The number of this formula is referenced with the `\ref` command. Its page is referenced using the `\pageref` command. For example, to get the reference see (1), type

```
see~(\ref{E:firstInt})
```

The amsmath package includes the `\eqref` command, which provides the reference number in parentheses. This command is smart: Even if the equation number appears in boldface or italic text, the reference will be typeset upright (in roman type).

Note the use of the tie (`~`) to ensure that the equation number is on the same line as the word `see`. You should always use ties to connect a `\ref` command to the name of its part (equation, page, section, chapter, etc.).

The main advantage of this cross-referencing system is that when you add, delete, or rearrange equations, LaTeX automatically renumbers the equations and adjusts the references that appear in your typeset document.

Rule ■ Typeset twice

For renumbering to work, you have to typeset the source file twice.

See Sections 12.2 and C.2.4. LaTeX will issue a warning if you forget.

LaTeX stores the labels in an auxiliary file while it typesets your source file (see Section 1.13). For each label, it stores the number of the equation and the page on which the equation appears. (A third round of typesetting may be necessary to get the correct page numbers in the table of contents.)

An equation will be numbered whether or not there is a `\label` command attached to it. Of course, if there is no `\label` command, the number generated for the equation by LaTeX cannot be referenced automatically.

The system described here is called *symbolic referencing*. The symbol for the number is the argument of the `\label` command, and that symbol can be referenced with `\ref` or `\pageref` commands. LaTeX uses the same mechanism for all of the numberings it automatically generates: sections, subsections, subsubsections, equations, theorems, lemmas, and bibliographic references—except that for bibliographic references, LaTeX uses the `\bibitem` command to define a bibliographic item and the `\cite` command to cite a bibliographic item (see Section 1.9.4 and Chapter 10).

With the amsmath package, equations can also be *tagged* by attaching a name to the formula with the `\tag` command. The tag replaces the equation number. Ⓐ

For example,

$$\int_{0}^{\pi} \sin x \, dx = 2 \tag{Int}$$

is typed as

```
\begin{equation}
  \int_{0}^{\pi} \sin x \, dx = 2 \tag{Int}
\end{equation}
```

Tags (of the type discussed here) are ***absolute:*** This equation should ***always*** be referred to as (Int). Equation numbers, on the other hand, are ***relative:*** They may change when equations are added, deleted, or rearranged.

1.6.2 Aligned formulas

LaTeX, with the help of the amsmath package, has many ways to typeset multiline formulas. We will discuss three constructs in this section: ***simple alignment, annotated alignment,*** and ***cases;*** see Chapter 5 for many others. Ⓐ

For simple and annotated alignment we use the `align` math environment. Each line in the `align` environment is a separate equation, which LaTeX will automatically number.

Simple alignment

Simple alignment is used to align two or more formulas. To obtain the formulas Ⓐ

$$\begin{aligned} r^2 &= s^2 + t^2, && (2)\\ 2u + 1 &= v + w^{\alpha}, && (3)\\ x &= \frac{y + z}{\sqrt{s + 2u}}; && (4) \end{aligned}$$

type the following, using `\\` as the line separator and `&` as the alignment point (note that you do not need a `\\` on the last line):

```
r^{2}  &= s^{2} + t^{2},                 \label{E:Pyth}\\
2u + 1 &= v + w^{\alpha},                \label{E:alpha}\\
     x &= \frac{y + z}{\sqrt{s + 2u}};   \label{E:frac}
```

alignment points
of formulas

$$r^2 = s^2 + t^2, \tag{2}$$
$$2u + 1 = v + w^\alpha, \tag{3}$$
$$x = \frac{y + z}{\sqrt{s + 2u}}; \tag{4}$$

alignment points
of formulas

Figure 1.1: Simple alignment: source and typeset.

```
\begin{align}
  r^{2}  &= s^{2} + t^{2},                 \label{E:Pyth}\\
  2u + 1 &= v + w^{\alpha},                \label{E:alpha}\\
       x &= \frac{y + z}{\sqrt{s + 2u}};   \label{E:frac}
\end{align}
```

(These formulas are numbered (2), (3), and (4) because they are preceded by one numbered equation earlier in this section.)

Ⓐ The intercolumn space is set by amsmath; if you want to set it yourself, use the alignat math environment (see Section 5.5.4).

The align environment can also be used to break a long formula into two (or more) parts. Since numbering both lines in such a case would be undesirable, you can prevent the numbering of the second line by using the \notag command in the second part of the formula.

For example,

$$\begin{aligned} h(x) &= \int \left(\frac{f(x) + g(x)}{1 + f^{2}(x)} + \frac{1 + f(x)g(x)}{\sqrt{1 - \sin x}} \right) \, dx \\ &= \int \frac{1 + f(x)}{1 + g(x)} \, dx - 2 \tan^{-1}(x - 2) \end{aligned} \tag{5}$$

is typed as follows:

```
\begin{align}\label{E:longInt}
  h(x) &= \int \left( \frac{ f(x) + g(x) } { 1+ f^{2}(x) }
    + \frac{ 1+ f(x)g(x) } { \sqrt{1 - \sin x} } \right) \, dx\\
```

```
        &= \int \frac{ 1 + f(x) } { 1 + g(x) } \, dx
          - 2 \tan^{-1}(x-2)\notag
\end{align}
```

The `multline` math environment (See Section 5.3) and the `split` subsidiary math environment (see Section 5.6.2) provide better ways to split a long formula into two or more aligned parts. `split` also centers the formula number vertically. Ⓐ

The rules for simple alignment are easy to remember:

Rule ■ Simple alignments Ⓐ

- Use the `align` environment.
- Separate the lines with `\\`.
- In each line, indicate the alignment point with `&`.
- Place a `\notag` command in each line that you do not wish numbered.
- Place a `\label` command in each numbered line you may want to reference with `\ref`, `\eqref`, or `\pageref`.

Annotated alignment

Annotated alignment allows you to align formulas and their annotations (explanatory text) separately (see Figure 1.2): Ⓐ

$$\begin{aligned} x &= x \wedge (y \vee z) && \text{(by distributivity)} \quad (6)\\ &= (x \wedge y) \vee (x \wedge z) && \text{(by condition (M))}\\ &= y \vee z. \end{aligned}$$

This example is typed as

```
\begin{align}\label{E:DoAlign}
   x &= x \wedge (y \vee z)
    &&\text{(by distributivity)}\\
   &= (x \wedge y) \vee (x \wedge z)
    &&\text{(by condition (M))} \notag\\
   &= y \vee z. \notag
\end{align}
```

The rules for annotated alignment are similar to the rules of simple alignment. In each line, in addition to the alignment point marked by `&`, there is also a mark for the start of the annotation: `&&`.

The `align` environment can be used for much more than simple and annotated alignments—see Section 5.5.

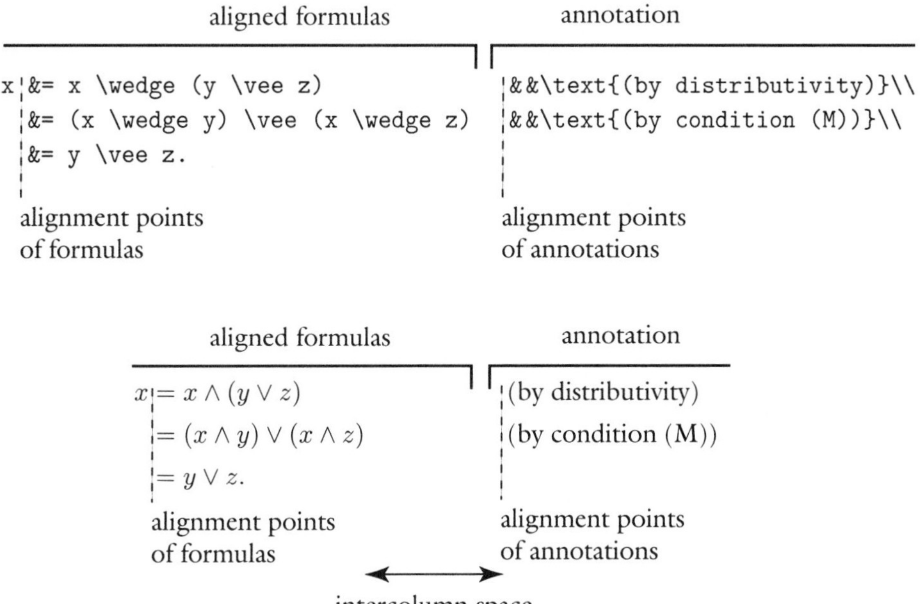

Figure 1.2: Annotated alignment: source and typeset.

1.6.3 *Cases*

Ⓐ The `cases` construct is another subsidiary math environment. It must be used in a displayed math environment (e.g., `align`) or within an `equation` environment (see Section 1.6.1). Here is a typical example:

$$f(x) = \begin{cases} -x^{2}, & \text{if } x < 0; \\ \alpha + x, & \text{if } 0 \leq x \leq 1; \\ x^{2}, & \text{otherwise.} \end{cases}$$

typed as follows:

```
\[
   f(x)=
   \begin{cases}
     -x^{2},         &\text{if $x < 0$;}\\
     \alpha + x,     &\text{if $0 \leq x \leq 1$;}\\
     x^{2}, &\text{otherwise.}
   \end{cases}
\]
```

The rules for using the cases environment are simple:

Rule ■ cases environments

- Separate the lines with \\. Ⓐ
- In each line, indicate the alignment point for the annotation with &.

1.7 *The anatomy of an article*

In this introductory chapter, I will use the popular LaTeX articledocument class and the sample article intrart.tex (in the samples directory) to examine the anatomy of an article. Type it in as we discuss the parts of an article.

The *preamble* of an article is everything from the first line of the source file up to the line

```
\begin{document}
```

```
\documentclass{...}
\usepackage{...}
...
```
preamble

```
\begin{document}
```

```
\title{...}
\author{...}
\date{...}
\maketitle
```
top matter

```
\begin{abstract}
...
\end{abstract}
```
abstract

body

```
\section{...}

\section{...}
```

```
\begin{thebibliography}{9}
...
\end{thebibliography}
```
bibliography

```
\end{document}
```

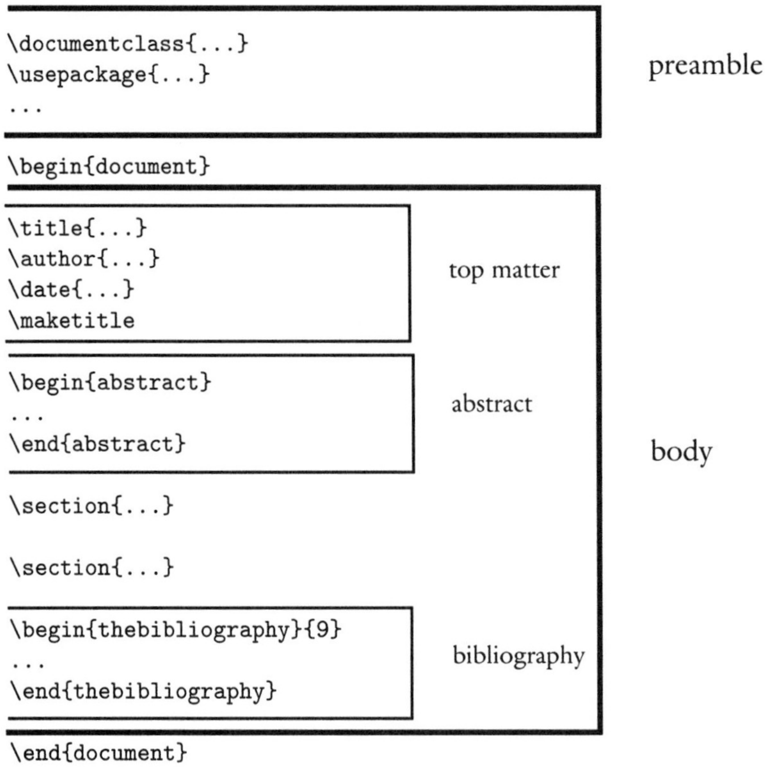

Figure 1.3: A schematic view of an article.

See Figure 1.3. The preamble contains instructions affecting the entire document. The `\documentclass` command is the *only* required command in the preamble. There are other commands (such as the `\usepackage` command) that must be placed in the preamble if they are used, but these commands do not have to be present in every document.

Here is the preamble of the introductory sample article:

```
% Introductory sample article: intrart.tex
% Typeset with LaTeX format

\documentclass{article}
\usepackage{latexsym}
\newtheorem{theorem}{Theorem}
\newtheorem{definition}{Definition}
\newtheorem{notation}{Notation}
```

The preamble specifies the document class and then the LaTeX enhancements, or *packages,* used by the article. It can also specify additional commands that will be used throughout the document (such as proclamation definitions, user-defined commands, and so on). `intrart.tex` specifies the `article` document class, and then loads the latexsym package that provides access to some additional LaTeX symbols.

A *proclamation* is a theorem, definition, corollary, note, or other similar construct. The `intrart.tex` article defines three proclamations. The first of these,

```
\newtheorem{theorem}{Theorem}
```

defines the `theorem` environment, which then can be used in the body of the article (as explained in Section 1.9.3). The other two are similar. LaTeX will automatically number and format proclamations.

The article proper, called the *body,* is contained within the `document` environment—between the lines

```
\begin{document}
```

and

```
\end{document}
```

as illustrated in Figure 1.3. The body of an article is also split into several parts, starting with the *top matter,* which contains title page information. The top matter follows the line

```
\begin{document}
```

and concludes with the line

```
\maketitle
```

Here is the top matter of the introductory sample article:

```
\title{A construction of complete-simple\\
       distributive lattices}
\author{George~A. Menuhin\thanks{Research supported
   by the NSF under grant number 23466.}\\
   Computer Science Department\\
   Winnebago, MN 23714\\
   menuhin@cc.uwinnebago.edu}
\date{March 15, 2000}
\maketitle
```

The body continues with an (optional) abstract, contained within an abstract environment:

```
\begin{abstract}
   In this note, we prove that there exist \emph{complete-simple
   distributive lattices,} that is, complete distributive
   lattices in which there are only two complete congruences.
\end{abstract}
```

And here is the rest of the body of the introductory sample article, exclusive of the bibliography (with one comment in the middle):

```
\section{Introduction}\label{S:intro}
In this note, we prove the following result:

\begin{theorem}
   There exists an infinite complete distributive lattice~$K$
   with only the two trivial complete congruence relations.
\end{theorem}

\section{The $\Pi^{*}$ construction}\label{S:P*}
The following construction is crucial in the proof of our Theorem:

\begin{definition}\label{D:P*}
   Let $D_{i}$, for $i \in I$, be complete distributive
   lattices satisfying condition~\textup{(J)}.  Their
   $\Pi^{*}$ product is defined as follows:
   \[
      \Pi^{*} ( D_{i} \mid i \in I ) =
       \Pi ( D_{i}^{-} \mid i \in I ) + 1;
   \]
   that is, $\Pi^{*} ( D_{i} \mid i \in I )$ is
```

```
   $\Pi ( D_{i}^{-} \mid i \in I )$ with a new unit element.
\end{definition}
```

Notice that we refer to condition (J) in the definition as `\textup{(J)}`. As a result, even if the text of the definition is emphasized (as it will be in the typeset article), `(J)` will still be typeset upright as (J) and not slanted as *(J)*.

```
\begin{notation}
   If $i \in I$ and $d \in D_{i}^{-}$, then
   \[
      \langle \ldots, 0, \ldots, d, \ldots, 0, \ldots \rangle
   \]
   is the element of $\Pi^{*} ( D_{i} \mid i \in I )$ whose
   $i$-th component is $d$ and all the other components
   are $0$.
\end{notation}

See also Ernest~T. Moynahan~\cite{eM57a}.

Next we verify the following result:

\begin{theorem}\label{T:P*}
   Let $D_{i}$, $i \in I$, be complete distributive
   lattices satisfying condition~\textup{(J)}.  Let $\Theta$
   be a complete congruence relation on
   $\Pi^{*} ( D_{i} \mid i \in I )$.
   If there exist $i \in I$ and $d \in D_{i}$ with
   $d < 1_{i}$ such that, for all $d \leq c < 1_{i}$,
   \begin{equation}\label{E:cong1}
      \langle \ldots, d, \ldots, 0, \ldots \rangle \equiv
      \langle \ldots, c, \ldots, 0, \ldots \rangle \pmod{\Theta},
   \end{equation}
   then $\Theta = \iota$.
\end{theorem}

\emph{Proof.} Since
\begin{equation}\label{E:cong2}
   \langle \ldots, d, \ldots, 0, \ldots \rangle \equiv
   \langle \ldots, c, \ldots, 0, \ldots \rangle \pmod{\Theta},
\end{equation}
and $\Theta$ is a complete congruence relation, it follows
from condition~(J) that
\begin{equation}\label{E:cong}
```

```
    \langle \ldots, d, \ldots, 0, \ldots \rangle \equiv
    \bigvee ( \langle \ldots, c, \ldots, 0, \ldots \rangle
    \mid d \leq c < 1 ) \pmod{\Theta}.
\end{equation}

Let $j \in I$, $j \neq i$, and let $a \in D_{j}^{-}$.
Meeting both sides of the congruence (\ref{E:cong2}) with
$\langle \ldots, a, \ldots, 0, \ldots \rangle$, we obtain that
\begin{equation}\label{E:comp}
   0 = \langle \ldots, a, \ldots, 0, \ldots \rangle \pmod{\Theta},
\end{equation}
Using the completeness of $\Theta$ and (\ref{E:comp}),
we get:
\[
   0 \equiv \bigvee ( \langle \ldots, a, \ldots, 0, \ldots
   \rangle \mid a \in D_{j}^{-} ) = 1 \pmod{\Theta},
\]
hence $\Theta = \iota$.
```

At the end of the body, the *bibliographic entries* are typed between the lines

```
\begin{thebibliography}{9}
```

and

```
\end{thebibliography}
```

There are fewer than 10 references in this article, so we tell LaTeX to make room for single-digit numbering by providing the argument 9 to the `thebibliography` environment; use 99 if the number of references is between 10 and 99. The typeset bibliography will be titled References.

Here is the bibliography from `intrart.tex`:

```
\begin{thebibliography}{9}
   \bibitem{sF90}
      Soo-Key Foo,
      \emph{Lattice Constructions},
      Ph.D. thesis,
      University of Winnebago, Winnebago, MN, December, 1990.
   \bibitem{gM68}
      George~A. Menuhin,
      \emph{Universal Algebra},
      D.~van Nostrand, Princeton, 1968.
   \bibitem{eM57}
```

```
      Ernest~T. Moynahan,
      \emph{On a problem of M. Stone},
      Acta Math. Acad. Sci. Hungar. \textbf{8} (1957), 455--460.
   \bibitem{eM57a}
      Ernest~T. Moynahan,
      \emph{Ideals and congruence relations in lattices.} II,
      Magyar Tud. Akad. Mat. Fiz. Oszt. K\"{o}zl. \textbf{9}
      (1957), 417--434.
\end{thebibliography}
```

The body (and the article) ends when the `document` environment is closed with

```
\end{document}
```

1.7.1 *The typeset sample article*

On pages 44 and 45, you will find the typeset `intrart.tex`, the introductory sample article. Notice that the equation numbers are on the right, which is the default in LaTeX's `article` document class. Elsewhere in this book you will find equation numbers on the left, which is the AMS default—see Sections 7.1.1, 8.5, and 12.1.3 to learn how to change the default.

A construction of complete-simple distributive lattices

George A. Menuhin*
Computer Science Department
Winnebago, MN 23714
menuhin@cc.uwinnebago.edu

March 15, 2000

Abstract

In this note, we prove that there exist *complete-simple distributive lattices,* that is, complete distributive lattices in which there are only two complete congruences.

1 Introduction

In this note, we prove the following result:

Theorem 1 *There exists an infinite complete distributive lattice K with only the two trivial complete congruence relations.*

2 The Π^* construction

The following construction is crucial in the proof of our Theorem:

Definition 1 *Let D_i, for $i \in I$, be complete distributive lattices satisfying condition* (J). *Their Π^* product is defined as follows:*

$$\Pi^*(D_i \mid i \in I) = \Pi(D_i^- \mid i \in I) + 1;$$

that is, $\Pi^*(D_i \mid i \in I)$ is $\Pi(D_i^- \mid i \in I)$ with a new unit element.

Notation 1 *If $i \in I$ and $d \in D_i^-$, then*

$$\langle \dots, 0, \dots, d, \dots, 0, \dots \rangle$$

is the element of $\Pi^*(D_i \mid i \in I)$ whose i-th component is d and all the other components are 0.

*Research supported by the NSF under grant number 23466.

See also Ernest T. Moynahan [4].
Next we verify the following result:

Theorem 2 *Let D_i, $i \in I$, be complete distributive lattices satisfying condition* (J). *Let Θ be a complete congruence relation on $\Pi^*(D_i \mid i \in I)$. If there exist $i \in I$ and $d \in D_i$ with $d < 1_i$ such that, for all $d \le c < 1_i$,*

$$\langle \dots, d, \dots, 0, \dots \rangle \equiv \langle \dots, c, \dots, 0, \dots \rangle \pmod{\Theta}, \tag{1}$$

then $\Theta = \iota$.

Proof. Since

$$\langle \dots, d, \dots, 0, \dots \rangle \equiv \langle \dots, c, \dots, 0, \dots \rangle \pmod{\Theta}, \tag{2}$$

and Θ is a complete congruence relation, it follows from condition (J) that

$$\langle \dots, d, \dots, 0, \dots \rangle \equiv \bigvee (\langle \dots, c, \dots, 0, \dots \rangle \mid d \le c < 1) \pmod{\Theta}. \tag{3}$$

Let $j \in I$, $j \ne i$, and let $a \in D_j^-$. Meeting both sides of the congruence (2) with $\langle \dots, a, \dots, 0, \dots \rangle$, we obtain that

$$0 = \langle \dots, a, \dots, 0, \dots \rangle \pmod{\Theta}, \tag{4}$$

Using the completeness of Θ and (4), we get:

$$0 \equiv \bigvee (\langle \dots, a, \dots, 0, \dots \rangle \mid a \in D_j^-) = 1 \pmod{\Theta},$$

hence $\Theta = \iota$.

References

[1] Soo-Key Foo, *Lattice Constructions*, Ph.D. thesis, University of Winnebago, Winnebago, MN, December, 1990.

[2] George A. Menuhin, *Universal Algebra*, D. van Nostrand, Princeton, 1968.

[3] Ernest T. Moynahan, *On a problem of M. Stone*, Acta Math. Acad. Sci. Hungar. **8** (1957), 455–460.

[4] Ernest T. Moynahan, *Ideals and congruence relations in lattices.* II, Magyar Tud. Akad. Mat. Fiz. Oszt. Közl. **9** (1957), 417–434.

2

1.8 LaTeX article templates

Before you start writing your first article, you should create two article templates using LaTeX's `article` document class:

- `article.tpl` for articles with one author
- `article2.tpl` for articles with two authors

You will find copies of these templates in the `samples` directory (see page 4). Start by copying them to your `work` directory, or type them in from the following listings:

```
% Sample file: article.tpl
% Typeset with LaTeX format
\documentclass{article}
\usepackage{amssymb,latexsym,amsmath}
\newtheorem{theorem}{Theorem}
\newtheorem{lemma}{Lemma}
\newtheorem{proposition}{Proposition}
\newtheorem{definition}{Definition}
\newtheorem{corollary}{Corollary}
\newtheorem{notation}{Notation}

\begin{document}
\title{titleline1\\
  titleline2}
\author{name\thanks{support}\\
  addressline1\\
  addressline2\\
  addressline3}
\date{date}
\maketitle

\begin{abstract}
  abstract text
\end{abstract}

\begin{thebibliography}{99}
  bibliographic entries
\end{thebibliography}
\end{document}
```

The document `article2.tpl` is identical to `article.tpl` except for the argument of the `\author` command which is expanded to accommodate two authors:

```
\author{name1\thanks{support1}\\
   address1line1\\
   address1line2\\
   address1line3
   \and
   name2\thanks{support2}\\
   address2line1\\
   address2line2\\
   address2line3}
```

Note the use of the `\and` command, which separates the two authors.

Once you have copies of the template files in your `work` directory, you can customize them by putting your own information into the arguments of the top-matter commands. You may also want to save your modified templates in another directory, with more meaningful names. My templates are named `ggart.tpl` and `ggart2.tpl`.

The top matter of my personalized template file looks like this:

```
\title{titleline1\\
       titleline2}
\author{G. Gr\"{a}tzer\thanks{Research supported by the
                              NSERC of Canada.}\\
   University of Manitoba\\
   Department of Mathematics\\
   Winnipeg, MB R3T 2N2\\
   Canada}
\date{date}
```

Notice that I did not edit the `\title` lines (or the `\date` command) because they change from article to article. I also left the second author's information unchanged in `ggart2.tpl`.

1.9 *Your first article*

Your first article will use the `article` document class. To start, open the personalized article template that you created in Section 1.8, and save a copy with an appropriate name. The name should be *one word* (no spaces, no special characters) and end with `.tex`.

1.9.1 *Editing the top matter*

Edit the top matter to contain the relevant information (e.g., title and date) for your article.

Here are some simple rules to follow:

Rule ■ Top matter for the `article` document class

1. If necessary, break the title into separate lines with `\\`. Do not put a `\\` at the end of the last line.
2. `\thanks` places a footnote at the bottom of the first page. If it is not needed, delete it.
3. Separate the lines of your address with `\\`. Do not put a `\\` at the end of the last line.
4. Multiple authors are separated by `\and`. There is only one `\author` command, and it contains all the information (name, address, support) about the authors. There is no `\\` command before the `\and` command.
5. If there is no `\date` command, LaTeX will insert the date on which you are typesetting the file (`\date{\today}` will produce the same result). If you do not want *any* date to appear, type `\date{}`. For a specific date, such as February 21, 2000, type `\date{February 21, 2000}`.
6. The `\title` command is the only required command. The others are optional.

1.9.2 Sectioning

An article, as a rule, is divided into sections. To start the section entitled Introduction, type

```
\section{Introduction}\label{S:intro}
```

`Introduction` is the title of the section; `S:intro` is its label. (I use the convention that `S:` starts the label for a section.) The section's number is automatically assigned by LaTeX; you can refer to this section number with `\ref{S:intro}`:

```
In Section~\ref{S:intro}, we introduce ...
```

`\section*` produces an unnumbered section.

Sections have subsections, and subsections have subsubsections, followed by paragraphs and subparagraphs. The corresponding commands are

```
\subsection  \subsubsection  \paragraph  \subparagraph
```

Their unnumbered variants are

```
\subsection*  \subsubsection*  \paragraph*  \subparagraph*
```

1.9.3 Invoking proclamations

In the preamble of `article.tpl`, you defined the theorem, lemma, proposition, definition, corollary, and notation proclamations. These proclamations define environments.

For example, you type a theorem within a `theorem` environment. The body of the theorem (that is, the part of the source file that produces the theorem) is typed between the lines

```
\begin{theorem}\label{T:xxx}
```

and

```
\end{theorem}
```

where `T:`*xxx* is the label for the theorem. (You should replace *xxx* with a label that is somewhat descriptive of the contents of your theorem.) LaTeX will automatically assign a number to the theorem, and the theorem can be referenced by using a command of the form `\ref{T:`*xxx*`}`.

1.9.4 Inserting references

Finally, we discuss the bibliography. Below are typical entries for the most frequently used types of references: an article in a journal, a book, an article in a volume of conference proceedings, an article (or a chapter) in a book, a Ph.D. thesis, and a technical report. For more examples, see the bibliographic template file, `bibl.tpl`, in the `samples` directory.

```
\begin{thebibliography}{9}
   \bibitem{sF90}
      Soo-Key Foo,
      \emph{Lattice Constructions},
      Ph.D. thesis,
      University of Winnebago, Winnebago, MN, December, 1990.
   \bibitem{gM68}
      George~A. Menuhin,
      \emph{Universal Algebra},
      D.~van Nostrand, Princeton, 1968.
   \bibitem{eM57}
      Ernest~T. Moynahan,
      \emph{On a problem of M. Stone},
      Acta Math. Acad. Sci. Hungar. \textbf{8} (1957), 455--460.
   \bibitem{eM57a}
      Ernest~T. Moynahan,
      \emph{Ideals and congruence relations in lattices.} II,
```

```
    Magyar Tud. Akad. Mat. Fiz. Oszt. K\"{o}zl. \textbf{9}
    (1957), 417--434.
\end{thebibliography}
```

I use the convention that the label for a `\bibitem` consists of the initials of the author and the year of publication: A publication by Andrew B. Reich in 1987 would have the label `aR87` (a second publication by that author from that year would be `aR87a`). For joint publications, the label consists of the initials of the authors and the year of publication: A publication by John Bradford and Andrew B. Reich in 1987 would have the label `BR87`. Of course, you can use any label you choose (subject to the rule in Section 6.4.2).

A reference to Bradford and Reich's 1987 article is made with `\cite{BR87}`. For instance,

this result was first published in [5]

typed as

```
this result was first published in~\cite{BR87}
```

You have to arrange the references in your document's `thebibliography` environment in the order you wish to see them. LaTeX only takes care of the numbering and the citations in the text.

If you use an AMS document class, then you can use the `\MR` command to add (A) a *Mathematical Reviews* number reference and the `\URL` command to add a Web page reference to a bibliographic item.

1.10 LaTeX error messages

You will probably make a number of mistakes in your first article. These mistakes will fall into one of the following categories:

1. Typographical errors, which LaTeX will blindly typeset.
2. Errors in mathematical formulas or in the formatting of the text.
3. Errors in your instructions to LaTeX (commands and environments).

can be corrected by viewing the typeset article, finding the errors, and then editing the source file.

Using a spelling checker before typesetting will help you catch many of these errors: See Section 1.13.4 for more information.

Mistakes in the second and third categories will probably trigger errors during the typesetting process (we looked at a few math errors in Section 1.2.2), some of which will require correction before your article can be completely typeset.

We will now look at some examples of the third class of errors by deliberately introducing a number of mistakes into the source file of the introductory LaTeX sample article, `intrart.tex` (in your `work` directory, source file on pages 39–43, and shown typeset on pages 44–45), and examining the error messages that occur.

When LaTeX displays a `?` prompt, you can either try to continue typesetting the document by pressing Return, or type `x` to stop typesetting immediately. See Section 1.13.2 for other options.

Example 1 In `intrart.tex`, go to line 21 (avoid counting lines by using your editor's `Go to Line` function or searching for some text) and remove the closing brace so that it reads

```
\begin{abstract
```

When you typeset `intrart.tex`, LaTeX reports a problem:

```
Runaway argument?
{abstract In this note, we prove that there exist \emph \ETC.
! Paragraph ended before \begin was complete.
<to be read again>
                   \par
l.26
```

Line 26 of the file is the line after `\end{abstract}`. From the error message, you can tell that something is wrong with the command that starts the `abstract` environment.

Example 2 Now correct line 21, then go to line 25 and change it from

```
\end{abstract}
```

to

```
\end{abstrac}
```

and typeset the article again. LaTeX will inform you of another error:

```
! LaTeX Error: \begin{abstract} on input line 21
  ended by \end{abstrac}.

See the LaTeX manual or LaTeX Companion for explanation.
Type  H <Return>  for immediate help.
 ...

l.25 \end{abstrac}
```

You may continue typesetting the article by pressing Return: LaTeX will recover from this error.

Example 3 Instead of correcting the error in line 25, comment it out:

```
% \end{abstrac}
```

Introduce an additional error in line 66. This line reads

```
lattices satisfying condition~\textup{(J)}.  Let $\Theta$
```

Change `\Theta` to `\Teta`:

```
lattices satisfying condition~\textup{(J)}.  Let $\Teta$
```

Now, when you typeset the article, LaTeX reports

```
! Undefined control sequence.
<recently read> \Teta

l.66 ...textup{(J)}.  Let $\Teta
                                $
```

Pressing Return results in the message

```
! LaTeX Error: \begin{abstract} on input line 21 ended
    by \end{document}.


See the LaTeX manual or LaTeX Companion for explanation.
Type  H <Return>  for immediate help.
 ...

l.126 \end{document}
```

These two mistakes are easy to identify: `\Teta` is a misspelling of `\Theta`, and (since `\end{abstract}` is missing) LaTeX is trying to match

```
\begin{abstract}
```

with

```
\end{document}
```

Now undo the changes you made to lines 25 and 66.

Example 4 In line 38, drop the closing brace of the `\label` command:

```
\begin{definition}\label{D:P*
```

This results in the message

```
Runaway argument?
{D:P* Let $D_{i}$, for $i \in I$, be complete distribu\ETC.
! Paragraph ended before \label was complete.
<to be read again>
                   \par
l.49
```

Line 49 is the blank line following `\end{definition}`. The error message is easy to understand: You cannot begin a new paragraph (`\par`) within the argument of a `\label` command.

Undo the change to line 38.

Example 5 Add a blank line following line 53:

```
      \langle \dots, 0, \dots, d, \dots, 0, \dots \rangle
```

This change results in the message

```
! Missing $ inserted.
<inserted text>
                $
l.54
```

There can be no blank lines within a displayed math environment. LaTeX catches the mistake, but the line number reported in the error message is incorrect and the message itself is misleading.

Example 6 Add a $ somewhere in line 53 (such errors often occur when copying and pasting formulas):

```
      \langle $\dots, 0, \dots, d, \dots, 0, \dots \rangle
```

This results in the message:

```
! Display math should end with $$.
<to be read again>
                   \protect
l.53       \langle $\dots
                         , 0, \dots, d, \dots, 0, \dots \rangle
```

You cannot have a $ (an inline math delimiter) in a displayed math formula. LaTeX catches the mistake, but the line number in the error message is wrong.

Example 7 Error messages from LaTeX are not always as helpful as they could be, but there is always some information that can be gleaned from them. In Theorem 1 of `intrart.tex`, delete the second `$` symbol, changing `$K$` to `$K`. You will get the error message

```
! LaTeX Error: Something's wrong--perhaps a missing \item.

See the LaTeX manual or LaTeX Companion for explanation.
Type  H <return>  for immediate help.
 ...

l.33 \end{theorem}
```

Since there is no list, there can be no missing `\item`. The last line of the error message tells you to look at the `theorem` environment.

As a rule, the error message should at least tell you the line number (or paragraph or formula) where LaTeX realizes that there is a problem. Try to identify the structure (the command or environment) that caused the error—read the section of this book that describes that command or environment. Doing so should help you correct the error. Keep in mind that the error could be quite far from the line LaTeX indicates, but will always be on or before that line in the source file.

If you have difficulty isolating a problem, create a `current.tex` file that has the same preamble as your current source file and an empty `document` environment. Then copy the paragraphs you suspect might have problems into this document one by one and track down the errors. Once your new document typesets correctly, copy the paragraph back into your real document, and work on another paragraph. If necessary, split a large paragraph into smaller pieces. See also Section 2.5 on how to use the `comment` environment to help you find errors.

To a large extent you can prevent having to isolate problems by typesetting often. For instance, if I were to typeset *First Steps into LaTeX* [30], with the closing brace of the first `\caption` command on line 480 of the source file missing, I would get the error message

```
! Text line contains an invalid character.
l.1227 ...pletely irreducible^^?
```

where the reference is to line 1227 (about 700 lines removed from the actual error). However, if the only thing I had done before typesetting was to insert that figure (with its incorrect caption command), at least I would know where to look for errors. If you make a dozen corrections and then typeset, you may not know where to start.

1.11 *Logical and visual design*

The typeset version of `intrart.tex` (pp. 44–45) looks impressive. I believe that the typeset version of `sampart.tex` (on pp. 286–288) is even more impressive. To produce such articles, you need to understand that there are two aspects to article design: *visual* and *logical.*

As an example, let us look at a theorem from `intrart.tex`, the LaTeX sample article (the typeset form of the theorem is on page 45). You tell LaTeX that you want to state a theorem by using a `theorem` environment:

```
\begin{theorem}\label{T:P*}
   Let $D_{i}$, $i \in I$, be complete distributive
   lattices satisfying condition~\textup{(J)}.  Let $\Theta$
   be a complete congruence relation on
   $\Pi^{*} ( D_{i} \mid i \in I )$.
   If there exist $i \in I$ and $d \in D_{i}$ with
   $d < 1_{i}$ such that, for all $d \leq c < 1_{i}$,
   \begin{equation}\label{E:cong1}
      \langle \ldots, d, \ldots, 0, \ldots \rangle \equiv
      \langle \ldots, c, \ldots, 0, \ldots \rangle \pmod{\Theta},
   \end{equation}
   then $\Theta = \iota$.
\end{theorem}
```

The logical part of the design is choosing to define a theorem by placing material inside a `theorem` environment. For the visual design, LaTeX must make hundreds of decisions. Could you have specified all of the spacing, font size changes, centering, numbering, and so on? Maybe, but would you *want* to? And would you want to repeat that process for every theorem in your document?

Even if you did, you would have spent a great deal of time and energy on the *visual design* of the theorem rather than on the *logical design* of your article. The idea behind LaTeX is that you should concentrate on what you have to say and let LaTeX take care of the visual design.

This approach allows you to easily alter the visual design by changing the document class (or its options; see Sections 7.1.1, 8.5, and 12.1). If you code the visual design into the article (hard coding it, as a programmer would say), such changes are much harder to accomplish.

LaTeX uses four major tools to separate the logical and visual design of a document:

1. **Commands** Information is given to LaTeX in the arguments of commands; it is up to LaTeX to process that information. For instance, titlepage information Ⓐ (especially in the `amsart` document class) is given in this form; the final organization and appearance of the title page is completely up to the document class and its options.

A more subtle example is the use of a command for distinguishing a term or notation. For instance, you may want to use an `\env` command for environment names. You may define `\env` as follows (`\newcommand` is explained in Section 9.1.1):

```
\newcommand{\env}[1]{\texttt{#1}}
```

giving you a command that typesets all environment names in typewriter style (see Section 2.6.2). Logically, you have decided that an environment name should be marked up. Visually, you may change your decision any time. By changing the definition to

```
\newcommand{\env}[1]{\textbf{#1}}
```

all environment names will be typeset in bold (see Section 2.6.6).

The following, more mathematical, example is taken from `sampartu.tex` (see Section 8.3 and the `samples` directory). This article defines the construct $D^{\langle 2 \rangle}$ with the command

```
\newcommand{\Ds}{D^{\langle 2 \rangle}}
```

If a referee or coauthor suggests a different notation, editing this *one line* will change the notation throughout the entire article.

2. **Environments** Important logical structures are placed within environments. For example, list items (see Section 3.1) are typed within a list environment and formatted accordingly. If you later decide to change the type of the list, you can do so by simply changing the name of the environment.

3. **Proclamations** You can change the style or numbering scheme of any proclamation at any time by changing that proclamation's definition in the preamble, especially if you use the `amsart` document class. See the typeset AMS sample article (`sampart.tex`, on pages 286–288) for examples of proclamations typeset with different styles. 

4. **Numbering and cross-referencing** Theorems, lemmas, definitions, sections, and equations are logical units that can be freely moved around. LaTeX automatically recalculates the numbers and cross-references.

You write articles to communicate your ideas. The closer you get to a separation of logical and visual design, the more you are able to concentrate on that goal. Of course, you can never quite reach this ideal. For instance, a `line too wide` warning (see Sections 1.1.3 and 2.7.1) is a problem of visual design. When a journal changes the document class, unless the new document class retains the same fonts and line width of the document class the author used, new `line too wide` problems will arise. LaTeX is successful in automatically solving visual design problems well over 95% of the time. That is getting fairly close to the ideal.

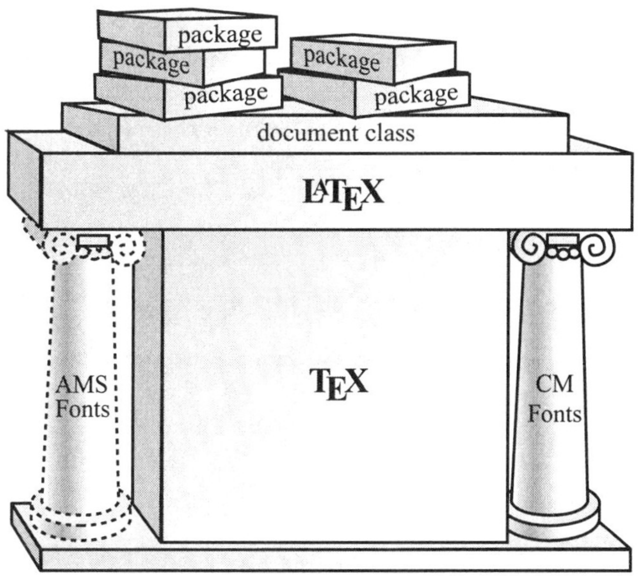

Figure 1.4: The structure of LaTeX.

1.12 *A brief overview*

Now that you have learned how to use LaTeX to typeset an article, I will give you a brief overview of how LaTeX works (see Figure 1.4). As I mentioned in the introduction, LaTeX's core is a programming language created by Donald E. Knuth called TeX, which provides low-level typesetting instructions. TeX comes with a set of fonts called *Computer Modern* (CM). (See Appendix D for a discussion of PostScript CM fonts.) The CM fonts and the TeX programming language form the foundation of a typical TeX system.

TeX is extensible—new commands can be defined in terms of more basic ones. LaTeX is one of the best known extensions of TeX, introducing the concept of *logical units,* which you read about in Section 1.11, and adding a large number of higher-level commands.

The visual layout of LaTeX documents is primarily determined by the *document class* (you now have some familiarity with the document class, `article`; other standard classes include `book`, `letter`, `report`, and `slides`). Many journals, publishers, and schools have their own document classes for formatting articles, books, and theses.

Extensions of LaTeX are called *packages* (we have already come across a number of them, including the amsmath, amssymb, eufrak, and latexsym packages); they add new functionality to LaTeX (by adding new commands and environments) or change the way previously defined commands and environments work. It is essential that you find the packages that make your work easier. (See Section 13.1.)

Ⓐ

My view of the structure of TeX and LaTeX is illustrated in Figure 1.4. This figure suggests that in order to work with a LaTeX document, you first have to install TeX and the CM fonts, then LaTeX, and finally specify the document class and the necessary packages. The AMSFonts font set is very useful, but not absolutely necessary.

1.13 Using LaTeX

Figure 1.5 illustrates the steps in the production of a typeset document.

You start by opening an existing LaTeX source file or creating a new one with a text editor (for this discussion, the source file will be called `myart.tex`). Once the source file is ready, you typeset it using the `LaTeX` format. Depending on the document class options you choose and the packages the document loads, you will end up with at least three additional files:

1. `myart.dvi` The typeset article in machine-readable format—DVI stands for DeVice Independent.
2. `myart.aux` The auxiliary file, used by LaTeX for internal bookkeeping, including cross-references and bibliographic citations.
3. `myart.log` The log file. LaTeX records the typesetting session in the log file, including any warnings and error messages that appear on your monitor.

Your computer uses a *video driver* (DVI *viewer*) to display the typeset article, `myart.dvi`, on your monitor; a (DVI) *printer driver* to print the typeset article on a printer; and a (DVI) *PostScript driver* (DVI *to PS converter*) to convert the typeset article to PostScript format. (For Macintosh and PC implementations of TeX, the PostScript converters are often in the `Save as` option of the printer driver dialog boxes; for most UNIX implementations, the printer driver and the PostScript driver are separate applications.)

It should be emphasized that of the four applications used (TeX and the three drivers), only one (TeX) is the same for all computers and all implementations. If you use TeX in an integrated environment, the four applications may even appear to be a single application.

1.13.1 AMS packages revisited

Now that you understand the structure of LaTeX, we can again discuss the AMS packages. As outlined in the introduction, the AMS enhancements to LaTeX fall into three groups: the AMS math enhancements, the document classes, and the AMSFonts. They consist of several packages.

An AMS document class automatically loads a number of AMS packages (see Section 8.6 for a more detailed discussion) including:

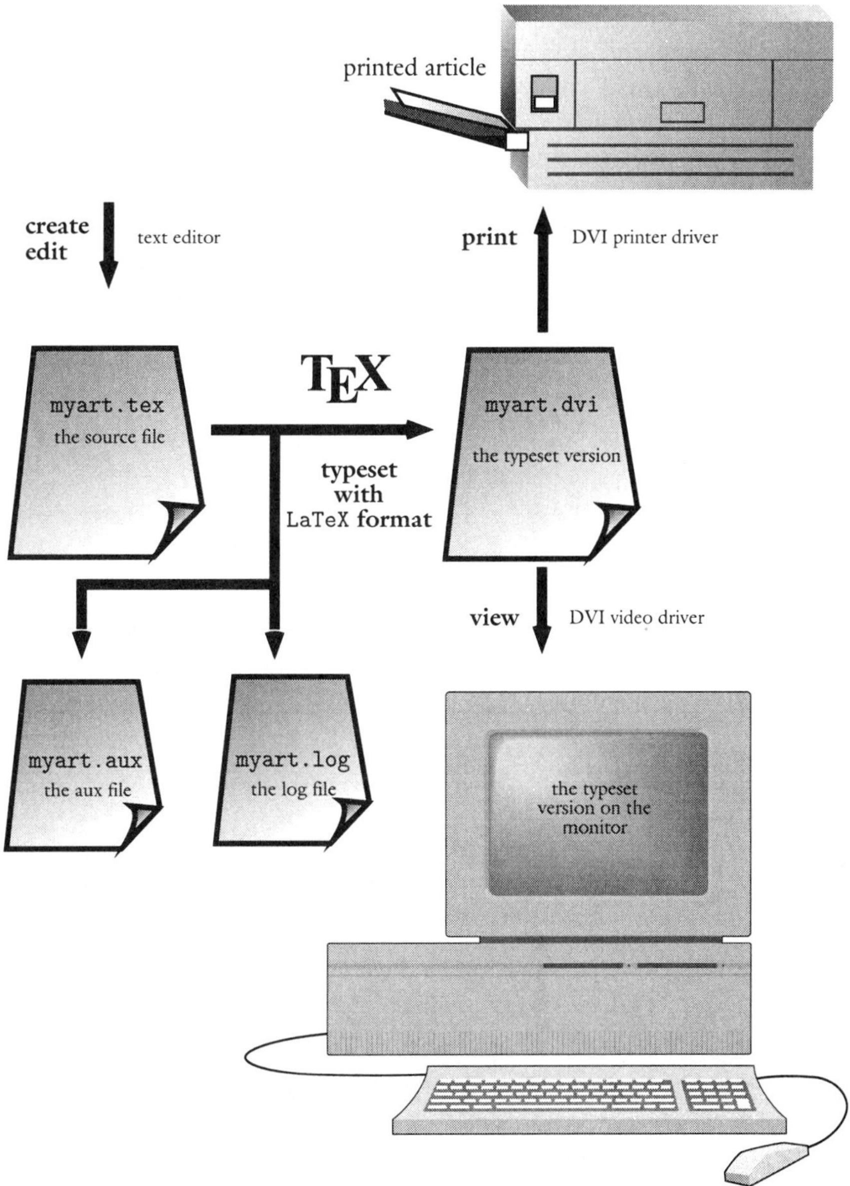

Figure 1.5: Using LaTeX.

- amsmath, the main AMS math package
- amsfonts, commands for math alphabets
- amsbsy, bold symbol commands

The AMS document classes do not automatically load the amssymb package, which Ⓐ provides math symbol names. This package and other AMS or LaTeX packages can be loaded as needed.

When we discuss a feature of LaTeX that requires a package, I mention it in the text. I do not always point out, however, the interdependencies of the document classes and of the packages. For instance, the `\text` command (Section 2.9) is provided by the amstext package, which is loaded automatically by the amsmath Ⓐ package, which is, in turn, loaded automatically by all the AMS document classes. These interdependencies are discussed in Section 8.6.

1.13.2 *Interactive LaTeX*

If LaTeX cannot carry out your instructions, it displays a *prompt* (and possibly an error message; see Section 1.10):

- The `**` prompt means that LaTeX needs to know the name of a source file to typeset. This usually means that you misspelled a file name, you are trying to typeset a document that is not located in TeX's current directory, or that there is a space in the name of your source file.
- The `?` prompt indicates that LaTeX has found an error in your source file, and wants you to decide what to do next. You can try to continue typesetting the file by pressing
  - Return
  - `q` to typeset in quiet mode, not stopping for errors (depending on the nature of the error, LaTeX may either recover or generate error messages)
  - `x` to stop typesetting your file
  - `h` to get advice on how to correct the error
- If you have misspelled the name of a package (in a `\usepackage` command), or if LaTeX cannot find a file, it will display a message similar to the following:

```
! LaTeX Error: File 'misspelled.sty' not found.

Type X to quit or <RETURN> to proceed,
or enter new name. (Default extension: sty)

Enter file name:
```

  You can either type the correct name of the file at the prompt, or type `x` to quit LaTeX.

- The * prompt signifies that LaTeX is in *interactive mode* and is waiting for instructions. To get such a prompt, comment out the line

  ```
  \end{document}
  ```

  in a source file by inserting a % symbol as the first character of the line; then typeset the file. Interactive instructions (such as `\show` and `\showthe`—see Section 9.1.7) may be given at the * prompt. To exit, type

  ```
  \end{document}
  ```

  at the * prompt, and press Return.
- If you get the * prompt and no error message, type `\stop` and press Return.

1.13.3 Versions

A complete LaTeX distribution consists of hundreds of files, all of which interact. Since most of these files have had many revisions, you should make sure that they are all up-to-date and compatible with each other. You can check the version numbers and dates by reading the first few lines of each file in a text editor or by checking the dates and version numbers that are shown on the list created by the command `\listfiles`, which I discuss later in this section.

LaTeX has been updated every six months; while writing this book, I used the version of LaTeX that was issued on June 1, 1999. Starting with the year 2000, updates will be issued once a year.

When you typeset a LaTeX document, LaTeX prints its release date in the log file with a line such as

```
LaTeX2e <1999/06/01>
```

If you use a LaTeX feature that was introduced recently, you can put a command such as the following into the preamble of your source file:

```
\NeedsTeXFormat{LaTeX2e}[1999/06/01]
```

This command specifies the date of the oldest version of LaTeX that may be used to typeset your file. If someone attempts to typeset your file with an older version, LaTeX will generate a warning.

The AMS math packages (in particular, amsmath) and document classes are at version 2.0; and the AMSFonts set is at version 2.2e. See Section 13.1 for more information on obtaining updated versions.

If you include the `\listfiles` command in the preamble of your document, the log file will contain a detailed listing of all the files used in the typesetting of your document. Here are the first few (truncated) lines from such a listing:

```
 *File List*
    book.cls    1999/01/07 v1.4a Standard LaTeX document class
   leqno.clo    1998/08/17 v1.1c Standard LaTeX option
    bk10.clo    1999/01/07 v1.4a Standard LaTeX file
 LaTeXB3.sty    1999/04/15 Commands for LaTeX book, third edition
 amsmath.sty    2000/01/06 v2.04 AMS math features
 amstext.sty    1999/11/15 v2.0
  amsgen.sty    1999/11/30 v2.0
  amsbsy.sty    1999/11/29 v1.2d
  amsopn.sty    1999/12/14 v2.01 operator names
  amsthm.sty    1999/12/16 v2.01
verbatim.sty    1997/04/30 v1.5k verbatim enhancements
 amsxtra.sty    1999/11/15 v1.2c
   eucal.sty    1995/01/06 v2.2 Euler Script fonts
 amssymb.sty    1996/11/03 v2.2b
amsfonts.sty    1997/09/17 v2.2e
 omxcmex.fd     1999/05/25 v2.5h Standard LaTeX font definitions
latexsym.sty    1998/08/17 v2.2e Standard LaTeX package
   amscd.sty    1999/11/29 v2.0
   alltt.sty    1997/06/16 v2.0g defines alltt environment
  xspace.sty    1997/10/13 v1.06 Space after command names
graphics.sty    1999/02/16 v1.01 Standard LaTeX Graphics
    trig.sty    1999/03/16 v1.09 sin cos tan
```

This list looks quite up-to-date (in fact, it is completely up-to-date). To confirm this, open the file alltt.sty in the latest LaTeX distribution; you will find the lines

```
\ProvidesPackage{alltt}
               [1997/06/16 v2.0g defines alltt environment]
```

that explain the date found in the listing.

1.13.4 *Spelling checkers and text editors*

It can be very frustrating to try to check the spelling of a LaTeX document with a regular spelling checker because it will try to check the spelling of your math! Luckily, there are LaTeX-aware spelling checker applications available for all three major platforms:

- Macintosh
  - Excalibur
    `http://www.eg.bucknell.edu/~excalibr/excalibur.html`

- PC
  - jspell
    `ftp://ftp.tex.ac.uk/pub/archive/support/jspell/`
  - Trigram Systems' Microspell
    Available from Y&Y (`http://www.yandy.com/`), among other sources.
  - TeXSpell
    Comes with PCTeX for Windows.
- UNIX
  - ispell is the spelling checker of choice.

All three computer platforms also have a variety of freeware, shareware, and commercial "TeX-aware" text editors with features that include syntax coloring, automatic completion of LaTeX commands and environments, and management of `\label` and `\ref` entries. Using such a text editor can make working with LaTeX much more pleasant and efficient.

If you look at the source files of the sample articles, your first impression may be how very verbose LaTeX is. In actual practice, however, LaTeX is fairly easy to type. You should be able to train your editor so that a single keystroke produces the text:

```
\begin{theorem}\label{T:}

\end{theorem}
```

with the cursor immediately following the colon (where you type the label).

Customizing LaTeX will make repetitious structures such as

```
\begin{equation}
   \langle 0, \dots, d, \dots, 0, \dots \rangle \equiv
   \langle 0, \dots, c, \dots, 0, \dots \rangle \pmod{\Theta},
\end{equation}
```

which typesets as

$$\langle 0, \dots, d, \dots, 0, \dots \rangle \equiv \langle 0, \dots, c, \dots, 0, \dots \rangle \pmod{\Theta}, \tag{3.1}$$

(see page 294) become much shorter and (with practice) more readable. Utilizing the user-defined commands `\con` (for congruence), `\vct` (for vector), and `\gQ` (for Greek theta), this formula can be typed as

```
\begin{equation}
   \con \vct{d}=\vct{c}(\gQ),
\end{equation}
```

which is quite succinct and readable.

User-defined commands are covered in Part IV.

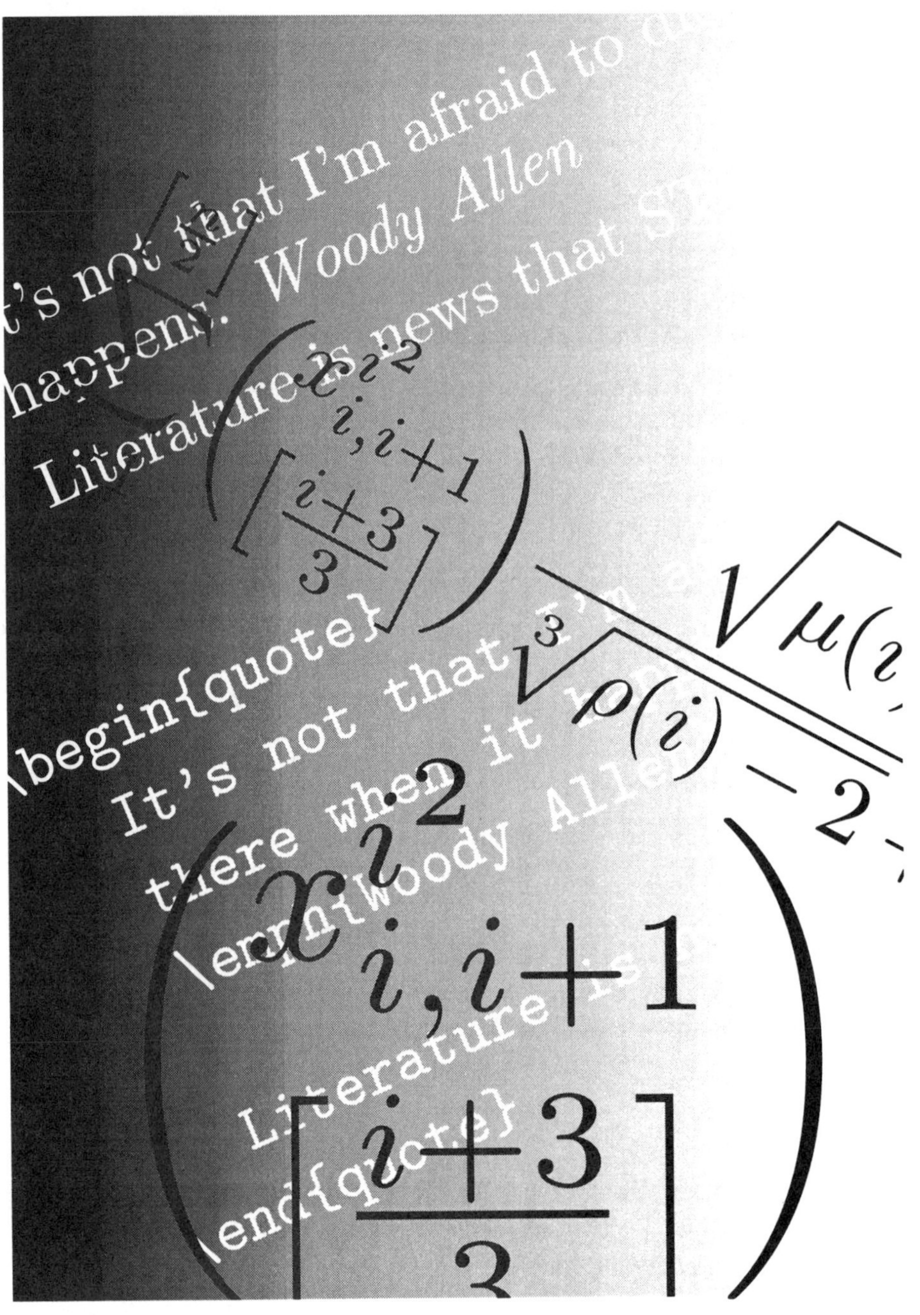

that I'm afraid to
happens. Woody Allen
Literature is news that
\begin{quote}
It's not that
there when it
\end{quote}

PART II

Text and math

CHAPTER

2

Typing text

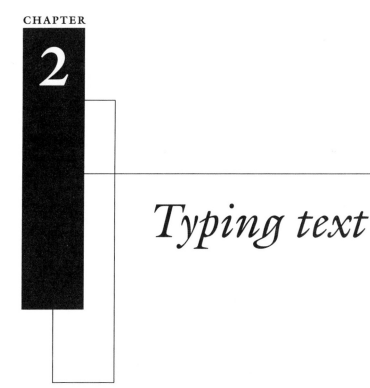

In Chapter 1, we briefly discussed how to type text in a document. Now we will take up this topic more fully.

This chapter starts with a discussion of the keyboard (Section 2.1) and the rules for spaces and tabs (Section 2.2). Section 2.3 covers a very important topic: How to control LaTeX with commands and environments. A document may contain symbols that cannot be found on your keyboard; in Section 2.4, we discuss how to get these symbols in our typeset documents. The % character plays a special role in the source document: It is used to comment out lines; see Section 2.5; this section concludes with a discussion of footnotes.

Section 2.6 discusses methods for changing fonts, shapes, and sizes. In Section 2.7, you will learn about lines, paragraphs, and pages. The judicious use of horizontal and vertical spacing is an important part of document formatting and also the topic of Section 2.8. In Section 2.9 you will learn how to typeset text as if it were a single large character.

2.1 *The keyboard*

Most of the keys on your computer's keyboard produce characters; others are function or modifier keys.

2.1.1 *Basic keys*

The basic keys are grouped as follows:

Letters The 52 letter keys:

`a b c ... z    A B C ... Z`

Digits The ten digits:

`1 2 ... 9 0`

Old-style digits are available with the `\oldstylenums` command; the next line shows the default digits followed by the old style digits:

1234567890   1234567890

Punctuation There are nine punctuation marks:

`, ; . ? ! : ‘ ’ -`

The first six are the usual punctuation marks. The ‘ is the *left single quote* (also known as the *grave accent*), while ’ doubles as the *right single quote* and *apostrophe* (see Section 2.4.1). The - key is the *dash* or *hyphen* (see Sections 2.4.2 and 2.4.9).

Parentheses There are four:

`( ) [ ]`

(and) are *parentheses;* [and] are called (*square*) *brackets.*

Math symbols There are seven math symbols that correspond to keys:

$$/ \quad * \quad + \quad = \quad - \quad < \quad >$$

(The minus sign − corresponds to - (hyphen)—see Section 4.4.1.) The last two characters when typed not in math mode typeset the Spanish punctuation marks ¡ and ¿. Note that there is also a version of colon ($:$) for math formulas (see Section 4.11).

Space keys Pressing the spacebar (or the tab key) gives the *space character;* pressing the *Return* (or *Enter*) key gives the *end-of-line character.* (These keys produce *invisible characters* that are normally not displayed by the text editor on your monitor.) Different computer systems have different end-of-line characters, which may cause some problems when transferring files from one system to another. A good text editor will translate end-of-line characters automatically or on demand.

Sometimes it is important to know whether a space is required. In such cases, I will use the symbol ␣ to indicate a space, for instance, `\in␣ut` and `\␣`.

The tilde ~ produces a *nonbreakable space* or *tie*; see Section 2.4.3.

2.1.2 *Special keys*

There are thirteen special keys on the keyboard:

```
# $ % & ~ _ ^ \ { } @ " |
```

They are mostly used to give instructions to LaTeX; some are used in math mode (see Chapter 4), and some in BibTeX (see Chapter 10). See Section 2.4.4 on how to print these characters in text. Only @ requires no special instructions; type `@` to print @.

2.1.3 *Prohibited keys*

Keys other than the those discussed in Sections 2.1.1 and 2.1.2 are prohibited! Specifically, do not use the computer's modifier keys (Control, Alt, Escape) to produce special characters, such as accented characters. LaTeX will either reject or misunderstand them.

LaTeX provides support for using some modifier keys. More about this in Appendix E.

Tip If there is a prohibited character in your document, you may receive an error message such as

```
! Text line contains an invalid character.
l.222 completely irreducible^^?
                                ^^?
```

Delete and retype the offending word or line until the error goes away.

2.2 *Words, sentences, and paragraphs*

Text consists of words, sentences, and paragraphs. In text, *words* are separated by one or more spaces (which may include a single end-of-line character, see the rule, Spacing in text, below). A group of words terminated by a period, exclamation point, or question mark forms a *sentence*. A group of sentences terminated by one or more blank lines constitutes a *paragraph*.

2.2.1 *Spacing rules*

Here are the most important LaTeX rules about spaces in text in the source file:

Rule ■ Spacing in text

1. Two or more spaces in text are the same as one.
2. A tab or end-of-line character is the same as a space.
3. A blank line (that is, two end-of-line characters separated only by spaces and tabs) indicates the end of a paragraph. The `\par` command is equivalent.
4. Spaces at the beginning of a line are ignored.

Rules 1 and 2 make cutting and pasting text less error-prone. In your source file, you do not have to worry about the line length or the number of spaces separating words or sentences, so long as there is at least one space or end-of-line character separating any two words. Thus

```
 You   do not have to    worry
 about the number of   spaces
separating words, as long as there
is  at least one space or end-of-line character
separating  any two words.
```

produces the same typeset text as

```
You do not have to worry about the number of spaces separating
words, as long as there is at least one space or end-of-line
character separating any two words.
```

However,

```
the number of   spaces separating words,
as long
```

and

```
the number of   spaces separating words
, as long
```

produce different results:

the number of spaces separating words, as long
the number of spaces separating words , as long

Notice the space between words and the comma in the second line: That space was produced by the end-of-line character according to Rule 2.

It is very important, however, to maintain the readability of your source file (see Section 1.4 for an example). LaTeX may not care about the number of spaces or line length, but you, your coauthor, or your editor might.

Rule 3 contradicts Rules 1 and 2; consider it an exception. Sometimes (especially when defining commands and environments—see Sections 9.1 and 9.2) it is more convenient to indicate the end of a paragraph with `\par`.

2.2.2 *Periods*

LaTeX uses the spacing rules in Section 2.2.1 to decide where to put a space when typesetting words and paragraphs. For sentences, the rules are slightly more complicated, however. LaTeX places a certain size space between words—the ***interword space***—and a somewhat larger space between sentences—the ***intersentence space***. To know which space to use, LaTeX must decide whether or not a period indicates the end of a sentence.

Rule 1 ■ Period

A period after a capital letter (for instance, A. or CAT.) signifies an abbreviation or an initial. Every other period signifies the end of a sentence.

This rule works most of the time. When it fails, you will have to specify the type of space you want, as stated in the following two rules.

Rule 2 ■ Period

If an abbreviation does not end with a capital letter (for instance, `etc.`) and it is not the last word in the sentence, then follow the period by an interword space (`\␣`) (or a tie, if appropriate; see Section 2.4.3).

Recall that `\␣` provides an interword space.

```
In 1994, the result was published in the Combin.\ Journal.\\
In 1994, the result was published in the Combin. Journal.
```

will print (since the two spaces are lined up, the small difference is easier to detect):

In 1994, the result was published in the Combin. Journal.
In 1994, the result was published in the Combin. Journal.

Notice that Combin. in the first line is followed by a regular interword space. The intersentence space following Combin. in the second line is wider.

A tie is more appropriate in phrases such as Prof. Smith and pp. 271-292; you should type `Prof.~Smith` and `pp.~271-292`.

Tip The `thebibliography` environment handles periods properly. You do not have to mark periods for abbreviations (in the form `.\␣`) in the name of a journal, so

```
Acta Math. Acad. Sci. Hungar.
```

is correct.

Rule 3 ■ Period

If a capital letter followed by a period is at the end of a sentence, precede the period with `\@`.

For example,

```
(1) follows from condition~H\@.  Therefore, we can proceed\\
(1) follows from condition~H.  Therefore, we can proceed
```

will print:

(1) follows from condition H. Therefore, we can proceed
(1) follows from condition H. Therefore, we can proceed

Notice that there is not enough space after H. in the second line.

Most typographers agree on the following rule (see, e.g., Robert Bringhurst's *The Elements of Typographic Style* [9], p. 30):

Rule 4 ■ Strings of initials

Add no space or a thin space (`\,`) within strings of initials and be consistent.

So W.H. Lampstone (no space) or W. H. Lampstone (thin space, `\,`) is preferred over W. H. Lampstone.

To make the intersentence space equal to the interword space, you can use the command

```
\frenchspacing
```

To switch back to using spaces of different sizes, give the command

```
\nonfrenchspacing
```

2.3 Commanding LATEX

How do you command LATEX to do something special for you, such as starting a new line, changing emphasis, or displaying the next theorem? You use *commands* and special pairs of commands called *environments.*

Commands, as a rule, are followed by their arguments, which are usually fairly brief. Environments can contain any amount of text.

2.3.1 Commands and environments

The `\emph{`*`text`*`}` *command* instructs LATEX to emphasize its argument, *`text`*. The `\&` command has no argument; it instructs LATEX to typeset & (Section 2.4.4).

The `flushright` *environment* instructs LATEX to right justify the text between the two commands

```
\begin{flushright}
\end{flushright}
```

Further examples: a `document` environment contains the body of the article, and an `abstract` environment contains an abstract (if the document class provides for one).

Rule 1 ■ Environments

An environment starts with the command

```
\begin{name}
```

and ends with

```
\end{name}
```

Between these two lines is the *body* of the environment, affected by the definition of the environment.

Rule 2 ■ Commands

A LaTeX command starts with a backslash (\) and is followed by the *command name.* The *name* of a command is either a *single non-alphabetic character* (other than a tab or end-of-line character) or a *string of letters* (one or more letters).

So # and ' are valid command names (the corresponding commands \# and \' are used in Sections 2.4.4 and 2.4.7, respectively), as are `input` and `date`. However, `input3`, `in#ut`, and `in␣ut` are not valid names (3, #, and ␣ should not occur in a multicharacter command name).

LaTeX has a few commands (for instance, $—see Section 4.1) that do not follow this naming scheme, that is, they are not of the form *name*. See also Section 9.1.8 for special commands with special termination rules.

Rule 3 ■ Command termination

LaTeX finds the end of a command name as follows:

- If the first character of the name is not a letter, the name is terminated after the first character.
- If the first character of the name is a letter, the command is terminated by the first nonletter.

If the command name is a string of letters, and is terminated by a space, then LaTeX discards all spaces following the command name.

While `input3` is an invalid name, `\input3` is not an incorrect command: It is the `\input` command followed by the character 3, which is either part of the text following the command or the argument of the command.

LaTeX also allows command names to be modified with *; such commands are referred to as **-ed commands.* Many commands have *-ed variants; for instance, `\hspace*` (see Section 2.8.1).

Rule 4 ■ Command and environment names

Command and environment names are *case sensitive:* `\ShowLabels` is not the same as `\showlabels`.

Rule 5 ■ Arguments

Arguments are enclosed in braces, { }.

Optional arguments are enclosed in brackets, [ ].

Commands may have *arguments,* typed in braces immediately after the command; the argument(s) are used in processing the command. Accents provide very simple examples. For instance, `\'{o}` (which typesets ó) consists of the command `\'` and the argument `o` (see Section 2.4.7). In `\bibliography{article1}`, the command is `\bibliography` and the argument is `article1` (see Section 10.2.2).

Sometimes, if the argument is a single character, the braces can be dropped: `\'o` also typesets as ó.

Some environments also have arguments; for example, the `alignat` environment (see Section 5.5.4) is delimited by the commands

```
\begin{alignat}{2}
```

and

```
\end{alignat}
```

A command or environment may have more than one argument. The `\frac` command (see Section 4.4.1) has two (`$\frac{1}{2}$` typesets as $\frac{1}{2}$); the user-defined command `\con` (see Section 9.1.2) has three.

Some commands (and a few environments) have one or more *optional arguments,* arguments that may or may not be present. The `\sqrt` command (see Section 4.4.5) has an optional argument for specifying roots other than the square root: `\sqrt[3]{25}` typesets as $\sqrt[3]{25}$; the `\documentclass` command (see Section 6.2) has an argument (the name of a document class) and an optional argument (a list of options).

Tip If you get an error when using a command, check that

1. The command is spelled correctly, including the use of uppercase and lowercase characters
2. You have specified all required arguments in braces
3. Any optional argument is in brackets, not braces
4. The command is properly terminated
5. The package providing the command is loaded with the `\usepackage` command

---

Most errors in the use of commands are caused by breaking the termination rule. We can illustrate some of these errors with the `\today` command, which produces today's date; you have already seen this command in Section 1.1.4 (see also Section 2.4.8). The correct use is

```
\today\␣is␣the␣day
```

or

```
\today{}␣is␣the␣day
```

which both typeset as

May 19, 2000 is the day

In the first case, `\today` was terminated by `\␣`, the command that produces an interword space; in the second case, by the *empty group* `{}`.

If there is no space after the `\today` command, as in

```
\todayis␣the␣day
```

you will get the error message

```
! Undefined control sequence.
l.3 \todayis
             the day
```

LaTeX thinks that `\todayis` is the command, and of course, does not recognize it.

If you type one or more spaces after `\today` (two, for example):

```
\today␣␣is␣the␣day%Incorrect!
```

LaTeX interprets the two spaces as a single space by the first space rule (see page 70), and will use that one space to delimit `\today` from the text that follows it. So LaTeX produces

May 19, 2000is the day

Section 9.1.8 discusses how to avoid such errors.

2.3.2 *Scope*

A command issued inside a pair of braces `{ }` has no effect beyond the right brace. You can have any number of pairs of braces:

```
{ ... { ... { ... } ... } ... }
```

The innermost pair containing a command is the *scope* of that command; the command has no effect outside its scope (see, however, Section 2.3.3). We can illustrate this concept using the `\bfseries` command that switches the font to boldface:

```
{some text \bfseries bold text} no more bold
```

typesets `bold text` in bold, but `no more bold` is not typeset in bold:

some text **bold text** no more bold

The commands `\begin{name}` and `\end{name}` bracketing an environment (including inline and displayed math environments—see Section 4.1), also act as a pair of braces; in particular, `$`, `\[`, and `\]` are special braces.

Remember the following obvious but very important rules about braces:

Rule ■ Braces

1. Braces must be balanced: An opening brace has to be closed, and a closing brace must have a matching opening brace.
2. Pairs of braces cannot overlap.

Violating the first brace rule generates warnings and error messages. If there is one more opening brace than closing brace, the document will be typeset, but you will get a warning:

```
(\end occurred inside a group at level 1)
```

For two or more unmatched opening braces, you will be warned that `\end` occurred inside a group at level 2, and so on. There is a tendency to disregard such warnings since your article is already typeset and the error may be difficult to find. However, such errors may have strange consequences. At one point in the writing of the second edition of this book, there were two extra opening braces in Chapter 2; as a result, the title of Chapter 7 was placed on a page by itself. So it is best not to disregard such warnings.

If you have one unmatched closing brace, you will get an error message such as

```
! Too many }'s
```

If a special brace (say, `\begin{name}` or `\end{name}`) does not balance, you will get an error message such as those discussed in Section 1.10:

```
! LaTeX Error: \begin{name} on input line 21
ended by \end{document}.
```

or

```
! LaTeX Error: \begin{document} ended by \end{name}.
```

To illustrate the second rule, here are two simple examples of overlapping braces:

Example 1

```
{\bfseries some text
\begin{lemma}
   more text} final text
\end{lemma}
```

Example 2

```
{some \bfseries text, then math: $\sqrt{2} }, \sqrt{3}$
```

In Example 1, the scope of `\bfseries` overlaps the special braces `\begin{lemma}` and `\end{lemma}`, whereas in Example 2, the scope of `\bfseries` overlaps the special braces `$` and `$`. Example 1 is easy to correct:

```
{\bfseries... }
\begin{lemma}
   {\bfseries... }
   ...
\end{lemma}
```

Example 2 may be corrected as follows:

```
{some \bfseries text, then math:} $\sqrt{2}, \sqrt{3}$
```

If the braces do overlap, and they are of the same kind, LaTeX will simply misunderstand the instructions: The closing brace of the first pair will be regarded as the closing brace of the second pair, an error that may be difficult to detect. Real conflicts can develop when using special braces. Typesetting Example 1 gives the error message

```
! Extra }, or forgotten \endgroup.
l.7 more text }
                final text
```

2.3.3 *Types of commands*

It may be useful at this point to mention that commands may be of various types.

Some commands have arguments, and some do not. It is more interesting that some commands effect change in their arguments, while some commands declare a change. For instance, `\textbf{This is bold}` typesets the phrase `This is bold` in bold, and has no effect on the text following the command. On the other hand, the command `\bfseries` declares that the following text should be bold; this command has no argument. I call a command that effects change a *command declaration.* So `\bfseries` is a command declaration, while `\textbf` is not. As a rule, command declarations are commands without arguments.

Commands with arguments are called *long* if their argument(s) can be more than a paragraph long; otherwise they are *short*. For example, `\textbf` is a short command; so are all the top-matter commands discussed in Section 8.2.

Finally, as discussed in Section 2.3.2, the effect of a command remains within its scope. This is true only of *local* commands. There are also *global* commands, such as the `\setcounter` command described in Section 9.5.1.

Fragile commands

As a rule, LaTeX reads a paragraph of the source file, typesets it, and then goes on to the next paragraph (see Section C.2). Some information from the source file, however, is separately stored for later use.

Examples include the title of an article, which is reused as a running head (Section 8.2.1); titles of parts, sections, subsections, and other sectioning commands, which are used in the table of contents (Sections 12.2 and 6.4.1); footnotes (Section 2.5); table and figure captions (Section 6.4.3); and index entries (Chapter 11).

These are *movable arguments,* and certain commands embedded in them must be protected from damage while being moved. LaTeX commands that need such protection are called *fragile.* The inline math delimiter commands `\(` and `\)` are fragile; `$` is not.

In a movable argument, fragile commands must be protected with a `\protect` command. Thus

```
The function \( f(x^{2}) \)
```

is not an appropriate section title, but

```
The function \protect \( f(x^{2}) \protect \)
```

is. Of course, so is

```
The function $f(x^{2})$
```

To be on the safe side, you should protect every command that might cause problems in a movable argument. Section 12.2 shows an example of what happens if a fragile command is not protected.

2.4 *Symbols not on the keyboard*

A typeset document may contain symbols that cannot be typed; some of these symbols may even be available on the keyboard, but you are prohibited from using them (see Section 2.1.3). In this section, we discuss the commands that typeset some of these symbols in text.

2.4.1 Quotation marks

To produce single and double quotes, as in

‘subdirectly irreducible’ and “subdirectly irreducible”

type

```
`subdirectly irreducible' and ``subdirectly irreducible''
```

Here, ` is the left single quote and ' is the right single quote. Note that the double quote is obtained by pressing the single quote key twice, and *not* by using the double quote key. If you need single and double quotes together, as in “She replied, ‘No.’ ”, separate them with `\,` (which provides a thin horizontal space):

```
``She replied, `No.'\,''
```

2.4.2 Dashes

Dashes come in three lengths. The shortest dash (called a *hyphen*) is used to connect words:

Mean-Value Theorem

This phrase is typed with a single dash:

```
Mean-Value Theorem
```

A medium-sized dash (called an *en dash*) is typed as `--` and is used

- For number ranges; for instance, the phrase see pages 23–45, is typed as

  ```
  see pages~23--45
  ```

  (Note: `~` is a nonbreakable space or tie—see Section 2.4.3).
- In place of a hyphen in a compound adjective when one of the elements of the adjective is an open compound (such as New York) or hyphenated (such as non-English); for instance, the phrase Jonathan Schmidt–Freid adjoint, is typed as

  ```
  Jonathan Schmidt--Freid adjoint
  ```

A long dash—called an *em dash*—is used to mark a change in thought or to add emphasis to a parenthetical clause, as in this sentence. The two em dashes in the last sentence are typed as follows:

```
A long dash---called an \emph{em dash}---is used
```

In math mode, a single dash is typeset as a minus sign $-$ (see Sections 2.1.1 and 4.4.1).

Note that there is no space before or after an en dash or em dash.

2.4.3 *Ties or nonbreakable spaces*

A *tie* or *nonbreakable space* (sometimes called a *blue space*) is an interword space that cannot be broken across lines; for instance, when referencing P. Neukomm in an article, you do not want the initial P. at the end of a line and the surname Neukomm at the beginning of the next line. To prevent such an occurrence, you should type `P.~Neukomm`.

The following examples show some typical uses:

```
Theorem~1
Section~4.2
Donald~E. Knuth
assume that $f(x)$ is (a)~continuous, (b)~bounded
```

Of course, if you add too many ties, as in

```
Peter~G.~Neukomm% Incorrect!
```

LaTeX may send you a line too wide error message (see Section 2.7.1).

In AMS document classes, the tie (`~`) absorbs spaces, so typing `P.␣~␣Neukomm` works just as well; this feature is very convenient when you have to add a tie during editing.

2.4.4 *Special characters*

The characters corresponding to nine of the thirteen special keys (see Section 2.1.2) are produced by typing a backslash (\) and then the key, as shown in Table 2.1.

If for some reason you want to typeset a backslash in your document, type `\textbackslash`, which typesets as \. You might think that you could get a backslash by typing

```
\texttt{\textbackslash}
```

Name	Type	Typeset
Ampersand	`\&`	&
Caret	`\^{}`	^
Dollar Sign	`\$`	$
Left Brace	`\{`	{
Right Brace	`\}`	}
Underscore (or Lowline)	`\_`	_
Octothorp	`\#`	#
Percent	`\%`	%
Tilde	`\~{}`	~

Table 2.1: Nine special characters.

but `\textbackslash` and `\texttt{\textbackslash}` produce the same symbol, \, which is different from the typewriter-style backslash: `\`. (Look at them side by side: \ `\`.) For a typewriter-style backslash you can use the `\bsl` command introduced in Section 9.1.1 or the `\texttt{\symbol{92}}` command introduced later in this section.

The `|` key is seldom used in text; if you need to typeset the math symbol | in text, type `\textbar`.

Note that `*` is typeset as * in text but typesets centered in a formula: $*$; to typeset a centered star in text: $*$, use the command `\textasteriskcentered`.

`@` typesets as @. (In $\mathcal{AMS}$-LaTeX, version 1.1, you had to type `@@` to typeset @.)

Finally, the `"` key should never be used in text; see Section 2.4.1 for the proper way to typeset double quotes. Nevertheless, sometimes " may be used to typeset ", as in the code segment `print("Hello!")`, typed as `\mon{print("Hello!")}`. In BIBTEX and *MakeIndex*, " also has special meanings; see Chapters 10 and 11.

Tip Be careful when typing `\{` and `\}` to typeset the braces { }. Typing a brace without its backslash will result in unbalanced braces, in violation of the first brace rule of Section 2.3.2.

See Section 2.3.2 for some consequences of unbalanced braces. You may avoid some of these problems by introducing user-defined commands as discussed in Section 9.3.

You can also produce special characters with the `\symbol` command:

`\symbol{94}` typesets as ˆ

`\symbol{126}` typesets as ˜

`\texttt{\symbol{92}}` typesets as `\`

The argument of the `\symbol` command is a number matching the slot of the symbol in the layout (encoding) of the font; the layout for the Computer Modern typewriter-style font is shown in Table 2.2.

You can obtain similar tables for any font by using the `fonttbl.tex` file in your `samples` directory. The tables in this file are used in Section 3.7 as examples of the `tabular` environment.

For more about font tables, see the `nfssfont.tex` file (part of the standard LaTeX distribution; see Section 7.3) and Chapter 7 of *The LaTeX Companion* [17] (Sections 7.3.4, 7.5.5, and Figure 7.8).

	0	1	2	3	4	5	6	7	8	9
x	Γ	Δ	Θ	Λ	Ξ	Π	Σ	ϒ	Φ	Ψ
1x	Ω	↑	↓	'	¡	¿	ı	ȷ	`	´
2x	ˇ	˘	¯	˚	¸	ß	æ	œ	ø	Æ
3x	Œ	Ø	␣	!	"	#	$	%	&	’
4x	(	)	*	+	,	-	.	/	0	1
5x	2	3	4	5	6	7	8	9	:	;
6x	<	=	>	?	@	A	B	C	D	E
7x	F	G	H	I	J	K	L	M	N	O
8x	P	Q	R	S	T	U	V	W	X	Y
9x	Z	[	\	]	^	_	‘	a	b	c
10x	d	e	f	g	h	i	j	k	l	m
11x	n	o	p	q	r	s	t	u	v	w
12x	x	y	z	{	|	}	~	¨		

Table 2.2: Font table for the Computer Modern typewriter-style font.

2.4.5 *Ellipses*

The text ellipsis, . . . , is produced using the `\ldots` command. Typing three periods produces ... (notice that the spacing is wrong).

`\ldots` is one of several commands that can be used to create ellipses in formulas; see Section 4.4.3.

2.4.6 *Ligatures*

Certain groups of characters, when typeset, are joined together; such compound characters are called *ligatures*. There are five ligatures that LaTeX typesets automatically (if you use the Computer Modern fonts): ff, fi, fl, ffi, and ffl.

If you want to prevent LaTeX forming a ligature, separate the characters with the command `\textcompwordmark`. Compare iff with iff, typed as `iff` and

```
if\textcompwordmark f
```

respectively. A crude method of preventing the ligature is shown in Formula 4 of the formula gallery (see Section 1.5), enclosing the second character in braces (`{}`); this method, as a rule, may interfere with LaTeX's hyphenation algorithm.

2.4.7 *Accents and symbols in text*

LaTeX provides 15 European accents. Type the command for the accent (\ and a character), followed by the letter (in braces) on which you want the accent placed; see Table 2.3.

For examples, to get Grätzer György, type

Name	Type	Typeset	Name	Type	Typeset
acute	\'{o}	ó	macron	\={o}	ō
breve	\u{o}	ŏ	overdot	\.{g}	ġ
caron/haček	\v{o}	ǒ	ring	\r{u}	ů
cedilla	\c{c}	ç	tie	\t{oo}	o͡o
circumflex	\^{o}	ô	tilde	\~{n}	ñ
dieresis/umlaut	\"{u}	ü	underdot	\d{m}	ṃ
double acute	\H{o}	ő	underbar	\b{o}	o̲
grave	\`{o}	ò			
dotless i	\i	ı	dotless j	\j	ȷ
	\'{\i}	í		\v{\j}	ǰ

Table 2.3: European accents.

Name	Type	Typeset	Type	Typeset
a-ring	\aa	å	\AA	Å
aesc	\ae	æ	\AE	Æ
ethel	\oe	œ	\OE	Œ
eszett	\ss	ß	\SS	SS
inverted question mark	?`	¿		
inverted exclamation mark	!`	¡		
slashed L	\l	ł	\L	Ł
slashed O	\o	ø	\O	Ø

Table 2.4: European characters.

```
Gr\"{a}tzer Gy\"{o}rgy
```

To place an accent on top of an "i" or a "j", you must use the *dotless* "i" and "j", obtained by \i and \j: \'{\i} typesets as í and \v{\j} typesets as ǰ. Tables 2.4 and 2.5 list some additional symbols and European characters available in LaTeX when typing text.

Note that the \textcircled command (in Table 2.5) takes an argument; it seems to work best with a single lowercase character; for instance, ⓐ or @. Capitals, such as Ⓐ, are not very satisfactory; Section 2.9.5 explains how we created the AMS alert symbol Ⓐ that appears in the margins of this book.

2.4.8 *Logos and numbers*

\TeX produces TeX, \LaTeX produces LaTeX, and \LaTeXe produces LaTeX 2_ε (the current version of LaTeX). Remember to type \TeX\␣ or \TeX{} if you need a space

Name	Type	Typeset
ampersand	`\&`	&
asterisk bullet	`\textasteriskcentered`	∗
backslash	`\textbackslash`	\
bar (caesura)	`\textbar`	|
brace left	`\{`	{
brace right	`\}`	}
bullet	`\textbullet`	•
circled a	`\textcircled{a}`	ⓐ
circumflex	`\textasciicircum`	^
copyright	`\copyright`	©
dagger	`\dag`	†
double dagger (diesis)	`\ddag`	‡
dollar	`\$`	$
double quotation left	`\textquotedblleft` or ``` `` ```	“
double quotation right	`\textquotedblright` or `''`	”
em dash	`\textemdash` or `---`	—
en dash	`\textendash` or `--`	–
exclamation down	`\textexclamdown` or ``!` ``	¡
greater than	`\textgreater`	>
less than	`\textless`	<
lowline	`\_`	_
midpoint	`\textperiodcentered`	·
octothorp	`\#`	#
percent	`\%`	%
pilcrow (paragraph)	`\P`	¶
question down	`\textquestiondown` or ``?` ``	¿
registered trademark	`\textregistered`	®
section	`\S`	§

Table 2.5: Extra text symbols.

after TeX (similarly for `\LaTeX` and `\LaTeXe`). A better way to handle this problem is discussed in Section 9.1.1.

The amsmath package adds the `\AmS` command, which produces AMS.

LaTeX also stores some useful numbers:

- `\time` is the time of day in minutes since midnight
- `\day` is the day of the month
- `\month` is the month of the year
- `\year` is the current year

You can include these numbers in your document by using the `\the` command:

```
The year: \the\year; the month: \the\month; the day: \the\day
```

produces a result such as

The year: 2000; the month: 2; the day: 19

Of more interest is the `\today` command, which produces today's date in the form: February 19, 2000. You may want to use `\today` as the argument of the `\date` command when using the AMS document classes (see Chapter 8). In some standard LaTeX document classes, such as `article`, leaving out the `\date` command will also typeset today's date on the title page of the document (see Section 1.9.1).

Remember the termination rule (Rule 3 in Section 2.3.1).

```
today's date in the form: \today (you may want
```

produces

today's date in the form: May 19, 2000(you may want

To get the desired effect, type `\␣` or `{}` after the `\today` command:

```
today's date in the form: \today\ (you may want
```

2.4.9 *Hyphenation*

LaTeX reads the source file one line at a time until it reaches the end of the current paragraph; then tries to balance the typeset lines (see Section C.2.2). To achieve this goal, LaTeX hyphenates long words using a built-in hyphenation algorithm and a database stored in the `hyphen.tex` file. This algorithm is very good, but sometimes you will have to help LaTeX to do a better job.

Rule 1 ■ Optional hyphen
If you find that LaTeX cannot properly hyphenate a word, put *optional hyphens* in the word. An optional hyphen is typed as `\-`, and will allow LaTeX to hyphenate the word where it is placed (and only at these points) if the need arises.

Examples: `data\-base`, `an\-ti\-thet\-ic`, `set\-up`
Note that

- Optional hyphens prevent hyphenation at any other point in the word

- Placing an optional hyphen in a particular occurrence of a word does not affect the hyphenation of any other occurrences of that word

Rule 2 ■ Hyphenation specifications

List the words that often need help in a command:

```
\hyphenation{set-up as-so-ciate}
```

All occurrences of the listed words following this command in your document will be hyphenated as specified where necessary.

Note that in the `\hyphenation` command the hyphens are designated by `-` and not by `\-`, and that the words are separated by spaces (not by commas).

You must use optional hyphens for words with accented characters, as in

```
Gr\"{a}t\-zer
```

Such words cannot be included in a `\hyphenation` list (unless you use the T1 encoding; see Appendix E).

Ⓐ If you use an AMS document class, many such exceptional words are contained in a long `\hyphenation` list in the class file; in particular, the word `database` is listed, so LaTeX will have no difficulty hyphenating it.

Rule 3 ■ Preventing hyphenation

To *prevent* hyphenation of a word, put it in the argument of an `\mbox` command or place it unhyphenated in a `\hyphenation` command.

For example, type

```
\mbox{database}
```

if you do not want this instance of `database` hyphenated, or type

```
\hyphenation{database}
```

to tell LaTeX not to hyphenate any occurrence of the word after this command in your document. Of course, `data\-base` will override the general prohibition for one instance.

You can have any number of `\hyphenation` commands in your document.

Tip LaTeX does not hyphenate a hyphenated word except at the hyphen; nor does it hyphenate a word followed by or preceding an em dash or en dash (see Section 2.4.2). LaTeX often needs help with such words.

Sometimes a hyphen in a phrase should not be broken. For instance, the phrase $\mathfrak{m}$-complete lattice should not be broken after $\mathfrak{m}$; so type it as

```
\mbox{$\mathfrak{m}$-com}\-plete lattice
```

(See Section 4.13.2 for `\mathfrak`.)

The `amsmath` package provides the command `\nobreakdash`, used as Ⓐ

```
\nobreakdash-   \nobreakdash--   \nobreakdash---
```

to prevent such breaks. For example,

```
pages~24\nobreakdash--47
```

Since LaTeX will not hyphenate a hyphenated word except at the hyphen,

```
\nobreakdash-
```

prevents the hyphenation of the whole word as though it were enclosed in an `\mbox`. The form

```
\nobreakdash-\hspace{0pt}
```

allows the normal hyphenation of the word that follows the hyphen; for example,

```
$\mathfrak{m}$\nobreakdash-\hspace{0pt}complete lattice
```

allows the word `complete` to be hyphenated.

This coding of the phrase $\mathfrak{m}$-complete lattice is a natural candidate for a user-defined command (see Section 9.1.1).

Tip If you want to know how LaTeX would hyphenate a list of words, place it in the argument of a `\showhyphens` command.

For instance,

```
\showhyphens{summation reducible latticoid}
```

The result,

```
sum-ma-tion re-ducible lat-ti-coid
```

will be shown in the log file.

Tip Some text editors wrap lines in a source file by breaking them at a hyphen, introducing errors in your typeset document.

For instance,

```
It follows from Theorems \ref{T:M} and~\ref{T:Ap} that complete-
simple lattices are very large.
```

is typeset by LaTeX as follows:

It follows from Theorems 2 and 5 that complete- simple lattices are very large.

As you can see, there is a space between the hyphen and the word `simple`. The text editor inserted an end-of-line character after the hyphen; by the second space rule (see Section 2.2.1), the end-of-line character was interpreted by LaTeX as a space. To correct the error, make sure that there is no such line break, or comment out (see Section 2.5) the end-of-line character:

```
It follows from Theorems \ref{T:M} and~\ref{T:Ap} that complete-%
simple lattices are very large.
```

Better yet, rearrange the two lines:

```
It follows from Theorems \ref{T:M} and~\ref{T:Ap} that
complete-simple lattices are very large.
```

Of course, LaTeX knows nothing about the English language's complicated hyphenation rules; consult *The Chicago Manual of Style* [12] and Lyn Dupré's *BUGS in Writing: A Guide to Debugging Your Prose* [15] for some guidance.

2.5 Comments and footnotes

2.5.1 Comments

The `%` symbol makes LaTeX ignore the rest of the line. A typical use might be a comment to yourself in your source file:

```
therefore, a reference to Theorem~1 % check this!
```

The `%` symbol has many uses. For instance, a typical document class command (see Section 7.1.1),

```
\documentclass[twocolumn,twoside,legalpaper]{article}
```

may be typed with explanations, as

```
\documentclass[%
twocolumn,%  option for two-column pages
twoside,%    format for two-sided printing
legalpaper%  print on legal-size paper
]{article}
```

so you can easily comment out some at a later time:

```
\documentclass[%
%twocolumn,%  option for two-column pages
%twoside,%    format for two-sided printing
legalpaper%  print on legal-size paper
]{article}
```

Notice that the first line is terminated with a `%` to comment out the end-of-line character.

Tip Some command arguments do not allow any spaces; if you want to break line within an argument list, you can terminate the line with a `%`, as shown in the previous example.

See also the example at the end of Section 2.4.9.

It is often useful to start a document with comment lines giving the file name and identifying the format and the version of LaTeX that must be used to typeset it.

```
% This is article.tex
% Typeset with LaTeX format
\NeedsTexFormat{LaTeX2e}[1994/12/01]
```

The third line specifies the December 1, 1994 (or later) release of LaTeX; use such a declaration if your document uses a feature that was not available in earlier releases.

Tip If the comment is too long, split it; otherwise your text editor may wrap it to the next line.

Of course, your editor may be smart enough not to do this, but what about your e-mail application's editor or the text editor a coworker uses? Long lines are a potential problem, so it is best to avoid them altogether.

Other uses of `%` include marking parts of the article for your own reference; for instance, comments explaining command definitions (as in `lattice.sty` in Section 9.3 and your `samples` directory). If something goes wrong inside a multiline math display (see Chapter 5), LaTeX will not tell you precisely where the error occurred. You can try commenting out all but one of the lines, until each line works separately.

Note that % does not comment out lines in a BibTeX database document (see Section 10.2.5).

Tip The 25% rule
If you want a % sign in text, make sure you type it as \%. Otherwise, % will comment out the rest of the line. LaTeX will not produce a warning.

Using % to comment out large blocks of text can be tedious. The verbatim package includes the `comment` environment:

```
\begin{comment}
   ...the commented out text...
\end{comment}
```

Rule ■ `comment` environments

1. `\end{comment}` must be on a line by itself.

2. There can be no `comment` within a `comment`.

In other words,

```
\begin{comment}
   commented out text...
   \begin{comment}
      some more commented out text...
   \end{comment}
   and some more commented out text...
\end{comment}
```

is not allowed. There may be one of several error messages, depending on the circumstances; for instance,

```
! Bad space factor (0).
<recently read> \@savsf

l.175 \end{comment}
```

The `comment` environment can be very useful when working with a large document. Commenting out large parts you are not working on should speed up the typesetting process. Remember to delete any comment environment(s) before the final typesetting. See also Section 12.3.3 for a different approach to managing long documents.

Tip The `comment` environment can also be very useful in locating errors. Suppose you have unbalanced braces in your source file (see Section 2.3.2). Working with a *copy* of your source file, comment out the first half at a safe point (not within an environment!) and typeset. If you still get the same error message, the error is in the second half; you can delete the first half of your copy of the source file. If there is no error message, the error is in the first half; delete the second half of the copy of the source file. Continue applying this method until you narrow down the error to a paragraph that you can visually inspect.

Since the `comment` environment requires the verbatim package, you must include the line

```
\usepackage{verbatim}
```

in the preamble of the file if you want to use it. You can find the verbatim package—if you do not already have it—on CTAN (see Section 13.1) in the

```
/tex-archive/macros/latex/required/tools/
```

directory.

2.5.2 Footnotes

The text of a footnote is typed as the argument of a `\footnote` command. To illustrate the use of footnotes, I have placed one here,[1] typed as

```
\footnote{Footnotes are easy to place.}
```

If you want to use symbols to designate the footnotes, instead of numbers, give the command (before the first footnote)

```
\renewcommand{\thefootnote}{\ensuremath{\fnsymbol{footnote}}}
```

which provides up to nine symbols. Section 9.1.1 discusses the `\ensuremath` command.

Section 3.4 of *The LaTeX Companion* [17] describes how to further customize footnotes.

---

[1]Footnotes are easy to place.

Ⓐ In addition, there are title-page footnotes used by some document classes, such as the `\thanks` and `\date` commands in the top matter of the `amsart` document class (see Section 8.2 and the typeset title page footnotes on page 286).

2.6 Changing font characteristics

Although the document class and its options choose how to typeset characters, there are occasions when you want control over the shape or size of the font used.

2.6.1 Basic font characteristics

You do not have to be a typesetting expert to recognize the following basic font attributes:

Shape Normal text is typeset upright (or roman), but for emphasis you may want to specify *slanted* or *italic* text. Occasionally, you may want to use the SMALL CAPS shape.

Monospace and proportional Typewriters use *monospaced* fonts: The width of all the characters is the same. Most text editors display text using a monospaced font. LaTeX calls monospaced fonts *typewriter style*. In this book, such a font is used to represent user input and LaTeX's responses, whereas normal text is typeset in a *proportional* font in which an i is narrow and an m is wide:

```
mmmmmm
iiiiii
```
} monospaced

mmmmmm
iiiiii
} proportional

Serifs A *serif* is a small horizontal stroke used to finish off a vertical stroke of a letter, as on the top and bottom of the letter M. LaTeX's standard serif font is Computer Modern roman. Fonts without serifs are called *sans serif*. LaTeX's standard sans-serif font is Computer Modern sans serif. Sans-serif fonts are often used for titles or special emphasis.

Series: weight and width The *series* is the combination of weight and width. A font's *weight* is the thickness of a stroke; the *width* is how wide the characters are.

light, ***medium*** (or ***normal***), and ***bold*** often describe weight.

narrow (or ***condensed***), ***medium*** (or ***normal***), and ***extended*** often describe width.

The Computer Modern family includes bold fonts. Traditionally, when the user asks for bold CM fonts, LaTeX actually provides ***bold extended*** (a somewhat wider version).

Size Most document classes cause LaTeX to typeset text at 10 points unless otherwise instructed. Larger sizes are used for titles, section titles, and so on. Abstracts and footnotes are often set in 8-point type.

2.6.2 Document font families

In a document class, the style designer designates three document font families:

1. Roman (upright and serifed) document font family
2. Sans-serif document font family
3. Typewriter-style document font family

and picks one of these (normally, the roman document font family) as the ***document font family*** or ***normal family***. In all the examples in this book, the document font family is the roman document font family. When you use Computer Modern fonts in LaTeX (which is the default), the three document font families are Computer Modern roman, Computer Modern sans serif, and Computer Modern typewriter; the document font family is Computer Modern roman.

In this book, the roman document font family is Galliard; the sans-serif document font family is Computer Modern sans serif; and the typewriter-style document font family is Computer Modern typewriter. The document font family is the roman document font family Galliard.

When typing a document, the document font family (normal family) is the default font. You can always switch back to it with

```
\textnormal{...}
```

or

```
{\normalfont ...}
```

Table 2.6 shows these two commands and three additional pairs of commands to help you switch among the three basic document font families.

2.6.3 Command pairs

As you have seen, most commands that change font characteristics come in two forms:

- A command with an argument, such as `\textrm{...}`, changes its argument; these are short commands (i.e., they cannot contain a blank line or a `\par` command; see Section 2.3.3).
- A command declaration, such as `\rmfamily`, carries out the font change within its scope; see Section 2.3.2.

You should always use commands with arguments for small changes within a paragraph. They have two advantages:

Command with Argument	Command Declaration	Switches to
`\textnormal{...}`	`{\normalfont ...}`	document font family
`\emph{...}`	`{\em ...}`	*emphasis*
`\textrm{...}`	`{\rmfamily ...}`	roman font family
`\textsf{...}`	`{\sffamily ...}`	sans-serif font family
`\texttt{...}`	`{\ttfamily ...}`	`typewriter-style font family`
`\textup{...}`	`{\upshape ...}`	upright shape
`\textit{...}`	`{\itshape ...}`	*italic shape*
`\textsl{...}`	`{\slshape ...}`	*slanted shape*
`\textsc{...}`	`{\scshape ...}`	SMALL CAPITALS
`\textbf{...}`	`{\bfseries ...}`	**bold**
`\textmd{...}`	`{\mdseries ...}`	normal weight and width

Table 2.6: Font family switching commands.

- You are less likely to forget to change back to the normal font
- You do not have to worry about italic corrections (see Section 2.6.5)

Note that *MakeIndex* requires you to use commands with arguments (see Section 11.1) to change the font in which page numbers are typeset.

For font changes involving more than one paragraph, use command declarations; these commands are also preferable in user-defined commands and environments (see Chapter 9).

2.6.4 *Shape commands*

There are five pairs of commands to change the font shape.

- `\textup{...}` or `{\upshape ...}` switch to the upright shape.
- `\textit{...}` or `{\itshape ...}` switch to the *italic shape*.
- `\textsl{...}` or `{\slshape ...}` switch to the *slanted shape*.
- `\textsc{...}` or `{\scshape ...}` switch to SMALL CAPITALS.
- `\emph{...}` or `{\em ...}` switch to *emphasis*.

The document class will specify how emphasis is typeset; normally, it is italic or slanted. Note that the font used for emphasis is context-dependent; for instance,

```
\emph{Rubin space}
```

in the statement of a theorem is typeset as

the space satisfies all three conditions, a so-called Rubin space *that ...*

The emphasis changed the style of Rubin space from italic to upright.

Tip Be careful not to interchange the command pairs. For instance, if by mistake you type `{\textit serif}`, the result is *s*erif. Only the *s* is italicized since `\textit` takes `s` as its argument.

Some typographical rules (for more, see Robert Bringhurst's *The Elements of Typographic Style* [9]):

Rule 1 ■ Font shape and punctuation
If italicized (or slanted) text is followed by a comma or semicolon, it also should be italicized (or slanted).

So in the following example, the first line is the correct one:

```
If the lattice is \emph{relatively complemented,} then \ldots\\
If the lattice is \emph{relatively complemented}, then \ldots
```

and typeset:

If the lattice is *relatively complemented,* then ...
If the lattice is *relatively complemented*, then ...

As Robert Bringhurst puts it in *The Elements of Typographic Style* [9] (p. 60), "italic punctuation normally gives better letterfit and thus looks less obtrusive."

We follow this rule in this book with one exception: The bibliographies are formatted by the AMS rules, which place a comma outside an emphasized title.

Experts are divided whether this rule applies to font weight, in particular, to bold; it is your choice whether a comma or semicolon terminating a bold phrase should be bold. But be consistent.

Rule 2 ■ Abbreviations and acronyms
For abbreviations and acronyms use small caps, except for two-letter geographical acronyms.

So The Proceedings of the AMS should be typed as

```
The Proceedings of the \textsc{ams}
```

Note that only the lowercase characters in the argument of the `\textsc` command are printed as small caps.

2.6.5 *Italic corrections*

The phrase

when using a *serif* font

should be typed as follows:

```
when using a {\itshape serif\/} font
```

The `\/` command before the closing brace is called an *italic correction*. Notice the emphasized M in *M*M typed as `{\itshape M}M`. The first *M* is leaning into the second M. To ensure the proper spacing, you should add an italic correction. This *M* M would be typed as `{\itshape M\/}M`. Compare the typeset phrase from the previous example with and without an italic correction:

when using a *serif* font
when using a *serif* font

The latter is not as pleasing to the eye.

Rule 1 ■ Italic correction before a period or comma
If the emphasized text is followed by a period or comma, you should not type the italic correction.

For example,

Do not forget. My party is on Monday.

should be typed as

```
{\itshape Do not forget}.  My party is on Monday.
```

Rule 2 ■ Italic correction suppressed
The shape commands with arguments do not require you to type an italic correction; it is provided automatically where needed.

Thus you can type the phrase when using a *serif* font the easy way:

```
when using a \textit{serif} font
```

Whenever possible, let LaTeX take care of the italic correction. However, if LaTeX is adding an italic correction where you feel it is not needed, you can override the correction with the `\nocorr` command. LaTeX will not add an italic correction before a period or a comma; these two punctuation marks are stored in the `\nocorrlist` command. By redefining this command, you can modify LaTeX's behavior.

Rule 3 ■ Italic correction necessary
The italic correction is required with the commands `\itshape`, `\slshape`, `\em`.

2.6.6 *Series*

These attributes play a very limited role with the Computer Modern fonts. There is only one important pair of commands,

```
\textbf{...}    {\bfseries ...}
```

to change the font to bold (actually, bold extended). The commands

```
\textmd{...}    {\mdseries ...}
```

which set both the weight and width to medium (normal) are seldom needed.

2.6.7 *Size changes*

Standard LaTeX documents are typeset in 10 point type; to typeset in 11 or 12 point type, use the `11pt` or `12pt` document class options (see Section 7.1.1). The AMS Ⓐ document classes also offer `8pt` and `9pt` document class options (see Sections 8.5 and 12.1.3). The sizes of titles, subscripts, and superscripts are automatically set by the document class. If you must change the font size (it is seldom necessary to do so), the following command declarations are provided:

```
\tiny  \scriptsize  \footnotesize  \small
\normalsize
\large  \Large  \LARGE  \huge  \Huge
```

These are listed in order of increasing (nondecreasing) size (a document class may implement some adjacent commands in the same size). Some document classes may provide additional size-changing commands (see Section 8.1.1).

For example, the size-changing commands in the `book` document class with the `10pt` option (which is the default; see Section 12.1.3) are implemented as follows:

`\tiny`	sample text
`\scriptsize`	sample text
`\footnotesize`	sample text
`\small`	sample text
`\normalsize`	sample text
`\large`	sample text
`\Large`	sample text
`\LARGE`	sample text
`\huge`	sample text
`\Huge`	sample text

Ⓐ The table in Section B.3.2 shows the LaTeX and AMS font-size commands side-by-side. Notice that the AMS document classes define a couple of extra sizes.

2.6.8 *Orthogonality*

You are now familiar with the commands that change the font family, shape, series, and size. Each of these commands affects one and only one font attribute. For example, if you change the series, then the font family, shape, and size do not change; these commands act independently. In LaTeX terminology, the commands are *orthogonal.* From the user's point of view this behavior has an important consequence: *The order in which these commands are given does not matter.* Thus

```
\Large \itshape \bfseries
```

has the same effect as

```
\bfseries \itshape \Large
```

Note that LaTeX 2.09's two-letter commands (see Section 2.6.9) are not orthogonal.

Orthogonality also means that you can combine these font attributes any way you like: for instance, the commands

```
\sffamily \slshape \bfseries \Large
```

instruct LaTeX to change the font family to sans serif, the shape to slanted, the series to bold, and the size to `\Large`. If the corresponding font is not available, LaTeX will use a font that is available, and issue a warning. The font-substitution algorithm (see Section 7.6.3 of *The LaTeX Companion* [17] for details) may not provide the font you really want, so it is your responsibility to make sure that the necessary fonts are available. We discuss this topic further in Section 12.5.

2.6.9 *Two-letter commands*

Users of LaTeX 2.09 and AMS-LaTeX version 1.1 are accustomed to using the two-letter commands: `\bf`, `\it`, `\rm`, `\sc`, `\sf`, `\sl`, and `\tt`. These commands are not part of the new standard LaTeX. They are, however, still defined in LaTeX and AMS document classes. The two-letter commands

1. Switch to the document font family
2. Change to the requested shape

There are a number of reasons not to use them; the two-letter commands

- Are not part of the standard LaTeX
- Require manual italic corrections
- They are not orthogonal (as defined in Section 2.6.8): `\slshape\bfseries` is the same as `\bfseries\slshape` (slanted bold), but `\sl\bf` (bold) is not the same as `\bf\sl` (slanted)

2.6.10 *Low-level commands*

The font-characteristic changing commands we have been discussing in this section are the *high-level* font commands. Each of these commands is implemented by LaTeX and the document class using *low-level* font commands. The low-level commands have been developed for document class and package writers; *The LaTeX Companion* [17] discusses these commands in great detail.

There is one use of low-level commands that comes up often: When you choose a font size for your document, you also choose the `\baselineskip`, the distance from the base of one line to the base of the next line. Typically, a 10-point font size will use a 12 point `\baselineskip`. Occasionally, you may want to change the font size along with the `\baselineskip`. The command for doing so is

```
\fontsize{9pt}{11pt}\selectfont
```

which changes the font size to 9 point and the `\baselineskip` to 11 point. To make this change for a single paragraph, you can type

```
{%special paragraph
\fontsize{9}{11}\selectfont

text

}%end special paragraph
```

2.6.11 Boxed text

Boxed text is very emphatic: Do not touch! typed as

```
\fbox{Do not touch!}
```

Boxed text cannot be broken, so if you want a frame around more than one line of text, you should first place it in the argument of a `\parbox` command or within a `minipage` environment (see Section 2.9.2), and then put that in the argument of an `\fbox` command. For instance (the `\bsl` command is defined in Section 9.1.1),

```
\fbox{\parbox[3in]{Boxed text cannot be broken,
so if you want to frame more than one line
of text, place it in the argument of a
\bsl\texttt{parbox}
command or within a
\texttt{minipage} environment.}}
```

produces

Boxed text cannot be broken, so if you want to frame more than one line of text, place it in the argument of a `\parbox` command or within a `minipage` environment.

See Section 4.17 for boxed formulas.

2.7 Lines, paragraphs, and pages

When typesetting a document, LaTeX breaks the text into lines, paragraphs, and pages. Sometimes you may want to influence how LaTeX does its work.

2.7.1 Lines

LaTeX typesets a document one paragraph at a time (see Section C.2.2). It tries to split the paragraph into lines of equal width; if it fails to do so successfully, and a line is too wide, you will get an `overfull \hbox` message. Here is a typical example:

```
Overfull \hbox (15.38948pt too wide) in paragraph at lines 11--16
[]\OT1/cmr/m/n/10 In sev-eral sec-tions of the course on ma-trix
the-ory, the strange term ''hamiltonian-
```

The log file records these error messages. To place a visual warning in the typeset version of your document as well, use the `draft` document class option:

```
\documentclass[draft]{article}
```

Lines that are too wide will be marked with a *slug* (a black box) on the margin; a slug is a vertical bar of width `\overfullrule`.

Do not worry about such messages while writing the document. If you are preparing the final version and receive such a message, the first line of defense for an `overfull \hbox` is to see whether optional hyphens would help (see Section 2.4.9). Read the warning message carefully to see which words LaTeX cannot hyphenate properly. If adding optional hyphens does not help, a simple rephrasing of the problem sentence often does the trick.

Recall that there are 72.27 points in an inch (see Section 1.1.3). So if the error message indicates a 1.55812 pt overflow, for instance, you may safely ignore it.

Tip If you do not want the 1.55812pt overflow reported whenever the document is typeset, you can enclose the offending paragraph (including the blank line indicating the end of the paragraph) with the lines

```
{\setlength{\hfuzz}{2pt}
```

and

```
}% end of \hfuzz=2pt
```

Choose an argument that is slightly more than the reported error (`2pt` in this case). This does not affect the typeset output, but the warning message—and the slug, if you are using the `draft` option—is suppressed.

Alternatively, enclose the offending paragraph (including the blank line indicating the end of the paragraph) in a `setlength` environment:

```
\begin{setlength}{\hfuzz}{2pt}
\end{setlength}
```

Breaking lines

There are two types of line-breaking commands:

- The `\\` and `\newline` commands break the line at the point of insertion but do not stretch it.
- The `\linebreak` command breaks the line at the point of insertion and stretches the line to make it the normal width.

The text following any of these commands starts at the beginning of the next line, without indentation. The `\\` command is often used; the `\linebreak` command is rarely seen. (See Section 12.6 for an application of the `\linebreak` command.)

I will illustrate the effect of these commands:

```
There are two types of line-breaking commands:

There are two types\\ of line-breaking commands:

There are two types\newline of line-breaking commands:

There are two types\linebreak of line-breaking commands:
```

typeset as

> There are two types of line-breaking commands:
> There are two types
> of line-breaking commands:
> There are two types
> of line-breaking commands:
> There are two types
> of line-breaking commands:

If you force a line break in the middle of a paragraph with the `\linebreak` command and LaTeX thinks that there is too little text left on the line to stretch it full width, you will get a message such as

```
Underfull \hbox (badness 4328) in paragraph at lines 8--12
```

The `\\` command has two important variants:

- `\\[`*length*`]`, where *length* is the interline space you wish to specify after the line break, for instance, `12pt`, `.5in`, or `1.2cm`.
- `\\*`, prohibits a page break following the line break.

The `\\*[`*length*`]` form combines the two variants.
Note how the units are abbreviated. For example,

```
Note how the units are abbreviated.\\[15pt]  For example,
```

is typeset as

> Note how the units are abbreviated.
>
> For example,

Since `\\` can be modified by `*` or by `[ ]`, LaTeX may get confused if the line after a `\\` command starts with a real `*` or `[`. In such cases, type `*` as `{*}` or `[` as `{[}`. For instance, to get

There are two sources of problems:
[a] The next line starts with [.

type

```
There are two sources of problems:\\
{[}a] The next line starts with \texttt{[}.
```

If you fail to type `{[}`, you will get the error message

```
! Missing number, treated as zero.
<to be read again>
                    a
l.16 [a]
         The next line starts with \texttt{[}.
```

Rule ■ `\\`

Without optional arguments, the `\\` command and the `\newline` command are the same *in text*, but not within environments or command arguments.

You can qualify the `\linebreak` command with an optional argument: `0` to `4`. The higher the argument, the more it forces. The `\linebreak[4]` command is the same as `\linebreak`; `\linebreak[0]` allows the line break but does not force it.

The `\nolinebreak` command plays the opposite role. The `\nolinebreak[0]` command is the same as `\linebreak[0]`; and `\nolinebreak[4]` is the same as `\nolinebreak`. You can visualize these relationships as follows:

```
                                                  \linebreak
                          \linebreak[0]     ...   \linebreak[4]
\nolinebreak[4]    ...    \nolinebreak[0]
\nolinebreak
```

The `\nolinebreak` command is seldom used since the tie (`~`), the `\mbox` command (see Section 2.4.3), and the AMS command `\text` (see Section 2.4.9) accomplish the same goal most of the time. Ⓐ

Double spacing

It is convenient to proofread documents double spaced. Moreover, some journals require submissions to be double spaced.

To typeset a document double spaced, include the command

```
\renewcommand{\baselinestretch}{2}
```

in its preamble. Similarly, line-and-a-half spacing can be obtained with

```
\renewcommand{\baselinestretch}{1.5}
```

Alternatively, get George D. Greenwade's setspace package, in the

`/tex-archive/macros/latex/contrib/supported/setspace/`

directory on CTAN (see Appendix 13). Load this package with a

```
\usepackage{setspace}
```

command in the preamble of the document and specify

```
\doublespacing
```

or

```
\onehalfspacing
```

in the preamble.

For more on this topic, see Section 3.1.5 of *The LaTeX Companion* [17].

2.7.2 *Paragraphs*

Paragraphs are separated by blank lines or by the `\par` command. Error messages always show paragraph breaks as `\par`. The `\par` form is also very useful in user-defined commands and environments (see Sections 9.1 and 9.2).

In some document classes, the first line of a paragraph is automatically indented. Indentation may be prevented with the `\noindent` command or forced with the `\indent` command.

Sometimes—for instance, in a schedule, glossary, or index—you may want a *hanging indent*, where the first line of a paragraph is not indented, and all the others are indented by a specified amount.

Hanging indents are created by specifying the indentation in the length command `\hangindent` using the `\setlength` command:

```
\setlength{\hangindent}{30pt}
\noindent
\textbf{sentence} a group of words terminated by
 a period, exclamation point, or question mark.

\setlength{\hangindent}{30pt}
\noindent
\textbf{paragraph} a group of sentences terminated by a
blank line or by the \verb|\par| command.
```

producing

sentence a group of words terminated by a period, exclamation point, or question mark.

paragraph a group of sentences terminated by a blank line or by the `\par` command.

Notice that the `\setlength` command must be repeated for each paragraph.

Sometimes you may want to change the value of `\hangafter`, the length command that specifies the number of lines not to be indented. The default value is 1. To change it to 2, use the command

```
\setlength{\hangafter}{2}
```

For more about the `\setlength` command, see Section 9.5.2. Section 3.1.4 of *The LaTeX Companion* [17] discusses the style parameters of a paragraph.

The preferred way to shape a paragraph or series of paragraphs is with a custom list environment; see Section 9.6.

2.7.3 Pages

There are two page-breaking commands:

- `\newpage`, which breaks the page at the point of insertion but does not stretch it
- `\pagebreak`, which breaks the page at the point of insertion and stretches the page to make it normal length

Text following either command starts at the beginning of the next page, indented.

As you see, the page-breaking commands are analogous to the line-breaking commands discussed in Section 2.7.1. This analogy continues with the optional argument, 0 to 4:

`\pagebreak[0]` to `\pagebreak[4]`
`\nopagebreak[0]` to `\nopagebreak[4]`

Again, you can visualize the relationships as follows:

				`\pagebreak`
		`\pagebreak[0]`	...	`\pagebreak[4]`
`\nopagebreak[4]`	...	`\nopagebreak[0]`		
`\nopagebreak`				

There are also special commands for allowing or forbidding page breaks in multiline math displays (see Section 5.9).

Sometimes, when preparing the final draft of a document (see Section 12.5), you may have to add or remove a line or two to a page to prevent it from breaking at an unsuitable line. You can do so with the `\enlargethispage` command. For instance,

```
\enlargethispage{\baselineskip}
```

will add one line to the page length; on the other hand,

```
\enlargethispage{-\baselineskip}
```

will make the page one line shorter.

```
\enlargethispage{10000pt}
```

will make the page very long, so that you can break it wherever you wish with a `\pagebreak`.

The `*`-ed version, `\enlargethispage*`, squeezes the page as much as possible.

There are two more variants of the `\newpage` command. The

```
\clearpage
```

command does a `\newpage` and also typesets all the figures and tables waiting to be processed (see Section 6.4.3). The variant,

```
\cleardoublepage
```

is used with the `twoside` document class option (see Sections 7.1.1 and 8.5); it does a `\clearpage` and in addition makes the next printed page a right-hand (odd-numbered) page, by inserting a blank page if necessary.

Section 12.6 discusses the use of some of these commands in the final preparation of books.

2.7.4 *Multicolumn printing*

LaTeX provides the `twocolumn` document class option for two-column typesetting (see Sections 7.1.1 and 8.5). In addition, there is a `\twocolumn` command which starts a new page (by issuing a `\clearpage`) and then typesets in two columns. An optional argument provides a two-column wide title. The `\onecolumn` command switches back to a one-column format.

Frank Mittelbach's multicol package provides the much more sophisticated `multicols` environment, which can start in the middle of a page. The environment is invoked with

```
\begin{multicols}{n}[title]
```

where *n* is the number of columns and *title* is an optional argument, a title. The `multicols` environment can also be customized; see Section 3.5.3 of *The LaTeX Companion* [17].

You can find the multicol package on CTAN (see Section 13.1) in the directory

```
/tex-archive/macros/latex/required/tools/
```

2.8 Spaces

The judicious use of horizontal and vertical space is an important part of the formatting of a document. Fortunately, most of the spacing decisions are made by the document class, but LaTeX has a large number of commands that allow the user to insert horizontal and vertical spacing. You should use them sparingly.

2.8.1 Horizontal spaces

When typing text, there are three commands that are often used to create horizontal space (shown between the bars in the display below):

`\␣`	␣
`\quad`	⎵
`\qquad`	⎵⎵

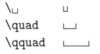

The `\quad` command creates a 1 em space; `\qquad` creates a 2 em space (see Section 2.8.3). The interword space created by `\␣` can both stretch and shrink. There are other commands that create smaller amounts of space. All the math spacing commands of Section 4.11.3 can be used in ordinary text, but the `\hspace` and `\phantom` commands are more appropriate.

The `\hspace` command takes a length as a parameter. For example,

`\textbar\hspace{12pt}\textbar`	| |
`\textbar\hspace{.5in}\textbar`	| |
`\textbar\hspace{1.5cm}\textbar`	| |

The `\phantom{`*argument*`}` command produces a space the width of the space that would be occupied by its typeset argument:

`\textbar need space\textbar`	|need space|
`\textbar\phantom{need space}\textbar`	| |

and

```
alpha \phantom{beta} gamma \phantom{delta}\\
\phantom{alpha} beta \phantom{gamma} delta
```

produces

alpha gamma
beta delta

The `\phantom` command is very useful for fine-tuning aligned math formulas; see Sections 4.11 and 5.6.2 for some examples.

See Section B.6 for a table of all horizontal text-spacing commands.

Horizontal space variant

When LaTeX typesets a line, it removes all spaces from the beginning of the line—including the space created by `\hspace`, `\quad`, and other spacing commands. Using the the `*`-ed variant of `\hspace`, `\hspace*`, will prevent LaTeX from removing the space you have specified.

For example,

```
And text\\
\hspace{20pt}And text\\
\hspace*{20pt}And text
```

is typeset as

And text
And text
    And text

Use the `\hspace*` command for creating customized indentation. To indent a paragraph by 24 points, give the command

```
\noindent\hspace*{24pt}And text
```

Similarly,

```
And text\\
\noindent\hspace*{24pt}And text
```

produces

And text
    And text

2.8.2 *Vertical spaces*

Vertical space may be required to make room for some graphics or to add some interline space for emphasis. The latter, as you have seen in Section 2.7.1, can be accomplished with the command `\\[length]`. Both goals are easily accomplished with the `\vspace` command, which works just like the `\hspace` command (see Section 2.8.1), except that it creates vertical space. For example,

```
\vspace{12pt}, \vspace{.5in}, \vspace{1.5cm}.
```

Standard amounts of vertical space are provided by the three commands

```
\smallskip, \medskip, \bigskip
```

The space these commands create depends on the document class and the font size. With the document class and font I am using for this book, they represent a vertical space of 3 points, 6 points, and 12 points, respectively (12 points is the distance from line to line—printers call this space the *leading*—in standard LaTeX documents with the default `10pt` option).

Rule ■ Vertical space commands

All vertical space commands add the vertical space *after* the typeset line in which the command appears.

To obtain

end of text.

New paragraph after vertical space

type

```
end of text.

\vspace{12pt}

New paragraph after vertical space
```

The following example illustrates the unexpected way the vertical space is placed if the command that creates it does not start a new paragraph:

```
end of text.
\vspace{12pt}
The following example illustrates the unexpected way
the vertical space is placed if the
command that creates it does not start a new paragraph:
```

It typesets as

end of text. The following example illustrates the unexpected way the vertical

space is placed if the command that creates it does not start a new paragraph:

Vertical space variant

LATEX removes vertical space from the beginning and end of each page, including space produced by `\vspace`. The space created by the variant `\vspace*` is not removed by LATEX under any circumstances.

2.8.3 *Relative spaces*

The length of a space is usually given in *absolute units:* `12pt` (points), `.5cm` (centimeters), `1.5in` (inches). Sometimes, *relative units* are more appropriate, that is, units that are relative to the size of the letters in the current font: em and ex. 1 em is approximately the width of an M in the current font; 1 ex is approximately the height of an x in the current font. (Historically, 1 em was exactly the width of an M; this is no longer true. For instance, in the Computer Modern roman 10-point font, 1 em is 10.00002 points, while the actual width of the letter M is 9.16669 points; and similarly for 1 ex.)

The units are used in commands such as `\hspace{12em}` and `\vspace{12ex}`; the `\quad` and `\qquad` commands (Section 2.8.1) produce 1 em and 2 em spaces.

2.8.4 *Expanding spaces*

The `\hfill`, `\dotfill`, and `\hrulefill` commands fill all available space in the line with spaces, dots, or a horizontal line, respectively. If there are two of these commands on the same line, the space will be divided equally between them. These commands can be used to center text, to fill lines with dots in a table of contents, and so on. To obtain

2. Boxes 34

type

```
2. Boxes\dotfill 34
```

ABC   and   ABC is typed

```
ABC\hfill and\hfill ABC
```

And finally, to get

ABC__________and__________ABC

type

```
ABC\hrulefill and\hrulefill ABC
```

In a centered environment—such as a `\title` (Section 8.2.1) or a `center` environment (Section 3.8)—you may use `\hfill` to set a line flush right:

This is the title

First Draft

Author

To achieve this effect, you would type

```
\begin{center}
  This is the title\\
  \hfill First Draft\\
  Author
\end{center}
```

2.9 Boxes

Sometimes it can be useful to typeset text in an imaginary box, and treat that box as a single large character. A single-line box can be created with the `\mbox` or `\makebox` commands, or with the `\text` command provided by the amstext or amsmath packages; a multiline box with a prescribed width can be created with the `\parbox` command or `minipage` environment. (A)

2.9.1 Line boxes

The `\mbox` command provides a *line box* that typesets its argument without line-breaks. The resulting box is handled by LaTeX as if it were a single large character. For instance,

```
\mbox{database}
```

causes LaTeX to treat the eight characters of the word `database` as if they were one. This technique has a number of uses: it prevents LaTeX from hyphenating the word (see Section 2.4.9) and allows you to use the word in a formula (see Section 4.5).

Ⓐ The `\text` command, provided by the amsmath package, is an improved version of the `\mbox` command; its argument is typeset in a size appropriate to its use; for example, as a subscript or superscript (see page 22 for a simple example).

Line boxes—a refinement

The `\mbox` command is the short form of the `\makebox` command. The full form of the command is

```
\makebox[width][alignment]{text}
```

where the arguments are

- *width,* the (optional) width of the box; if omitted, the box is as wide as necessary to enclose its contents
- *alignment,* (optionally) one of `c` (the default), `l`, `r`, or `s`; `l` sets the argument flush left; `r` right; the text is centered by default; `s` stretches the text the full length of the box if there is stretchable space in the argument
- *text,* the text in the box

A *width* argument can be specified in inches (in), centimeters (cm), points (pt), or relative units such as em or ex (see Sections 2.8.3 and 9.5.2).

The following examples,

```
\makebox{Short title.}End\\
\makebox[2in][l]{Short title.}End\\
\makebox[2in]{Short title.}End\\
\makebox[2in][r]{Short title.}End\\
\makebox[2in][s]{Short title.}End
```

typeset as

```
Short title.End
Short title.                   End
          Short title.         End
                    Short title.End
Short                      title.End
```

There are four length commands corresponding to the dimensions of the box that would be produced without the optional width argument; these commands can be used in the specification of *width*:

`\height`, `\depth`, `\totalheight`, and `\width`

To be more specific, `\height` is the height above the baseline, `\depth` is the depth below the baseline, `\totalheight` is the sum of `\height` and `\depth`, and `\width` is the width of the box.

So to typeset hello in a box three times the width of the word:

```
start\makebox[3\width]{hello}end
```

which typesets as

start   hello   end

The `\framebox` command works exactly like `\makebox`, except that it draws a frame around the box.

```
\framebox[2in][l]{Short title}
```

produces

Short title

You can use this command to typeset the number 1 in a square box, as required by the title of Michael Doob's *TEX Starting from* 1 [14]:

```
\framebox{\makebox[\totalheight]{1}}
```

which typesets as

1

Note that

```
\framebox[\totalheight]{1}
```

typesets as

1

which is not a square box. Indeed, `\totalheight` is the height of 1, which becomes the width of the box. The total height of the box, however, is the height of the character 1 to which you have to add twice the `\fboxsep` (the separation between the contents of the box and the frame, defined as 3 points) and twice the `\fboxrule` (the width of the line—or rule—defined as 0.4 points).

2.9.2 *Paragraph boxes*

A paragraph box works like a paragraph: The text it contains is broken into lines, but the width of these lines is set by the user.

The `\parbox` command typesets the contents of its second argument as a paragraph with a line width supplied as the first argument; the resulting box is handled by LaTeX as a single large character. To create a 3-inch wide column (the `\bsl` command is defined in Section 9.1.1),

The `\parbox` command typesets the contents of its second argument as a paragraph with a line width supplied as the first argument.

type

```
\parbox{3in}{The \bsl\texttt{parbox} command typesets the
contents of its second argument as a paragraph
with a line width supplied as the first argument.}
```

Paragraph boxes are especially useful when working within a `tabular` environment; see the subsection on refinements in Section 3.7 for examples of multiline entries.

The width of the paragraph box can be specified in inches (in), centimeters (cm), points (pt), or the relative measurements em and ex (see Section 2.8.3), among others. (See Section 9.5.2 for a complete listing of measurement units.)

Tip The `\parbox` command requires two arguments. Dropping the first argument results in an error message such as

```
! Missing number, treated as zero.
<to be read again>
                   T
l.175
```

Dropping the second argument does not yield an error message but the result will probably not be what you intended.

Paragraph box refinements

The "character" created by a `\parbox` command is placed on the line such that its vertical center is aligned with the center of the line. An optional first argument `b` or `t` forces the paragraph box to align along its bottom or top. For an example, see Section 3.7.

The full syntax of \parbox is

\parbox[*alignment*][*height*][*inner-alignment*]{*width*}{*text*}

Just like for the \makebox command (Section 2.9.1), the

\height, \depth, \totalheight, and \width

commands may be used in the *height* argument instead of a numeric argument.

The *inner-alignment* argument is the vertical equivalent of the *alignment* argument for \makebox, determining the position of *text* within the box; it may be any one of t, b, c, or s, denoting top, bottom, centered, or stretched alignment, respectively. When the *inner-alignment* argument is not specified, it defaults to *alignment*.

Paragraph box as an environment

The minipage environment is very similar to the \parbox command: It typesets the text in its body using a line width supplied as an argument. It has an optional argument for bottom or top alignment, and the other \parbox refinements also apply. The difference is that the minipage environment can contain displayed text environments (see Chapter 3).

The minipage environment can also contain footnotes (see Section 2.5.2) that are displayed within the minipage. See Section 3.4.1 of *The LaTeX Companion* [17] for complications that may arise from this usage.

2.9.3 Marginal comments

A variant of the paragraph box, the \marginpar command, allows you to add marginal comments. For example, the AMS warning in this book is defined as 

```
\marginpar{{\Large%
\textcircled{\raisebox{.7pt}{\normalsize\textbf A}}}}
```

(\textcircled was discussed in Section 2.4.7; \raisebox will be taken up in Section 2.9.5.)

Do not use marginal comments in equations or multiline math environments.

Tip Avoid using too many marginal comments on any given page—LaTeX may have to place some of them on the next page.

If the document is typeset two-sided, then the marginal comments are set in the outside margin. The form

\marginpar[*left-comment*]{*right-comment*}

uses the required argument *right-comment* when the marginal comment set in the right margin and the optional argument *left-comment* when the marginal comment is set in the left margin.

The width of the paragraph box for marginal comments is stored in the length command `\marginparwidth` (see Section 9.5.2 for length commands). If you want to change it, use

```
\setlength{\marginparwidth}{new_width}
```

as in

```
\setlength{\marginparwidth}{90pt}
```

The default value of this width is set by the document class. If you want to know the present setting, type

```
\the\marginparwidth
```

in your document and typeset it, or, in interactive mode (see Section 1.13.2 and also Section 9.1.7), type

```
*\showthe\marginparwidth
```

See Sections 3.4.2 and 4.1 of *The LaTeX Companion* [17] for other style parameters pertaining to marginal notes.

2.9.4 Solid boxes

A solid filled box is created with a `\rule` command; the first argument is the width and the second is the height. For instance, to obtain

end of proof symbol: ■

type

```
end of proof symbol: \rule{1.6ex}{1.6ex}
```

In fact, you may have noticed that this symbol is usually slightly lowered:

end of proof symbol: ■

This positioning is done with an optional first argument:

```
end of proof symbol: \rule[-.23ex]{1.6ex}{1.6ex}
```

Here is an example combining `\rule` with `\makebox` and `\hrulefill`:

```
1 inch:\quad\makebox[1in]{\rule{.4pt}{4pt}%
   \hrulefill\rule{.4pt}{4pt}}
```

which produces

1 inch: ⌊________________⌋

Solid boxes of zero width and any height are called *struts*. Struts are invisible, but they force LaTeX to make room for them, changing the vertical alignment of lines. Struts are especially useful for fine-tuning formulas and tables; see the end of Section 3.7 and Section 4.14 for examples.

Rule ■ Zero distance
`0pt, 0in, 0cm, 0em` all stand for zero width; `0` by itself is not acceptable.

For example, `\rule{0}{1.6ex}` gives the error message

```
! Illegal unit of measure (pt inserted).
<to be read again>
                       h
l.251 \rule{0}{1.6ex}
```

Tip If a command expects two arguments, and none or only one is supplied, LaTeX generates an error message.

For instance, `\rule{1.6ex}` will give the message

```
! Paragraph ended before \@rule was complete.
```

or

```
! Missing number, treated as zero.
```

In the first error message, the reference to `\@rule` suggests that the problem is with the `\rule` command. Checking the syntax of the `\rule` command, you will find that an argument is missing. The second error message is more informative, since there is, indeed, a missing number.

2.9.5 *Fine-tuning boxes*

The command

```
\raisebox{displacement}{text}
```

typesets *text* in a box with a vertical *displacement*. If *displacement* is positive, the box is raised; if negative, the box is lowered.

The \raisebox command allows us to play games:

```
fine-\raisebox{.5ex}{tun}\raisebox{-.5ex}{ing}
```

produces fine-$^{\text{tun}}{}_{\text{ing}}$.

The \raisebox command has two optional arguments:

```
\raisebox{0ex}[1.5ex][0.75ex]{text}
```

forces LaTeX to typeset *text* as if it extended 1.5 ex above and 0.75 ex below the line, resulting in a change in the interline space above and below the line. A simple version of this command, \smash, is discussed in Section 4.14.

In the AMS warning marginal comment in this book, the \raisebox command is used to properly center the Galliard bold A in the circle:

```
\Large\textcircled{\raisebox{.7pt}{\normalsize\textbf A}}
```

CHAPTER

3

Text environments

There are three types of text environments in LaTeX:

1. Displayed text environments: Text within the environment is typeset usually with some vertical space around it.
2. Text environments that create a "large symbol."
3. Style and size environments.

We will start by discussing the general displayed text environments: lists (Section 3.1), the `tabbing` environment (Section 3.2), `quote`, and a few others (Section 3.3). Then we will consider some displayed text environments that are very important in mathematical typesetting: proclamations (theorem-like structures), proclamations with style, and the `proof` environment (Sections 3.4 and 3.5).

We will only discuss one environment that produces a "large symbol": the `tabular` environment (Section 3.7). We conclude with an examination of the style and size environments in Section 3.8.

The examples in this chapter (along with the custom list examples from Chapter 9) are collected in the `textenv.tpl` file in the `samples` directory (see page 4).

3.1 List environments

LaTeX provides three ready-to-use list environments: `enumerate`, `itemize`, and `description`. LaTeX also provides a generic `list` environment that can be customized to fit your needs; see Section 9.6 to learn how to create custom lists.

In this section, the list environments will be formatted as they normally are by the `book` document class. Throughout the rest of the book, lists are formatted as specified by this book's designer.

3.1.1 Numbered lists

A *numbered list* is created with the `enumerate` environment,

This space has the following properties:

1. Grade 2 Cantor
2. Half-smooth Hausdorff
3. Metrizably smooth

Therefore, we can apply the Main Theorem …

typed as

```
\noindent This space has the following properties:
\begin{enumerate}
   \item Grade 2 Cantor\label{Cantor}
   \item Half-smooth Hausdorff\label{Hausdorff}
   \item Metrizably smooth\label{smooth}
\end{enumerate}
Therefore, we can apply the Main Theorem \ldots
```

Each item is introduced with an `\item` command. The numbers LaTeX generates can be labeled and cross-referenced (see Section 6.4.2). This construct can be used in theorems and definitions, and for listing conditions or conclusions. Note that the stylistic details are determined by the document class; in particular, the AMS style is (1), (2), and so on, for enumerated lists (and these numbers remain upright even if the text in which the list appears is emphasized). 

3.1.2 Bulleted lists

A *bulleted list* is created with the `itemize` environment:

In this lecture, we set out to accomplish a variety of goals:

- To introduce the concept of smooth functions
- To show their usefulness in the differentiation of Howard-type functions
- To point out the efficacy of using smooth functions in Advanced Calculus courses

In addition to these mathematicians …

is typed as

```
\noindent In this lecture, we set out to accomplish a variety
of goals:
\begin{itemize}
   \item To introduce the concept of smooth functions
   \item To show their usefulness in the differentiation
      of Howard-type functions
   \item To point out the efficacy of using smooth functions
      in Advanced Calculus courses
\end{itemize}
In addition to these mathematicians \ldots
```

3.1.3 Captioned lists

In a *captioned list* each item has a title (caption) specified as the optional argument of the `\item` command. A captioned list is created with the `description` environment:

In this introduction, we outline the history of this concept. The main contributors were:

J. Perelman, the first to introduce smooth functions.

T. Kovács, who showed the usefulness of smooth functions in the differentiation of Howard-type functions.

A.P. Fein, the main advocate of using smooth functions in Advanced Calculus courses.

In addition to these mathematicians …

is typed as

```
In this introduction, we outline the history of this concept.
The main contributors were:
\begin{description}
  \item[J. Perelman,] the first to introduce smooth functions.
  \item[T. Kov\'{a}cs,] who showed the usefulness of smooth
    functions in the differentiation of Howard-type functions.
  \item[A.P. Fein,] the main advocate of using smooth
      functions in Advanced Calculus courses.
\end{description}
In addition to these mathematicians \ldots
```

3.1.4 Rule and combinations

There is only one rule you must remember:

Rule ■ List environments
An `\item` command must immediately follow
`\begin{enumerate}`, `\begin{itemize}`, or `\begin{description}`.

If you break this rule, you will get an error message. For instance,

```
\begin{description}
   This is wrong!
   \item[J. Perelman] the first to introduce smooth functions.
```

gives the error message

```
! LaTeX Error: Something's wrong--perhaps a missing \item.

l.11    \item[J. Perelman]
                            the first to introduce smooth func...
```

If you see this error message, remember the rule for list environments and check for text preceding the first `\item`.

You can nest and mix up to four list environments; for instance,

1. First item of Level 1.
   (a) First item of Level 2.
      i. First item of Level 3.
         A. First item of Level 4.

B. Second item of Level 4.

ii. Second item of Level 3.

(b) Second item of Level 2.

2. Second item of Level 1.

Referencing the second item of Level 4: 1(a)iB

which is typed as

```
\begin{enumerate}
   \item First item of Level 1.
   \begin{enumerate}
      \item First item of Level 2.
      \begin{enumerate}
         \item First item of Level 3.
         \begin{enumerate}
            \item First item of Level 4.
            \item Second item of Level 4.\label{level4}
          \end{enumerate}
          \item Second item of Level 3.
       \end{enumerate}
       \item Second item of Level 2.
   \end{enumerate}
   \item Second item of Level 1.
\end{enumerate}
Referencing the second item of Level 4: \ref{level4}
```

Note that the label `level4` collected all four of the counters (see Section 6.4.2).

Here is a mixed example:

1. First item of Level 1.
    - First item of Level 2.
        (a) First item of Level 3.
            – First item of Level 4.
            – Second item of Level 4.
        (b) Second item of Level 3.
    - Second item of Level 2.
2. Second item of Level 1.

Referencing the second item of Level 4: 1a

which is typed as

```
\begin{enumerate}
   \item First item of Level 1.
   \begin{itemize}
      \item First item of Level 2.
      \begin{enumerate}
         \item First item of Level 3.
         \begin{itemize}
            \item First item of Level 4.
            \item Second item of Level 4.\label{enums}
          \end{itemize}
          \item Second item of Level 3.
       \end{enumerate}
       \item Second item of Level 2.
   \end{itemize}
   \item Second item of Level 1.
\end{enumerate}
Referencing the second item of Level 4: \ref{enums}
```

Now the label `enums` collects only the two enumerate counters (see Section 6.4.2).

In all three types of list environments, the `\item` command may be followed by an optional argument, which will be displayed at the beginning of the typeset item:

`\item[`*`label`*`]`

This form of the `\item` command is particularly useful in a `description` environment, whose items have no default label.

Tip The text following an `\item` may start with an opening square bracket, `[`, and then LaTeX would think that `\item` has an optional argument. To prevent this problem from occurring, type `[` as `{[}`. Similarly, a closing square bracket, `]`, *inside* the optional argument should be typed as `{]}`.

Tip You may want to use a list environment solely for the way the items are displayed, without any labels. You can achieve this effect by using `\item[]`.

You can change the style of the numbers in an `enumerate` environment by redefining the counter as suggested in Section 9.5.1:

```
\renewcommand{\labelenumi}{{\normalfont (\roman{enumi})}}
```

The labels then will be displayed as (i), (ii), and so on. This modification only works if you do not want to reference these items. If you want the `\ref` command to work properly, use David Carlisle's enumerate package (see Section 7.3.1); for an example of how to use Carlisle's environment, see Section 9.2.1.

Section 3.2 of *The LaTeX Companion* [17] explains how to customize the three list environments.

3.2 Tabbing environments

Although of limited use for mathematical typesetting, the `tabbing` environment can be useful for typing algorithms, computer programs, and so forth. LaTeX calculates the width of a column in the `tabular` environment based on the widest entry (Section 3.7); the `tabbing` environment allows you to control the width of the columns.

The `\\` command is the line separator, tab stops are set by `\=` (and are remembered by LaTeX in the order they are given), and `\>` moves to the next tab position.

You can easily reset tab positions. For instance, if you are past the second tab position (you used `\>` twice), and there is a third tab position, the `\=` command resets it.

Lines of comments may be inserted with the `\kill` command (see the examples below) or with the `%` character. The difference is that a line with `\kill` can be used to set tab stops, whereas a commented-out line cannot.

A simple example:

```
PrintTime
     Block[{timing},
          timing = Timing[expr];
          Print[ timing[[1]] ];
     ]
End[]
```

typed as

```
\begin{tabbing}
   Print\= Time\\
   \>Block\=[{timing},\\
   \>\>timing = Timing[expr];\\
   (careful with initialization)\kill
   \>\>Print[ timing[[1]] ];\\
```

```
  \>]\\
  End[]
\end{tabbing}
```

An alternative method is to use a line to set the tab stops, and then `\kill` the line so it does not print:

```
\begin{tabbing}
  \hspace*{.25in}\=\hspace{2ex}\=\hspace{2ex}\=\hspace{2ex}\kill
  \>  $k := 1$\\
  \>  $l_k := 0$; $r_k := 1$\\
  \>  \texttt{loop}\\
  \>  \> $m_k := (l_k + r_k)/2$\\
  \>  \> \texttt{if} $w < m_k$ \texttt{then}\\
  \>  \>  \> $b_k := 0$; $r_k := m_k$\\
  \>  \> \texttt{else if} $w > m_k$ \texttt{then}\\
  \>  \>  \> $b_k := 1$; $l_k := m_k$\\
  \>  \> \texttt{end if}\\
  \>  \> $k := k + 1$\\
  \>  \texttt{end loop}
\end{tabbing}
```

which typesets as

$k := 1$
$l_k := 0$; $r_k := 1$
`loop`
  $m_k := (l_k + r_k)/2$
  `if` $w < m_k$ `then`
    $b_k := 0$; $r_k := m_k$
  `else if` $w > m_k$ `then`
    $b_k := 1$; $l_k := m_k$
  `end if`
  $k := k + 1$
`end loop`

Some simple rules:

- There is no `\\` command on a line containing the `\kill` command
- You may set the tabs in a `\kill` line with `\hspace` commands
- The `\>` command moves to the next tab stop, even if the text you have already typed extends past that stop, which can result in overprinting

To illustrate the last rule, type

```
\begin{tabbing}
   This is short.\=\\
   This is much longer, \> and jumps back.
\end{tabbing}
```

which typesets as

This is short.
This is much longer, and jumps back.

There are about a dozen more commands peculiar to this environment; if you find yourself needing to use `tabbing` often, please consult Chapter 5 of *The LaTeX Companion* [17].

3.3 Miscellaneous displayed text environments

There are four more displayed text environments: `quote`, `quotation`, `verse`, and `verbatim`. We will also discuss an inline version of the `verbatim` environment, the `\verb` command.

Quotes

The `quote` environment is used for short (one paragraph) quotations:

> It's not that I'm afraid to die. I just don't want to be there when it happens. *Woody Allen*
>
> Literature is news that STAYS news. *Ezra Pound*

Typed as:

```
\begin{quote}
   It's not that I'm afraid to die.  I just don't want to be
   there when it happens.
   \emph{Woody Allen}

   Literature is news that STAYS news.
   \emph{Ezra Pound}
\end{quote}
```

Note that multiple quotes are separated by blank lines.

Quotations

In the quotation environment, blank lines mark new paragraphs:

> KATH: Can he be present at the birth of his child?
>
> ED: It's all any reasonable child can expect if the dad is present at the conception.
>
> *Joe Orton*

typed as

```
\begin{quotation}
   KATH: Can he be present at the birth of his child?

   ED: It's all any reasonable child can expect if the dad
   is present at the conception.
   \begin{flushright}
      \emph{Joe Orton}
   \end{flushright}
\end{quotation}
```

Verses

A verse environment,

> I think that I shall never see
> A poem as lovely as a tree.
>
> Poems are made by fools like me,
> But only God can make a tree.
>
> *Joyce Kilmer*

is typed as

```
\begin{verse}
   I think that I shall never see\\
   A poem as lovely as a tree.

   Poems are made by fools like me,\\
   But only God can make a tree.
```

```
   \begin{flushright}
      \emph{Joyce Kilmer}
   \end{flushright}
\end{verse}
```

Lines are separated by \\; stanzas by blank lines. Long lines are typeset with their wrapped portions indented (hanging indent).

Verbatim typesetting

Finally, there is the `verbatim` text environment. You may need it if you write *about* TEX or some other computer program or if you have to include source code or user input in your writing (most of the displayed source in this book was written in a `verbatim` environment). For instance, you may have to write to a journal about an article you are proofreading:

Formula (2) in Section 3 should be typed as follows:

```
\begin{equation}
   D^{\langle 2 \rangle} = \{\, \langle x_0, x_1 \rangle
    \mid x_0, x_1 \in D,\ x_0 = 0 \Rightarrow x_1 = 0 \,\}.
\end{equation}
```

Please make the necessary corrections.

The problem is that if you just type

```
Formula (2) in Section 3 should be typed as follows:
\begin{equation}
   D^{\langle 2 \rangle} = \{\, \langle x_0, x_1 \rangle
    \mid x_0, x_1 \in D,\ x_0 = 0 \Rightarrow x_1 = 0 \,\}.
\end{equation}
Please make the necessary corrections.
```

it will be typeset as

Formula (2) in Section 3 should be typed as follows:

$$D^{\langle 2 \rangle} = \{\, \langle x_0, x_1 \rangle \mid x_0, x_1 \in D,\ x_0 = 0 \Rightarrow x_1 = 0 \,\}. \tag{2}$$

Please make the necessary corrections.

If you want the LaTeX source printed (as above) exactly as typed, place the LaTeX source inside a `verbatim` environment:

```
Formula (2) in Section 3 should be typed as follows:
\begin{verbatim}
\begin{equation}
   D^{\langle 2 \rangle} = \{\, \langle x_0, x_1 \rangle
    \mid x_0, x_1 \in D,\ x_0 = 0 \Rightarrow x_1 \,\}
\end{equation}
\end{verbatim}
Please make the necessary corrections.
```

Rule ■ `verbatim` text environments

A `verbatim` environment cannot be placed within

- Another `verbatim` environment
- The argument of a command

A violation of the first rule will result in unmatched environment delimiters. You will get an error message such as

```
! \begin{document} ended by \end{verbatim}.
```

A violation of the second rule will give an error message such as

```
! Argument of \@xverbatim has an extra }.
<inserted text>
                \par
l.3 ...atim} text \end{verbatim}}
```

Tip There are two traps to avoid when using the `verbatim` environment.

1. If the `\end{verbatim}` line starts with spaces, a blank line will be added to the typeset version.
2. Any characters following `\end{verbatim}` on the same line are dropped (and you get a LaTeX warning).

To illustrate the first trap, type the last two lines of the previous example as follows:

```
␣\end{verbatim}
Please make the necessary corrections.
```

Then examine the typeset version:

Formula (2) in Section 3 should be typed as follows:

```
\begin{equation}
   D^{\langle 2 \rangle} = \{\, \langle x_0, x_1 \rangle
    \mid x_0, x_1 \in D,\ x_0 = 0 \Rightarrow x_1 = 0 \,\}.
\end{equation}
```

Please make the necessary corrections.

There is an unintended blank line before the last line.

The second trap can be seen if you type the last line of the above example as

```
\end{verbatim} Please make the necessary corrections.
```

When typeset, Please make the necessary corrections. will not appear, and you will receive a warning

```
LaTeX Warning: Characters dropped after
 '\end{verbatim}' on input line 17.
```

An improved version of the `verbatim` environment (as well as the `comment` environment) is provided by the verbatim package (see Section 7.3.1); in fact, the rules discussed in this section are those of the verbatim package. The `verbatim` environment has some interesting variants; a number of them are discussed in Section 3.3 of *The LaTeX Companion* [17]. For instance, the alltt package (which is part of the standard LaTeX distribution; see Section 7.3) is used to type the command syntax in this book (see page 116 for an example).

Verbatim typesetting inline

The `verbatim` environment also has an inline version called `\verb`. Here is an example:

```
Some European e-mail addresses contain \texttt{\%};
recall that you have to type \verb+\%+ to get \texttt{\%}.
```

which prints

Some European e-mail addresses contain `%`; recall that you have to type `\%` to get `%`.

The character following the `\verb` command is a delimiter; in this example I have used `+`. The argument starts with the character following the delimiter, and it is terminated by the next occurrence of the delimiter. So in this example, the argument is \%.

Choose the delimiter character carefully. For instance, if you want to typeset

```
$\sin(\pi/2 + \alpha)$
```

verbatim, and you type

```
\verb+$\sin(\pi/2 + \alpha)$+
```

then you will get the error message

```
! Missing $ inserted.
<inserted text>
                  $
l.5 \verb+$\sin(\pi/2 + \alpha
                                    )$+
```

Indeed, the argument of `\verb` is `$\sin(\pi/2` because the second + terminates the `\verb` command. Then LaTeX tries to typeset `\alpha)$+`, but cannot because it is not in math mode. Use another character, such as `!`, in place of +:

```
\verb!$\sin(\pi/2 + \alpha)$!
```

Rule ■ verb commands

- The entire `\verb` command must be on a single line of your source file.
- There can be no space between the `\verb` command and the delimiter.
- The `\verb` command cannot appear in the argument of another command.
- The `\verb` command cannot be used within an amsmath aligned math environment. 

If you violate the first rule, as in

```
\verb!$\sin(\pi/2 +
\alpha)$!
```

you will get the error message

```
! LaTeX Error: \verb command ended by end of line.

l.6 \verb!$\sin(\pi/2 +
```

The `\verb` command has a `*`-ed version which prints spaces as ␣ symbols. For example, `\today␣the` is typed as `\verb*+\today the+`.

3.4 Proclamations (theorem-like structures)

Theorems, lemmas, definitions, and so forth are a major part of mathematical writing. In LaTeX, these constructs are typed in displayed text environments called *proclamations* (some LaTeX documentation calls them *theorem-like structures*).

In the `intrart.tex` sample article (see pp. 44–45), there are two theorems, a definition, and a notation. These four environments have similar structures; only their names are different.

Ⓐ In the `amsart` sample article (see pp. 286–288), there are a number of different proclamations in a variety of styles, with varying degrees of emphasis. Proclamations with style will be discussed in Section 3.4.2.

You saw in Section 1.7 that proclamations require two steps:

Step 1. In the preamble of your LaTeX document, you *define* the proclamation with a `\newtheorem` command. For instance, the line

```
\newtheorem{theorem}{Theorem}
```

defines a `theorem` environment.

Step 2. *Invoke* the proclamation in the body of your document as an environment. Using the proclamation definition from Step 1, type

```
\begin{theorem}
   My first theorem.
\end{theorem}
```

to produce a theorem:

Theorem 1. My first theorem.

In the proclamation definition

```
\newtheorem{theorem}{Theorem}
```

the first argument, `theorem`, is the name of the environment that will invoke the theorem; the second argument, `Theorem`, is the name that will be used when the proclamation is typeset. LaTeX will number the theorems automatically and typeset them with vertical space above and below. The phrase **Theorem 1** will appear (its precise form is dependent on the document class), followed by the theorem itself, which may be emphasized (again, depending on the document class).

You may also specify an optional argument,

```
\begin{theorem}[The Fuchs-Schmidt Theorem]
   The statement of the theorem.
\end{theorem}
```

that will appear as the name of the theorem:

Theorem 2. (The Fuchs-Schmidt Theorem) The statement of the theorem.

LaTeX is very fussy about how proclamations are defined. For example, in the introductory article `intrart.tex` (see Section 1.7), if the closing brace is dropped from the end of the second line,

```
\newtheorem{theorem}{Theorem}
\newtheorem{definition}{Definition
\newtheorem{notation}{Notation}
```

you will get an error message such as

```
Runaway argument?
{Definition \newtheorem {notation}{Notation}
! Paragraph ended before \@nthm was complete.
<to be read again>
                   \par
1.12
```

The line number indicated follows the paragraph, so you may have to check all your `\newtheorem` commands to locate the source of the error.

If you forget an argument, as in

```
\newtheorem{definition}
```

LaTeX will produce an error message such as

```
! LaTeX Error: Missing \begin{document}.

1.11 \newtheorem{n
                  otation}{Notation}
```

In the error message, the line

```
! LaTeX Error: Missing \begin{document}.
```

usually means that LaTeX became confused and believes that some text typed in the preamble should be moved past the line

```
\begin{document}
```

The mistake could be anywhere in the preamble above the line LaTeX indicates. If you encounter such an error message, try to isolate the problem by commenting out parts of the preamble (see Section 2.5 and also Section 1.10).

Tip If a proclamation starts with a list environment, precede the list by `\hfill`.

If you do not, as in

```
\begin{definition}\label{D:prime}
   \begin{enumerate}
      \item $u$ is \emph{meet-irreducible} if
         $u = x \wedge y$ implies that
         $u = x$ or $u = x$.\label{mi1}
      \item $u$ is \emph{meet-irreducible} if
         $u = x \wedge y$ implies that
         $u = x$ or $u = x$.\label{mi2}
      \item $u$ is \emph{completely join-irreducible} if
         $u = \bigvee X$ implies that $u \in X$.
          \label{mi3}
   \end{enumerate}
\end{definition}
```

your typeset list will start on the same line as the label:

Definition 1. *1. u is* meet-irreducible *if $u = x \wedge y$ implies that $u = x$ or $u = y$.*
2. u is join-irreducible *if $u = x \vee y$ implies that $u = x$ or $u = y$.*
3. u is completely join-irreducible *if $u = \bigvee X$ implies that $u \in X$.*

If you add the `\hfill` command,

```
\begin{definition}\hfill
\begin{enumerate}
```

the list will typeset correctly:

Definition 1.

1. u is meet-irreducible *if $u = x \wedge y$ implies that $u = x$ or $u = y$.*
2. u is join-irreducible *if $u = x \vee y$ implies that $u = x$ or $u = y$.*
3. u is completely join-irreducible *if $u = \bigvee X$ implies that $u \in X$.*

Consecutive numbering

If you want to number two sets of proclamations consecutively, you can do so by first defining one, and then using its name as an optional argument of the second. For example, to number the lemmas and propositions in your paper consecutively, you would type the following two lines in your preamble:

```
\newtheorem{lemma}{Lemma}
\newtheorem{proposition}[lemma]{Proposition}
```

Lemmas and propositions will be consecutively numbered as **Lemma 1**, **Proposition 2**, **Proposition 3**, and so on.

Let me emphasize: The optional argument of a proclamation definition must be the environment name of a proclamation that *has already been defined.*

Numbering within a section

The `\newtheorem` command may also have a different optional argument, which causes LaTeX to number the lemmas within sections. For example,

```
\newtheorem{lemma}{Lemma}[section]
```

will cause lemmas in Section 1 to be numbered like **Lemma 1.1** and **Lemma 1.2**; in Section 2, you would have **Lemma 2.1** and **Lemma 2.2**; and so on.

Instead of `section`, you may use any sectioning command provided by the document class: `chapter`, `section`, and `subsection` are the most commonly used.

Consecutive numbering and numbering within a section can be combined. For example,

```
\newtheorem{lemma}{Lemma}[section]
\newtheorem{proposition}[lemma]{Proposition}
```

sets up the `lemma` and `proposition` environments so that they are numbered consecutively within sections such as **Lemma 1.1**, **Proposition 1.2**; **Proposition 2.1**, **Lemma 2.2**, and so on.

3.4.1 The full syntax

The full form of `\newtheorem` is

```
\newtheorem{envname}[procCounter]{Name}[secCounter]
```

where the two optional arguments are mutually exclusive, and

envname is the name of the environment to be used in the body of the document.

For instance, you may use `theorem` for the *envname* of a theorem, so that a theorem is typed inside a `theorem` environment. Of course, *envname* is just a label; you are free to choose any environment name, such as `thm` or `george` (so long as the name is not in use as the name of another command or environment). This argument is also the name of the counter LaTeX uses to number these text environments.

procCounter is an optional argument; it sets the new proclamation to use the counter of a previously defined proclamation. As a result, the two proclamations will be consecutively numbered.

Name is the text that is typeset when the proclamation is invoked. So if `Theorem` is given as *Name*, then you would get **Theorem 1**, **Theorem 2**, and so on in your document.

secCounter is an optional argument that causes *Name* environments to be numbered within the appropriate sectioning units. So if `theorem` is the *envname* and `section` is the *secCounter*, then in Section 1 you will have **Theorem 1.1**, **Theorem 1.2**, and so on; and in Section 2, **Theorem 2.1**, **Theorem 2.2**, and so on. Proclamations may be numbered within subsections, sections, chapters, or any other sectioning unit automatically numbered by LaTeX.

3.4.2 Proclamations with style

Ⓐ In the AMS document classes[1] (or in any document class if you load the amsthm package) you can choose one of three styles for your proclamations by preceding the definitions with the `\theoremstyle{style}` command, where *style* is one of the following:

- `plain`, the most emphatic
- `definition`
- `remark`, the least emphatic

You also get a few extra options, including the `\newtheorem*` command, an unnumbered version of `\newtheorem`.

The following commands set the styles in the `sampart.tex` sample article (see page 290); the typeset sample article (on pages 286–288) shows how the chosen styles affect the typeset proclamations.

```
\theoremstyle{plain}
\newtheorem{theorem}{Theorem}
\newtheorem{corollary}{Corollary}
\newtheorem*{main}{Main Theorem}
```

[1] Since this entire section deals with an AMS topic, the marginal warnings will be omitted.

```
\newtheorem{lemma}{Lemma}
\newtheorem{proposition}{Proposition}

\theoremstyle{definition}
\newtheorem{definition}{Definition}

\theoremstyle{remark}
\newtheorem*{notation}{Notation}
```

The document class determines how the various styles are implemented; however, `plain` is intended to be the most emphatic while `remark` is the least emphatic.

A proclamation created by a `\newtheorem` command has the style of the last `\theoremstyle` command preceding it. The default style is `plain`.

Five examples

Here are five example sets of proclamation definitions; these are reproduced in the `amsart.tpl` file in the `samples` directory (see page 4).

Example 1

```
\theoremstyle{plain}
\newtheorem{theorem}{Theorem}
\newtheorem{lemma}{Lemma}
\newtheorem{definition}{Definition}
```

A document using these definitions may have theorems, lemmas, and definitions, each typeset in the most emphatic (`plain`) style. They are numbered separately, so that you might have **Definition 1**, **Definition 2**, **Theorem 1**, **Lemma 1**, **Lemma 2**, **Theorem 2**, and so on.

Example 2

```
\theoremstyle{plain}
\newtheorem{theorem}{Theorem}
\newtheorem{lemma}[theorem]{Lemma}
\newtheorem{definition}[theorem]{Definition}
\newtheorem{corollary}[theorem]{Corollary}
```

This document may have theorems, lemmas, definitions, and corollaries, typeset in the most emphatic (`plain`) style. They are all numbered consecutively: **Definition 1**, **Definition 2**, **Theorem 3**, **Corollary 4**, **Lemma 5**, **Lemma 6**, **Theorem 7**, and so on.

Example 3

```
\theoremstyle{plain}
\newtheorem{theorem}{Theorem}
```

```
\newtheorem{proposition}{Proposition}[section]
\newtheorem{lemma}[proposition]{Lemma}
\newtheorem{definition}{Definition}

\theoremstyle{definition}
\newtheorem*{notation}{Notation}
```

This document may have theorems, propositions, lemmas, and definitions in the most emphatic (`plain`) style, and notations in the less emphatic `definition` style. Notations are not numbered. Propositions and lemmas are consecutively numbered *within sections*, so you might have **Definition 1**, **Definition 2**, **Theorem 1**, **Lemma 1.1**, **Lemma 1.2**, **Proposition 1.3**, **Theorem 2**, **Lemma 2.1**, and so on.

Example 4

```
\theoremstyle{plain}
\newtheorem{theorem}{Theorem}
\newtheorem*{main}{Main Theorem}
\newtheorem{definition}{Definition}[section]
\newtheorem{lemma}[definition]{Lemma}

\theoremstyle{definition}
\newtheorem*{Rule}{Rule}
```

This document may have theorems, definitions, and lemmas in the most emphatic (`plain`) style, and unnumbered rules in the less emphatic (`definition`) style. Definitions and lemmas are numbered consecutively within sections. There is also an unnumbered Main Theorem. So, for example, you may have **Definition 1.1**, **Definition 1.2**, **Main Theorem**, **Rule**, **Lemma 1.3**, **Lemma 2.1**, **Theorem 1**, and so on.

Example 5

```
\theoremstyle{plain}
\newtheorem{theorem}{Theorem}
\newtheorem{corollary}{Corollary}
\newtheorem*{main}{Main Theorem}
\newtheorem{lemma}{Lemma}
\newtheorem{proposition}{Proposition}

\theoremstyle{definition}
\newtheorem{definition}{Definition}

\theoremstyle{remark}
\newtheorem*{notation}{Notation}
```

This document may have theorems, corollaries, lemmas, and propositions in the most emphatic (`plain`) style, and an unnumbered Main Theorem. It has definitions in the less emphatic (`definition`) style. All are separately numbered. With these definitions, you might have **Definition 1**, **Definition 2**, **Main Theorem**, **Lemma 1**, **Proposition 1**, **Lemma 2**, **Theorem 1**, **Corollary 1**, and so on. Notations are unnumbered and typeset in the least emphatic (`remark`) style.

Number swapping

To number a proclamation on the left, as, for instance, **3.2 Theorem**, type the `\swapnumbers` command before the `\newtheorem` command corresponding to the proclamation definition you want to change. This command affects all of the proclamation definitions that follow it, so the proclamation definitions in the preamble should be in two groups: the regular ones should be listed first, followed by the `\swapnumbers` command, then all the proclamations that swap numbers.

Exercises

Exercises are produced using the `xca` and `xcb` environments.

The `xca` environment is available in all AMS document classes; it is used for exercises within a section. To use the `xca` environment, define it in the preamble:

```
\theoremstyle{definition}
\newtheorem{xca}{Exercise}
```

Then,

```
\begin{xca}
Prove that if $\inf H$ exists for all nonempty subsets $H$ of a
poset $P$, then $\sup \varnothing$ also exists in~$P$.
\end{xca}
```

will typeset as

Exercise 1. Prove that if $\inf H$ exists for all nonempty subsets H of a poset P, then $\sup \varnothing$ also exists in P.

The `xcb` environment is available only for the AMS book document class (it is not provided by the amsthm package or by the `amsart` or `amsproc` document classes); it is used for a series of exercises at the end of a section or chapter. The argument of the environment specifies the phrase (such as `Exercises`) to begin the list:

```
\begin{xcb}{Exercises}
\begin{enumerate}
\item A finite lattice $L$ is modular if{f} it does not
contain a pentagon.\label{E:pentagon}
\item Can the numbers of covering pairs in
Exercise~\ref{E:pentagon} be increased?\label{E:increased}
\end{enumerate}
\end{xcb}
```

which typesets as

Exercises

(1) A finite lattice L is modular iff it does not contain a pentagon.
(2) Can the numbers of covering pairs in Exercise 1 be increased?

As an alternative to the amsthm package you might wish to use Frank Mittelbach's theorem package (see Section 7.3.1) from which amsthm evolved.

3.5 *Proof environments*

Ⓐ The AMS document classes and the amsthm package define a proof environment.[2] For example,

Proof. This is a proof, delimited by the q.e.d. symbol. □

typed as

```
\begin{proof}
  This is a proof, delimited by the q.e.d.\ symbol.
\end{proof}
```

A proof is set off from the surrounding text with some vertical space. The end of the proof is marked with the symbol □ at the end of the line. There are a few examples of the proof environment in the sampart.tex sample article (pages 286–297).

If you want to suppress the symbol at the end of a proof, give the command

```
\begin{proof}
  ...
  \renewcommand{\qedsymbol}{}
\end{proof}
```

[2]Since this entire section deals with an AMS topic, the marginal warnings will be omitted.

To substitute another phrase for *Proof,* such as *Necessity,* as in

Necessity. This is the proof of necessity. □

use the proof environment with an optional argument:

```
\begin{proof}[Necessity]
   This is the proof of necessity.
\end{proof}
```

The optional argument may contain a reference, as in

```
\begin{proof}[Proof of Theorem~\ref{T:smooth}]
```

which might be typeset as

Proof of Theorem 5. This is the proof. □

It is easy to make the mistake of placing the optional argument after `\begin`, as in

```
\begin[Proof of Theorem 5]{proof}
```

Depending on the circumstances, you may get any one of a number of error messages, such as

```
! LaTeX Error: Something's wrong--perhaps a missing \item.
```

or

```
! Missing } inserted.
```

There is a problem with the placement of the q.e.d. symbol if the proof ends with a displayed formula (or a list environment). For instance,

```
\begin{proof}
Now the proof follows from the equation
\[
   a^2 = b^2 + c^2.
\]
\end{proof}
```

typesets as

Proof. Now the proof follows from the equation

$$a^2 = b^2 + c^2.$$

□

To correct the placement of the q.e.d. symbol, use the \qedhere command:

```
\begin{proof}
Now the proof follows from the equation
\[
   a^2 = b^2 + c^2.\qedhere
\]
\end{proof}
```

which typesets as

Proof. Now the proof follows from the equation

$$a^2 = b^2 + c^2. \qquad \square$$

You can use the proof environment and the \qedhere command in any document class if you load the amsthm package.

3.6 Some general rules for displayed text environments

As you know, blank lines play a special role in LaTeX, usually indicating a paragraph break.

Since displayed text environments structure the printed display themselves, the rules about blank lines are somewhat relaxed. However, a blank line trailing the environment signifies a new paragraph for the text following the environment.

Rule ■ Blank lines in displayed text environments

1. Blank lines are ignored immediately after \begin{*name*} or immediately before \end{*name*} except in a verbatim environment.
2. A blank line after \end{*name*} forces the following text to start a new paragraph.
3. As a rule, you should not have a blank line before \begin{*name*}.
4. If you use the amsthm package, then the line after any theorem or proof will always be treated as a new (indented) paragraph, even if there is no blank line or \par command.

The page-breaking commands in Section 2.7.3 apply to text environments, as does the \\ command discussed in Section 2.7.1 (including the use of its optional argument, as in \\[22pt]).

3.7 Tabular environments

A tabular environment creates a table that LaTeX treats as a "large symbol." Here is a simple table,

Name	1	2	3
Peter	2.45	34.12	1.00
John	0.00	12.89	3.71
David	2.00	1.85	0.71

, typeset inline (which looks awful, but does make the point that the table is just a "large symbol"). The table is typed as

```
\begin{tabular}{ | l | r | r | r | }
   \hline
   Name     & 1      & 2      & 3     \\ \hline
   Peter    &   2.45 & 34.12 & 1.00\\ \hline
   John     &   0.00 & 12.89 & 3.71\\ \hline
   David    &   2.00 & 1.85  & 0.71\\ \hline
\end{tabular}
```

with no blank line before or after the environment.

This table can be horizontally centered (with a center environment—see Section 3.8). It can also be placed within a table environment (see Section 6.4.3), which sets the table off from the surrounding text with vertical space (you can also use the float controls b, t, h, p to specify where the table should appear; see Section 6.4.3) and allows you to define a caption (which can be placed before or after the table):

```
\begin{table}
   \begin{center}
     \begin{tabular}{ | l | r | r | r | }
       \hline
       Name     & 1      & 2      & 3     \\ \hline
       Peter    &   2.45 & 34.12 & 1.00\\ \hline
       John     &   0.00 & 12.89 & 3.71\\ \hline
       David    &   2.00 & 1.85  & 0.71\\ \hline
     \end{tabular}
     \caption{Tabular table.}\label{Ta:first}
   \end{center}
\end{table}
```

This table is displayed as Table 3.1. It will be listed in a list of tables (see Section 6.4.3 and the front of this book) and the table number may be referenced

Name	1	2	3
Peter	2.45	34.12	1.00
John	0.00	12.89	3.71
David	2.00	1.85	0.71

Table 3.1: Tabular table.

using the command `\ref{Ta:first}`. Note that the label must be typed *between* the caption and the `\end{table}` command.

For another example, look at the two tables in the `fonttbl.tex` file in your `samples` directory. The first is typed as

```
\begin{tabular}{r|l|l|l|l|l|l|l|l|l|l}
 & 0 & 1 & 2 & 3 & 4 & 5 & 6 & 7 & 8 & 9\\\hline

0& \symbol{0} &\symbol{1}&\symbol{2}&\symbol{3}&
\symbol{4}&\symbol{5}&\symbol{6}&\symbol{7}&
\symbol{8}&\symbol{9}\\ \hline

                    .
                    .
                    .

120& \symbol{120} &\symbol{121}&\symbol{122}&\symbol{123}&
\symbol{124}&\symbol{125}&\symbol{126}&\symbol{127} & & \\ \hline
\end{tabular}
```

The second table is the same except that the numbers run from 128 to 255. The typeset table is shown in Section 2.4.4.

Rule ■ `tabular` environments

1. `\begin{tabular}` requires an argument consisting of a character `l`, `r`, or `c` (meaning left, right, or center alignment) for each column, and (optionally) the | symbols; each | indicates a vertical line in the typeset table. Spaces in the argument are ignored (but can be used for readability).
2. Columns are separated by ampersands (`&`) and rows are separated by `\\`.
3. `&` absorbs spaces on either side.
4. The `\hline` command creates a horizontal line in the typeset table.
5. If you use a horizontal line to finish the table, you must separate the last row of the table from the `\hline` command with the `\\` command.

6. `\begin{tabular}` takes an optional argument, `b` or `t`, to specify bottom or top vertical alignment of the table with the baseline. The default is center alignment.

Remember to put the optional argument `b` or `t` in square brackets, as in

```
\begin{tabular}[b]{ | l | r | r | r | }
```

If you forget to place a `\\` command at the end of the last row before `\hline`, you will get an error message such as

```
! Misplaced \noalign.
\hline ->\noalign
                 {\ifnum 0=`}\fi \hrule \@height \arrayrulew...
1.9 ....00 & 1.85  & 0.71 \hline
```

More column-formatting commands

The required argument of the `tabular` environment may contain other column-formatting commands.

An `@`*-expression,* for instance, `@{.}`, replaces the space LaTeX normally inserts between two columns with its argument. For example,

```
\begin{tabular}{r @{.} l}
   3&78\\
   4&261\\
   4
\end{tabular}
```

creates a table with two columns separated by a decimal point. In effect, you get a single, decimal-aligned column:

3.78
4.261
4.

This example is an illustration; you should use David Carlisle's dcolumn package if you need a decimal-aligned column (see Section 7.3.1).

The width of a column depends on the entries in the column by default; you can specify a width by using the p column specifier:

```
p{width}
```

For instance, if you want the first column of Table 3.1 to be 1 inch wide, then type

```
\begin{tabular}{ | p{1in} | r | r | r | }\hline
   Name    &  1    & 2     & 3    \\ \hline
   Peter   &  2.45 & 34.12 & 1.00\\ \hline
   John    &  0.00 & 12.89 & 3.71\\ \hline
   David   &  2.00 & 1.85  & 0.71\\ \hline
\end{tabular}
```

which typesets as

Name	1	2	3
Peter	2.45	34.12	1.00
John	0.00	12.89	3.71
David	2.00	1.85	0.71

The items in the first column are placed flush left. To center them, precede *each* item with a `\centering` command (see Section 3.8). Note that the first column is actually somewhat over 1 inch wide, on account of the extra space provided around the column boundaries.

Refinements

`\hline` draws a horizontal line the whole width of the table; `\cline{`*a*`-`*b*`}` may replace the `\hline` command; it draws a horizontal line from column *a* to column *b*. For instance,

`\cline{1-3}` or `\cline{4-4}`

Another useful command is `\multicolumn`, which is a single entry for one or more columns; for example,

```
\multicolumn{3}{c}{\emph{absent}}
```

The first argument is the number of columns spanned by the entry, the second is the alignment (and optional vertical line designators | for this row only), and the third argument is the entry. An example is shown in Table 3.2, typed as follows:

```
\begin{table}[b]
   \begin{center}
      \begin{tabular}{ | l | r | r | r | } \hline
         Name    & 1    & 2     & 3\\ \hline
         Peter   & 2.45 & 34.12 & 1.00\\ \hline
         John    & \multicolumn{3}{c |}{\emph{absent}}\\ \hline
         David   & 2.00 & 1.85  & 0.71\\ \hline
      \end{tabular}
      \caption{Table with \bsl\texttt{multicolumn}.}\label{Ta:mc}
```

Name	1	2	3
Peter	2.45	34.12	1.00
John	*absent*		
David	2.00	1.85	0.71

Table 3.2: Table with \multicolumn.

```
  \end{center}
\end{table}
```

The next example, shown in Table 3.3, uses \multicolumn and \cline together:

```
\begin{table}[b]
  \begin{center}
    \begin{tabular}{ | c  c  | c | r | } \hline
      Name  & Month & Week & Amount\\ \hline
      Peter & Jan.  & 1    & 1.00\\ \cline{3-4}
            &       & 2    & 12.78\\ \cline{3-4}
            &       & 3    & 0.71\\ \cline{3-4}
            &       & 4    & 15.00\\ \cline{2-4}
            & \multicolumn{2}{| l}{Total} & 29.49\\  \hline
      John  & Jan.  & 1    & 12.01\\ \cline{3-4}
            &       & 2    & 3.10\\ \cline{3-4}
            &       & 3    & 10.10\\ \cline{3-4}
            &       & 4    & 0.00\\ \cline{2-4}
            & \multicolumn{2}{| l}{Total} & 25.21\\  \hline
       \multicolumn{3}{|l}{Grand Total} & 54.70\\ \hline
    \end{tabular}
    \caption{Table with \bsl\texttt{multicolumn} and
     \bsl\texttt{cline}.}\label{Ta:multicol+cline}
  \end{center}
\end{table}
```

The \parbox command (see Section 2.9.2) can be used for multiline entries; recall that the first argument of \parbox is the width of the box. As an example, to replace Grand Total by Grand Total for Peter and John, type the last line as

```
\multicolumn{3}{l}{ \parbox[b]{10em}{Grand Total\\
for Peter and John} } & 54.70\\ \hline
```

(note the use of the bottom alignment option—see Section 2.9.2). The last row of the modified table prints

Grand Total	
for Peter and John	54.70

The spacing above Grand Total is not quite right. It can be adjusted with a strut (see Section 2.9.4),

```
\parbox[b]{10em}{\rule{0ex}{2ex}Grand Total\\
                 for Peter and John:}
```

where 2ex is the height of the strut.

Finally, vertical spacing can be adjusted by redefining \arraystretch. For instance, in the table

	Area	**Students**
5th Grade:	63.4 m^2	22
6th Grade:	62.0 m^2	19
Overall:	62.6 m^2	20

typed as

```
\begin{center}
  \begin{tabular}{|r|c|c|}\hline
       & \textbf{Area}  & \textbf{Students}\\ \hline
    \textbf{5th Grade}: & 63.4 m\textsuperscript{2} & 22\\ \hline
    \textbf{6th Grade}: & 62.0 m\textsuperscript{2} & 19\\ \hline
      \textbf{Overall}: & 62.6 m\textsuperscript{2} & 20\\ \hline
   \end{tabular}
\end{center}
```

Name	Month	Week	Amount
Peter	Jan.	1	1.00
		2	12.78
		3	0.71
		4	15.00
	Total		29.49
John	Jan.	1	12.01
		2	3.10
		3	10.10
		4	0.00
	Total		25.21
Grand Total			54.70

Table 3.3: Table with \multicolumn and \cline.

you may find that the rows are too crowded. The vertical spacing may be adjusted by adding the line

```
\renewcommand{\arraystretch}{1.25}
```

to the tabular environment; to limit its scope, add it after

```
\begin{center}
```

The adjusted table is typeset as

	Area	**Students**
5th Grade:	63.4 m^2	22
6th Grade:	62.0 m^2	19
Overall:	62.6 m^2	20

In some tables, horizontal and vertical lines do not always intersect as desired; fine control over these intersections is provided by the hhline package (see Section 7.3.1).

Chapter 5 of *The LaTeX Companion* [17] deals with tabular material, discussing many extensions, including multipage tables, decimal-point alignment, footnotes in tables, tables within tables, and so on.

3.7.1 *Table styles*

LaTeX can draw double horizontal and vertical lines in tables with ease. As a result, there are far too many double lines in LaTeX tables, resulting in cluttered and confusing tables. *The Chicago Manual of Style* [12] has 80 pages on tables; for simple tables it advocates a simple style, as shown in Table 3.4.

Table 3.4: Smokers and Nonsmokers, by Sex.

	Smoke	Don't Smoke	Total
Males	1,258	2,104	3,362
Females	1,194	2,752	3.946
Total	2,452	4,856	7,308

Notice a generous space above and below the column heads (this has been achieved with a `\rule[-8pt]{0pt}{22pt}` command), some extra space above the first line of data (achieved with the `\rule{0pt}{14pt}` command), columns of equal width (achieved with `p{70pt}` commands), and no vertical lines. Most tables in this book have been designed according to this style using Simon Fear's booktabs package, which you can find on CTAN (see Section 13.1) in the directory

```
/tex-archive/macros/latex/contrib/supported/booktabs/
```

3.8 Style and size environments

There are several text environments that allow you to set font characteristics. They have the same names as their corresponding command declarations:

```
        rmfamily  sffamily  ttfamily
upshape  itshape  em  slshape  scshape
              bfseries
```

For instance,

```
\begin{ttfamily}
   text
\end{ttfamily}
```

typesets *text* just like `{\ttfamily text}` would. Remember to use the command-declaration names for the environment names; that is, use `rmfamily`, not `textrm`; `ttfamily`, not `texttt` (see Section 2.6.3). There are also text environments for changing the font size, from `tiny` to `Huge` (see Section 2.6.7). The AMS document classes provide two additional font-size environments, discussed in Section 8.1.1.

Horizontal alignment of a paragraph is controlled by the `flushleft`, `flushright`, and `center` environments. Within the `flushright` and `center` environments, it is customary to indicate linebreaks with the `\\` command, while in the `flushleft` environment, you normally allow LaTeX to wrap the lines.

These text environments can be used separately or in combination, as in

> The **simplest** text environments set the printing style and size.
> The commands and the environments have similar names.

typed as

```
\begin{flushright}
   The \begin{bfseries}simplest\end{bfseries}
   text environments set the
   printing style and size.\\
```

```
    The commands and the environments have similar names.

\end{flushright}
```

Note the blank line at the end delimiting the paragraph.

There are command declarations that correspond to these environments:

- `\centering` centers text
- `\raggedright` left aligns text
- `\raggedleft` right aligns text

The effect of one of these commands is almost the same as that of the corresponding environment except that the environment places additional vertical space before and after the displayed paragraphs. For such a command declaration to affect the way a paragraph is formatted, the scope must include the whole paragraph, including the blank line at the end of the paragraph.

CHAPTER

4

Typing math

TEX and LATEX were designed for typesetting math. I now address this most crucial topic in detail.

A math formula can be typeset *inline*, as part of the current line, or *displayed*, on a separate line or lines with vertical space before and after the formula.

In this chapter we will discuss formulas that are set inline or displayed on a single line; Chapter 5 addresses (displayed) multiline math formulas.

We start with a discussion of LATEX's basic math environments (Section 4.1), spacing rules in math (Section 4.2), and continue with the `equation` environment (Section 4.3). The basic constructs of a formula—arithmetic (including subscripts and superscripts), binomial coefficients, ellipses, integrals, and roots—are discussed in detail in Section 4.4. Another basic construct, text in math, is the subject of Section 4.5.

Delimiters, operators, large operators, and math accents are dealt with in Sections 4.6–4.9. In Section 4.10, we discuss three types of stretchable horizontal lines that can be used above or below a formula: braces, bars, and arrows; there are also stretchable arrow math symbols.

Ⓐ LATEX and the AMS packages provide a very large number of math symbols. Section 4.11 classifies and describes them; Section 4.12 discusses how to build new symbols from existing ones. Math alphabets and symbols are discussed in Section 4.13. Horizontal spacing commands in math are described in Section 4.14.

The amsmath package provides a variety of ways to number and tag equations; Ⓐ these techniques are described in Section 4.15. Section 4.16 discusses the generalized fraction command provided by the amsmath package. Finally, Section 4.17 Ⓐ describes boxed formulas.

4.1 *Math environments*

A math formula in a LaTeX document can be typeset *inline*, as in $a \equiv b \pmod{\theta}$ or $\int_{-\infty}^{\infty} e^{-x^2}\, dx = \sqrt{\pi}$, or *displayed* as in

$$a \equiv b \pmod{\theta}$$

or

$$\int_{-\infty}^{\infty} e^{-x^2}\, dx = \sqrt{\pi}.$$

Notice how changing these two formulas from inline to displayed affects their appearance. In LaTeX documentation, *math mode* refers to being inside an inline or displayed math environment, while *text mode* refers to being outside of inline or displayed math environments.

Inline and displayed math formulas are typeset using the *math environments* `math` and `displaymath`, respectively. Because math formulas occur so frequently, LaTeX has abbreviations: the special braces `\(` and `\)` or `$` are used for the `math` environment, and `\[` and `\]` for the `displaymath` environment. So our inline example may be typed as

```
$a \equiv b \pmod{\theta}$
```

or

```
\( a \equiv b \pmod{\theta} \)
```

or

```
\begin{math}
   a \equiv b \pmod{\theta}
\end{math}
```

The displayed example can be typed as

```
\[
   \int_{-\infty}^{\infty} e^{-x^{2}} \, dx = \sqrt{\pi}
\]
```

or

```
\begin{displaymath}
   \int_{-\infty}^{\infty} e^{-x^{2}} \, dx = \sqrt{\pi}
\end{displaymath}
```

Using `$` as a delimiter for a `math` environment is a bit of an anomaly, since the same character is used as both an opening and closing delimiter. This dual purpose use can easily cause trouble. Leave one `$` out and LaTeX will detect a problem, but will not know whether an opening or a closing delimiter is missing. For instance,

```
Let $a be a real number, and let $f$ be a function.
```

would be interpreted by LaTeX as follows:

- "`Let`" is ordinary text
- "`$a be a real number, and let $`" is math
- "`f`" is interpreted as ordinary text
- "`$ be a function.`" is thought to be a `math` environment (opened by `$`) that should be closed by the next `$` in the paragraph

Because the paragraph ends with no more dollar signs appearing, you get the error message

```
! Missing $ inserted.
```

indicating the line number of the end of the paragraph. This message tells you that LaTeX placed a `$` at the end of the paragraph and typeset it. In this case, we end up with the following:

Let $a be a real number, and let$f$be a function.$

The text that ended up in a math environment is run together because math environments ignore spaces (see Section 4.2). It is now obvious that a `$` is missing after the first math letter a.

If you use `\(` and `\)` as special braces for the `math` environment, LaTeX handles the same mistake more elegantly:

```
Let \( a be a real number, and let \( f \) be a function
```

gives the error message

```
! LaTeX Error: Bad math environment delimiter.

l.6 ...a real number, and let \(
                                f \) be a function
```

LaTeX realizes that the first `\(` opens a `math` environment, so the second `\(` must be in error. In this case, the line number in the error message is correct.

Throughout this book, I will use `$` to delimit inline math.

Rule ■ Math environments
No blank lines are permitted in a `math` or `displaymath` environment.

If you violate this rule, LaTeX will generate an error message,

```
! Missing $ inserted.
<inserted text>
                $
...
l.7
```

where the line number indicates the first blank line in the environment.

Multiline math displays (such as the examples in Sections 1.6.2–1.6.3) are also implemented as math environments; they are discussed in Chapter 5.

4.2 Spacing rules

In text, the most important spacing rule is that any number of spaces in the source file equals one space in the typeset document. The spacing rule for math mode is even more straightforward:

Rule ■ Spacing in math
LaTeX ignores spacing in math.

In other words, all spacing in math mode is provided by LaTeX. For instance,

```
$a+b=c$
```

and

```
$a + b = c$
```

are both typeset as $a + b = c$.

There are two exceptions to this rule:

1. Spaces delimiting commands must be present. For instance, in

   ```
   $a \quad b$
   ```

   you cannot drop the space between `\quad` and `b`.

Ⓐ 2. If you switch back to text mode inside a math formula with an `\mbox` or `\text` command (see Section 4.5), then the text spacing rules apply in the argument of such a command.

So the spaces you type in math do not affect the typeset document. But you should still

---

Tip Format your source file so that it is easy to read.

When typing a source file, it is good practice to

- Place `\[` and `\]` on lines by themselves
- Leave spaces before and after binary operations and binary relations, including the equal sign (=)
- Indent the contents of environments so they stand out (by three spaces, for example)
- Keep formulas on one line of the source file

Develop your own distinctive style of typing math, and stick with it.

Tip The spacing after a comma is different in math and text.

I use the following rule: If the comma could be replaced with the word "and", I break the formula and move the comma out of the formula.

Example 1. Type "a, $b \in B$" as

```
$a$, $b \in B$
```

and not as

```
$a, b \in B$
```

Example 2. Type "$x = a$, b, or c" as

```
$x = a$, $b$, or $c$
```

and not as

```
$x = a, b$, or $c$
```

Compare the last two typeset:

$x = a$, b, or c

$x = a, b$, or c

Example 3. Type "for $i = 1$, 2, …, n" as

```
"for $i = 1$,~$2$, \ldots,~$n$"
```

Tip Do not leave a trailing comma in inline math.

The alert reader will notice that this parallels Rule 1 in Section 2.6.4. So do not type `If $a = b,$ then`, but move the comma out.

4.3 Equations

An *equation* is a numbered formula displayed on a single line.

Equations are typed in an `equation` environment. The `equation` environment and `displaymath` environment are exactly the same except that the `equation` environment assigns the displayed formula a number:

$$\int_{-\infty}^{\infty} e^{-x^{2}} \, dx = \sqrt{\pi} \tag{1}$$

This example is typed as

```
\begin{equation}\label{E:int}
   \int_{-\infty}^{\infty} e^{-x^{2}} \, dx = \sqrt{\pi}
\end{equation}
```

By default, the LaTeX document classes place the equation numbers on the right, while the AMS document classes place them on the left. The default choice of the document class can be overridden in the standard document classes with a document class option (see Sections 7.1.1, 8.5, and 12.1.3). In this book the equation numbers are on the left except for the typeset `intrart.tex` sample article. Ⓐ

The `\label` command in the equation environment is optional. If you use a `\label` command, the number assigned to the equation can be referenced with the `\ref` command. Using the above example,

```
see~(\ref{E:int})
```

will be typeset as see (1). The amsmath package includes the `\eqref` command, which places the parentheses automatically: Ⓐ

```
see~\eqref{E:int}
```

will also be typeset as see (1). In fact, the `\eqref` command does more: It typesets the reference *upright*, even in italicized or slanted text. For more information about cross-referencing, see Section 6.4.2.

LaTeX numbers equations consecutively. The exact form depends on the document class. As a rule, equations are numbered consecutively throughout articles, whereas in books, numbering starts from 1 at the start of each chapter. If you use the amsmath package, you may also choose to have equations numbered within each section—(1.1), (1.2), ..., in Section 1; (2.1), (2.2), ..., in Section 2; and so on—by including the command Ⓐ

```
\numberwithin{equation}{section}
```

in the preamble of your document (see Section 6.2). "Manual control" of numbering is discussed in Section 9.5.1, group numbering in Section 5.4.3.

Ⓐ The amsmath package also includes a *-ed form of the equation environment that suppresses numbering; so that when typeset,

```
\begin{equation*}
   \int_{-\infty}^{\infty} e^{-x^{2}} \, dx = \sqrt{\pi}
\end{equation*}
```

appears the same as

```
\[
   \int_{-\infty}^{\infty} e^{-x^{2}} \, dx = \sqrt{\pi}
\]
```

There is, however, one difference: The equation* environment allows you to use the \tag command (see Section 4.15).

Rule ■ Equation environments
No blank lines are permitted within an equation or equation* environment.

If you type

```
\begin{equation}\label{E:int}
   \int_{-\infty}^{\infty} e^{-x^{2}} \, dx = \sqrt{\pi}

\end{equation}
```

LaTeX will generate the error message

```
! Missing $ inserted.
<inserted text>
                $
l.8
```

Ⓐ or, if you have loaded the amsmath package, the error message would be

```
Runaway argument?
\def \\{\@amsmath@err {\Invalid@@ \\}\@eha } \label {E\ETC.
! Paragraph ended before \equation was complete.
<to be read again>
                   \par
l.8
```

4.4 Basic constructs

A formula is built up by combining various basic constructs. This section discusses the following constructs:

- Arithmetic operations
  - Subscripts and superscripts
- Binomial coefficients
- Ellipses
- Integrals
- Roots

Additional constructs will be discussed in subsequent sections.

4.4.1 Arithmetic operations

The *arithmetic operations* are typed pretty much as you would expect. To get $a + b$, $a - b$, $-a$, a/b, and ab, you would type

```
$a + b$, $a - b$, $-a$, $a / b$, $a b$
```

There are also two other forms of multiplication and one of division: $a \cdot b$, $a \times b$, and $a \div b$. They are typed as follows:

```
$a \cdot b$,  $a \times b$,  $a \div b$
```

In displayed formulas, *fractions* are usually typed with the `\frac` command. To get

$$\frac{1 + 2x}{x + y + xy}$$

you would type

```
\[
   \frac{1 + 2x}{x + y + xy}
\]
```

The amsmath package provides some refinements to the `\frac` command. You can specify displayed math style fractions with `\dfrac` and inline math style fractions with `\tfrac`: Ⓐ

$$\dfrac{3 + a^{2}}{4 + b} \qquad \tfrac{3 + a^{2}}{4 + b}$$

typed as

```
\[
   \dfrac{3 + a^{2}}{4 + b}  \qquad  \tfrac{3 + a^{2}}{4 + b}
\]
```

The `\dfrac` command is often used in matrices whose entries are not normally typeset in displayed math style. See Formula 20 in the formula gallery (Section 1.5) for an example, and Section 4.16 for other fraction variants.

Subscripts and superscripts

Subscripts are typed with _ and *superscripts* with ^. Remember to enclose the subscripted or superscripted expression in braces:

```
\[
   a_{1}, a_{i_{1}}, a^{2}, a^{b^{c}}, a^{i_{1}}, a_{i} + 1,
    a_{i + 1}, a_{1}^{2}, a^{2}_{1}
\]
```

typesets as

$$a_1, a_{i_1}, a^2, a^{b^c}, a^{i_1}, a_i + 1, a_{i+1}, a_1^2, a_1^2$$

For a^{b^c}, type `$a^{b^{c}}$`, not `$a^{b}^{c}$`. If you type the latter, you will get the error message

```
! Double superscript.
l.6 $a^{b}^
           {c}$
```

Similarly, a_{b_c} is typed as `$a_{b_{c}}$`, not as `$a_{b}_{c}$`.

In many instances, the braces for the subscripts and superscripts could be omitted, but you should type them anyway.

Tip You may safely omit the braces for a subscript or superscript that is a single digit or letter, as in `$a_1$` and `$(a + b)^x$`, which are typeset as a_1 and $(a+b)^x$. Be careful, however. If you have to edit `$a_1$` to make it a_{12}, then the braces can no longer be omitted; you must type `$a_{12}$` to obtain a_{12} because `$a_12$` will be typesets as $a_1 2$.

There is one symbol that is automatically superscripted in math mode, the prime ('). To get $f'(x)$, you type `$f'(x)$`. However, to get f'^2 you must type `$f^{\prime 2}$`; typing `${f'}^{2}$` results in ${f'}^{2}$, with the 2 too high; typing

Ⓐ it as `$f'^{2}$` will cause a double superscript error if you are using the amsmath package.

Sometimes you may want a symbol to appear superscripted (or subscripted) by itself, as in the phrase

use the symbol † to indicate the dualspace

typed as

```
use the symbol ${}^{\dagger}$ to indicate the dualspace
```

where {} is the *empty group*. The empty group can be used to separate symbols, to terminate commands, or as the base for subscripting and superscripting.

The \sb and \sp commands also typeset subscripts and superscripts, respectively, as in

```
$a\sb{1} - a\sp{x + y}$
```

which prints $a_1 - a^{x+y}$. These commands are seldom used, however, except in the alltt environment (see Section 7.3) and in the *Mathematical Reviews* of the AMS.

For multiline subscripts and superscripts, see Section 4.8.1.

4.4.2 Binomial coefficients

Standard LaTeX[1] defines the \choose command for binomial coefficients. ${a \choose b+c}$ is typed as

```
$a \choose {b + c}$
```

This command is unusual in LaTeX in that it uses *infix* notation: Its two arguments come before and after the command rather than in braces following the command name. The amsmath package considers \choose to be obsolete and issues Ⓐ the following warning if you use the \choose command with the amsmath package loaded:

```
Package amsmath Warning: Foreign command \atopwithdelims;
\frac or \genfrac should be used instead.
```

The amsmath package replaces \choose with the \binom command, which Ⓐ uses the normal syntax: The arguments follow the command. Here are two examples shown inline, $\binom{a}{b+c}$ and $\binom{\frac{n^2-1}{2}}{n+1}$, and displayed:

$$\binom{a}{b + c} \text{ and } \binom{\frac{n^{2} - 1}{2}}{n + 1}$$

The latter are typed as

```
\[
  \binom{a}{b + c}\text{ and }\binom{\frac{n^{2} - 1}{2}}{n + 1}
\]
```

You can use display-style binomials inline with \dbinom, and inline-style binomials in displayed math environments with \tbinom; for example, $\dbinom{a}{b + c}$ is typed as $\dbinom{a}{b + c}$. You may want to use \tbinom for matrix entries in a displayed formula. See Section 4.16 for other variants.

[1] In this book, we do not distinguish between LaTeX and Plain TeX commands. But from the syntax of \choose, you might guess that this command preceded LaTeX; it is, in fact, a Plain TeX command. (See Section C.2.1.)

4.4.3 *Ellipses*

LaTeX's \ldots command produces a *low* or *on-the-line ellipsis*, as in

$$F(x_1, x_2, \ldots, x_n)$$

typed as

```
\[
   F(x_{1}, x_{2}, \ldots, x_{n})
\]
```

The \cdots command provides a *centered ellipsis*, as in $x_1 + x_2 + \cdots + x_n$, typed as

```
$x_{1} + x_{2} + \cdots + x_{n}$
```

I recommend that you avoid using the \ldots and \ldots commands with the amsmath package. The \dots command will do what you want most of the time; the amsmath package uses the symbol following a \dots command to decide whether to use a low or centered ellipsis. For instance,

```
\[
   F(x_{1}, x_{2}, \dots , x_{n})\quad
   x_{1} + x_{2} + \dots + x_{n}\quad
   \alpha(x_{1} + x_{2} + \dots)
\]
```

is typeset as

$$F(x_1, x_2, \ldots, x_n) \quad x_1 + x_2 + \cdots + x_n \quad \alpha(x_1 + x_2 + \ldots)$$

if the amsmath package is loaded. The first two ellipses are correct but the last is not (there is no symbol following \ldots command to guide amsmath); to get the desired ellipsis for this formula, type

```
\[
   \alpha(x_{1} + x_{2} + \cdots)
\]
```

and it will be typeset correctly as

$$\alpha(x_1 + x_2 + \cdots)$$

If \dots or \cdots produce the wrong ellipsis, you should specify the ellipsis with one of the following amsmath commands:

- `\dotsc`, for an ellipsis followed by a comma
- `\dotsb`, for an ellipsis followed by a binary operation or relation
- `\dotsm`, for an ellipsis followed by multiplication
- `\dotsi`, for an ellipsis with integrals
- `\dotso`, for an "other" ellipsis

These commands not only force the ellipsis to be low or centered, but also adjust the spacing.

See Section 5.7.1 for an example of *vertical dots* with the `\vdots` command and *diagonal dots* with the `\ddots` command.

4.4.4 *Integrals*

You have already seen the formula $\int_{-\infty}^{\infty} e^{-x^2}\,dx = \sqrt{\pi}$ in both inline and displayed forms in the first section of this chapter. In the inline version, the lower limit is typeset as a subscript and the upper limit is typeset as a superscript; in the displayed version the limits are typeset below and above the integral symbol. To force the limits below and above the integral symbol, use the `\limits` command (the `\nolimits` command does the reverse): To typeset $\int\limits_{-\infty}^{\infty} e^{-x^{2}} \, dx = \sqrt{\pi}$, type

`$\int\limits_{-\infty}^{\infty} e^{-x^{2}} \, dx = \sqrt{\pi}$`

See Section 8.5.1 for a discussion of the `intlimits` option of the `amsmath` package. Ⓐ

There are five commands to produce variants of the basic integral symbol:

`\oint` `\iint` `\iiint` `\iiiint` `\idotsint`

they typeset as

$$\oint \qquad \iint \qquad \iiint \qquad \iiiint \qquad \idotsint$$

Except for the first (`\oint`), all of these commands require the `amsmath` package. Ⓐ

For complicated bounds, use the AMS `\substack` command or the `subarray` environment (see Section 4.8.1). Ⓐ

4.4.5 *Roots*

The `\sqrt` command produces a square root; for instance,

`$\sqrt{5}$`	produces	$\sqrt{5}$
`$\sqrt{a + 2b + c^{2}}$`	produces	$\sqrt{a + 2b + c^{2}}$

Here is a more interesting example:

$$\sqrt{1 + \sqrt{1 + \frac{1}{2}\sqrt{1 + \frac{1}{3}\sqrt{1 + \frac{1}{4}\sqrt{1 + \cdots}}}}}$$

typed as

```
\[
   \sqrt{1 + \sqrt{1 + \frac{1}{2}\sqrt{1 + \frac{1}{3}
    \sqrt{1 + \frac{1}{4}\sqrt{1 + \cdots}}}}}
\]
```

For roots other than the square root (that is, $n \neq 2$), specify n with an optional argument: To get $\sqrt[3]{5}$, for example, type `$\sqrt[3]{5}$`.

Root refinement

In $\sqrt[g]{5}$, typed as `$\sqrt[g]{5}$`, the placement of g is not very pleasing. The

Ⓐ amsmath package provides two additional commands to allow you to adjust the position of g: `\leftroot` moves g *left* (or *right* with a negative argument) and `\uproot` moves g *up* (or *down* with a negative argument). You may prefer one of the following variants:

$\sqrt[\leftroot{2}\uproot{2} g]{5}$ typed as `$\sqrt[ \leftroot{2} \uproot{2} g ]{5}$`
$\sqrt[\uproot{2} g]{5}$ typed as `$\sqrt[ \uproot{2} g ]{5}$`

Experiment with `\leftroot` and `\uproot` to find the best spacing.

4.5 Text in math

LaTeX allows you to include text in formulas with the `\mbox` command. The formula

$$A = \{\, x \mid x \in X_{i}, \mbox{ for some } i \in I \,\}$$

is typed as

```
\[
   A = \{\, x \mid x \in X_{i}, \mbox{ for some } i \in I \,\}
\]
```

Note that you have to leave space before `for` and after `some` inside the argument of `\mbox`. The argument of `\mbox` is always typeset on one line.

Sometimes it is more convenient to go into math mode within the argument of an `\mbox` command rather than end the `\mbox` and start another, as in

$$A = \{\, x \mid \mbox{for x large} \,\}$$

which is typed as

```
\[
   A = \{\, x \mid \mbox{for $x$ large} \,\}
\]
```

It is better to enter text in formulas with the \text command provided by the amsmath package. Ⓐ

The \text command is similar to the \mbox command except that \text correctly sizes its argument to match the context. The formula

$$a_{\text{left}} + 2 = a_{\text{right}}$$

is typed as

```
\[
   a_{\text{left}} + 2 = a_{\text{right}}
\]
```

Note that \text typesets its argument *in the size and shape* of the surrounding text. If you want the text in a formula to be typeset in the document font family (see Section 2.6.2) independent of the surrounding text, use

\textnormal{ ... } or {\normalfont ...}

Any of the text font commands with arguments (see Section 2.6.4) can also be used in math formulas. For instance, \textbf will use the size and shape of the surrounding text to typeset its argument in bold (extended). By default, commands behave like the \mbox command, that is, they do not change the size of the argument in a math formula. If the amsmath package is loaded, these commands behave like \text, changing the size of the argument in a math formula as needed. Ⓐ

4.6 Delimiters

Parentheses and square brackets are examples of *delimiters;* they are used to enclose some subformulas, as in $[(a*b)+(c*d)]^2$, which typesets as $[(a * b) + (c * d)]^2$. Note that if you type [in a math formula, you will always get the same size bracket—it is a fixed-size delimiter. Some delimiters can "stretch" to enclose the subformula, as in

$$\left(\frac{1}{2} \right)^{\alpha}$$

typed as

```
\[
   \left( \frac{1}{2} \right)^{\alpha}
\]
```

The commands \left and \right instruct LaTeX to stretch the parentheses.

Source	Name	Type	Typeset
LaTeX			
	left parenthesis	`(`	$($
	right parenthesis	`)`	$)$
	left bracket	`[` or `\lbrack`	$[$
	right bracket	`]` or `\rbrack`	$]$
	left brace	`\{` or `\lbrace`	$\{$
	right brace	`\}` or `\rbrace`	$\}$
	backslash	`\backslash`	$\backslash$
	forward slash	`/`	$/$
	left angle bracket	`\langle`	$\langle$
	right angle bracket	`\rangle`	$\rangle$
	vertical line	`|` or `\vert`	$\vert$
	double vertical line	`\\|` or `\Vert`	$\Vert$
	left floor	`\lfloor`	$\lfloor$
	right floor	`\rfloor`	$\rfloor$
	left ceiling	`\lceil`	$\lceil$
	right ceiling	`\rceil`	$\rceil$
	upward	`\uparrow`	$\uparrow$
	double upward	`\Uparrow`	$\Uparrow$
	downward	`\downarrow`	$\downarrow$
	double downward	`\Downarrow`	$\Downarrow$
	up-and-down	`\updownarrow`	$\updownarrow$
	double up-and-down	`\Updownarrow`	$\Updownarrow$
amsmath(A)			
	upper-left corner	`\ulcorner`	$\ulcorner$
	upper-right corner	`\urcorner`	$\urcorner$
	lower-left corner	`\llcorner`	$\llcorner$
	lower-right corner	`\lrcorner`	$\lrcorner$

Table 4.1: Standard delimiters.

4.6.1 *Delimiter tables*

The standard delimiters are shown in Table 4.1.

LaTeX knows that the symbols in these tables are delimiters, and spaces them accordingly. Notice the difference between $||a||$ and $\|a\|$. The first, $||a||$, was typed incorrectly: `$|| a ||$`. As a result, the vertical bars are too far apart. The second was typed correctly using the appropriate delimiter commands: `$\| a \|$`.

Delimiters are normally used in pairs but they can also be used singly. For instance, `$F(x) |^{b}_{a}$` is typeset as $F(x)|^{b}_{a}$.

The delimiters `|`, `\|`, and all the arrows are special: The same symbol represents both left and right delimiters, which can sometimes cause problems; for instance, a multiline formula might have the two |-s on different lines (see also Example 2 in Section 4.11). In such cases, you should use the \left and \right commands to tell LaTeX whether the delimiter is a left or right delimiter (see Section 4.6.3). The amsmath package defines the \lvert and \rvert commands for | as left and right delimiters, respectively, and \lVert and \rVert for \|, respectively. Ⓐ

4.6.2 *Delimiters of fixed size*

The delimiters listed in Table 4.1 are typeset in a fixed size, normally 10 points.

LaTeX provides the \big, \Big, \bigg, and \Bigg commands to produce delimiters of larger sizes. For example,

```
\[
   (\quad \big(\quad \Big(\quad \bigg(\quad \Bigg(
\]
```

typesets as

$$(\quad \big(\quad \Big(\quad \bigg(\quad \Bigg($$

LaTeX also provides the more specific

\bigl, \Bigl, \biggl, \Biggl, \bigr, \Bigr, \biggr, and \Biggr

commands to produce larger left and right delimiters, but these are seldom used.

For integral evaluation, you can choose one of the following:

$$F(x) |^{b}_{a} \quad F(x) \bigr|^{b}_{a} \quad F(x) \Bigr|^{b}_{a}$$

typed as

```
\[
   F(x) |^{b}_{a}        \quad
   F(x) \bigr|^{b}_{a}  \quad
   F(x) \Bigr|^{b}_{a}
\]
```

\biggr and \Biggr provide even larger symbols.

4.6.3 *Delimiters of variable size*

To enclose the formula

$$\frac{x^2 + 1}{a_2 b_2 \times c_2 d_2}$$

with square brackets of the appropriate size,

$$\left[\frac{x^2 + 1}{a_2 b_2 \times c_2 d_2} \right]^2$$

type

```
\[
  \left[ \frac{x^2 + 1}{a_2 b_2 \times c_2 d_2} \right]^2
\]
```

The general construction is

`\left` *`delim1`* and `\right` *`delim2`*

where *`delim1`* and *`delim2`* are chosen from Table 4.1, usually, but not always, a matching pair (see the examples below). LaTeX inspects the formula between the `\left` and `\right` commands and decides what size delimiters to use. Such delimiters *must be paired* in order for LaTeX to know the extent of the material to be vertically measured; however, the matching delimiters need not be the same. If you want to use a single delimiter of variable size, you will have to pair it with a *blank delimiter*, represented by the `\left.` and `\right.` commands.

Here are some examples of delimiters of variable size:

$$\left| \frac{a + b}{2} \right|, \quad \left\| A^{2} \right\|, \quad \left(\frac{a}{2}, b \right], \quad \left. F(x) \right|_{a}^{b}$$

typed as

```
\[
   \left| \frac{a + b}{2} \right|, \quad
   \left\| A^{2} \right\|,         \quad
   \left( \frac{a}{2}, b \right],  \quad
   \left. F(x) \right|_{a}^{b}
\]
```

There are also some convenient abbreviations:

`\left<` for `\left\langle` and `\right>` for `\right\rangle`

Limitations

As the AMS points out in *User's guide for the* `amsmath` *package* (*version* 2.0) [7], in a number of situations the automatic delimiter sizing done by LaTeX is not ideal.

Here are some typical examples:

1. Large operators.

```
\[
  \left[ \sum_i a_i \right]^{1/p} \quad
     \biggl[ \sum_i a_i \biggr]^{1/p}
\]
```

typesets as

$$\left[\sum_i a_i \right]^{1/p} \quad \biggl[\sum_i a_i \biggr]^{1/p}$$

You may prefer the second version with `\biggl[` and `\biggr]`.

2. Groupings.

```
\[
  \left( (a_1 b_1) - (a_2 b_2) \right)
  \left( (a_2 b_1) + (a_1 b_2) \right)
  \quad
  \bigl( (a_1 b_1) - (a_2 b_2) \bigr)
  \bigl( (a_2 b_1) + (a_1 b_2) \bigr)
\]
```

typesets as

$$\left((a_1 b_1) - (a_2 b_2) \right) \left((a_2 b_1) + (a_1 b_2) \right) \quad \bigl((a_1 b_1) - (a_2 b_2) \bigr) \bigl((a_2 b_1) + (a_1 b_2) \bigr)$$

You may prefer the clearer groupings provided by `\bigl(` and `\bigr)`.

3. Inline formulas. The delimiters produced by `\left` and `\right` use too much interline space in $\left\lvert \frac{b'}{d'} \right\rvert$, typed as

```
\left\lvert \frac{b'}{d'} \right\rvert
```

Use `\bigl` and `\bigr` to produce delimiters that fit within the normal line spacing: $\bigl\lvert \frac{b'}{d'} \bigr\rvert$, typed as

```
\bigl\lvert \frac{b'}{d'} \bigr\rvert
```

4.6.4 Delimiters as binary relations

The symbol | can be used as a delimiter, as in $|x + y|$, and also as a binary relation, as in $\{\, x \in \mathcal{R} \mid x^2 \leq 2 \,\}$. As a binary relation it is typed as `\mid`. The previous formula is typed as

```
$\{\, x \mid x^{2} \leq 2 \,\}$
```

`\bigm` and `\biggm` produce larger variants of the delimiters, with spacing on either side like binary relations. For example,

$$\left\{\, x \biggm| \int_{0}^x t^{2} \, dt \leq 5 \,\right\}$$

is typed as

```
\[
   \left\{ \, x \biggm| \int_{0}^x t^{2} \, dt \leq 5 \,\right\}
\]
```

4.7 Operators

You cannot just type `sin x` to typeset the sine function in math mode; indeed,

```
$sin x$
```

produces $sinx$ instead of $\sin x$, as you intended. The correct way to type this function is

```
$\sin x$
```

The `\sin` command prints sin with the proper style and spacing. LaTeX calls `\sin` an *operator* (or log*-like function*).

4.7.1 Operator tables

There are two types of operators:

1. *Operators without limits*, such as `\sin`
2. *Operators with limits*, such as `\lim`, that take a subscript in inline mode and a "limit" in displayed math mode; for example, $\lim_{x \to 0} f(x) = 1$ is typed as

   ```
   $\lim_{x \to 0}  f(x) = 1$
   ```

   The same formula displayed,

   $$\lim_{x \to 0} f(x) = 1$$

   is typed as

   ```
   \[
      \lim_{x \to 0} f(x) = 1
   \]
   ```

Type	Typeset	Type	Typeset	Type	Typeset	Type	Typeset
`\arccos`	$\arccos$	`\cot`	$\cot$	`\hom`	$\hom$	`\sin`	$\sin$
`\arcsin`	$\arcsin$	`\coth`	$\coth$	`\ker`	$\ker$	`\sinh`	$\sinh$
`\arctan`	$\arctan$	`\csc`	$\csc$	`\lg`	$\lg$	`\tan`	$\tan$
`\arg`	$\arg$	`\deg`	$\deg$	`\ln`	$\ln$	`\tanh`	$\tanh$
`\cos`	$\cos$	`\dim`	$\dim$	`\log`	$\log$		
`\cosh`	$\cosh$	`\exp`	$\exp$	`\sec`	$\sec$		

Table 4.2: Operators without limits.

Source	Type	Typeset	Type	Typeset
LaTeX				
	`\det`	$\det$	`\limsup`	$\limsup$
	`\gcd`	$\gcd$	`\max`	$\max$
	`\inf`	$\inf$	`\min`	$\min$
	`\lim`	$\lim$	`\Pr`	$\Pr$
	`\liminf`	$\liminf$	`\sup`	$\sup$
amsmath Ⓐ				
	`\injlim`	$\injlim$	`\projlim`	$\projlim$
	`\varliminf`	$\varliminf$	`\varlimsup`	$\varlimsup$
	`\varinjlim`	$\varinjlim$	`\varprojlim`	$\varprojlim$

Table 4.3: Operators with limits.

The operators are listed in Tables 4.2 and 4.3 (see also Section A.6). The entries in the last two rows of Table 4.3 can be illustrated by

$$\varliminf_{x \to 0} \quad \varlimsup_{x \to 0} \quad \varinjlim_{x \to 0} \quad \varprojlim_{x \to 0}$$

which are typed as

```
\[
   \varliminf_{x \to 0} \quad  \varlimsup_{x \to 0}  \quad
   \varinjlim_{x \to 0} \quad  \varprojlim_{x \to 0}
\]
```

The following examples illustrate some more entries from Table 4.3:

$$\injlim_{x \to 0} \quad \liminf_{x \to 0} \quad \limsup_{x \to 0} \quad \projlim_{x \to 0}$$

These operators were typed as

```
\[
   \injlim_{x \to 0} \quad \liminf_{x \to 0} \quad
   \limsup_{x \to 0} \quad \projlim_{x \to 0}
\]
```

You can force the limits in a displayed formula into the subscript position with the `\nolimits` command. For example,

$$\operatorname{inj\,lim}\nolimits_{x\to 0} \quad \liminf\nolimits_{x\to 0} \quad \limsup\nolimits_{x\to 0} \quad \operatorname{proj\,lim}\nolimits_{x\to 0}$$

are typed as

```
\[
   \injlim\nolimits_{x \to 0} \quad
   \liminf\nolimits_{x \to 0} \quad
   \limsup\nolimits_{x \to 0} \quad
   \projlim\nolimits_{x \to 0}
\]
```

4.7.2 Declaring operators

(A) The amsmath package provides the powerful `\DeclareMathOperator` command to define a new operator:

`\DeclareMathOperator{\opCommand}{opName}`

You invoke the new operator with `\opCommand`; the operator as it will appear typeset is *opName*. The `\DeclareMathOperator` command must be placed in the preamble. For example, to define the operator Trunc, issue the command

`\DeclareMathOperator{\Trunc}{Trunc}`

An operator is typeset in math roman with a little space after it; so `$\Trunc A$` will be typeset as $\operatorname{Trunc} A$.

The second argument is typeset in math mode but - and * are typeset as they would be in text. Here are some more examples: Define

```
\DeclareMathOperator{\Trone}{Trunc_{1}}
\DeclareMathOperator{\Ststar}{Star-one*}
```

and then
`$\Trone A$` is typeset as $\operatorname{Trunc}_{1} A$
`$\Ststar A$` is typeset as Star-one* A

To define an operator with limits, use the *-ed form

`\DeclareMathOperator*{\doublesum}{\sum\sum}`

and then (see Section 4.8.1 for multiline subscripts)

```
\[
   \doublesum_{\begin{subarray}{l}
            i^2+j^2 = 50\\
            i,\ j \leq 10
            \end{subarray}}
            \frac{x^i + y^j}{(i + j)!}
\]
```

will be typeset as

$$\sum\sum_{\substack{i^2+j^2=50\\ i,\ j\leq 10}} \frac{x^i + y^j}{(i + j)!}$$

For more on declaring operators, see Section 4.12.3.

4.7.3 *Congruences*

The `mod` function is a special operator used for congruences. Congruences are usually typeset using the `\pmod` command; the `\bmod` command is used as a binary operation: $a \bmod b$ (the remainder of a divided by b), is typed as `$a \bmod b$`.

If you use the amsmath package, then you can use two additional commands, `\mod` and `\pod`, as shown in Table 4.4. The amsmath package changes the LaTeX `\pmod` command slightly: reducing the spacing in inline math mode. See Sections 9.1.2 and 9.1.8 for a discussion of related user-defined commands. Ⓐ

Type	Typeset
`$a \equiv v \mod{\theta}$`	$a \equiv v \mod \theta$
`$a \bmod b$`	$a \bmod b$
`$a \equiv v \pmod{\theta}$`	$a \equiv v \pmod{\theta}$
`$a \equiv v \pod{\theta}$`	$a \equiv v \ (\theta)$

Table 4.4: Congruences.

4.8 *Large operators*

Here is a sum typeset inline, $\sum_{i=1}^{n} x_i^2$, and displayed,

$$\sum_{i=1}^{n} x_i^2$$

In the latter form, the sum symbol is larger, and the subscript and superscript are displayed as limits.

Type	Inline	Displayed
`\int_{a}^{b}`	$\textstyle\int_{a}^{b}$	$\displaystyle\int_{a}^{b}$
`\oint_{a}^{b}`	$\textstyle\oint_{a}^{b}$	$\displaystyle\oint_{a}^{b}$
`\prod_{i=1}^{n}`	$\textstyle\prod_{i=1}^{n}$	$\displaystyle\prod_{i=1}^{n}$
`\coprod_{i=1}^{n}`	$\textstyle\coprod_{i=1}^{n}$	$\displaystyle\coprod_{i=1}^{n}$
`\bigcap_{i=1}^{n}`	$\textstyle\bigcap_{i=1}^{n}$	$\displaystyle\bigcap_{i=1}^{n}$
`\bigcup_{i=1}^{n}`	$\textstyle\bigcup_{i=1}^{n}$	$\displaystyle\bigcup_{i=1}^{n}$
`\bigwedge_{i=1}^{n}`	$\textstyle\bigwedge_{i=1}^{n}$	$\displaystyle\bigwedge_{i=1}^{n}$
`\bigvee_{i=1}^{n}`	$\textstyle\bigvee_{i=1}^{n}$	$\displaystyle\bigvee_{i=1}^{n}$
`\bigsqcup_{i=1}^{n}`	$\textstyle\bigsqcup_{i=1}^{n}$	$\displaystyle\bigsqcup_{i=1}^{n}$
`\biguplus_{i=1}^{n}`	$\textstyle\biguplus_{i=1}^{n}$	$\displaystyle\biguplus_{i=1}^{n}$
`\bigotimes_{i=1}^{n}`	$\textstyle\bigotimes_{i=1}^{n}$	$\displaystyle\bigotimes_{i=1}^{n}$
`\bigoplus_{i=1}^{n}`	$\textstyle\bigoplus_{i=1}^{n}$	$\displaystyle\bigoplus_{i=1}^{n}$
`\bigodot_{i=1}^{n}`	$\textstyle\bigodot_{i=1}^{n}$	$\displaystyle\bigodot_{i=1}^{n}$
`\sum_{i=1}^{n}`	$\textstyle\sum_{i=1}^{n}$	$\displaystyle\sum_{i=1}^{n}$

Table 4.5: Large operators.

Operators that behave in this way are called *large operators.* Table 4.5 gives a complete list of large operators.

You can use the `\nolimits` command if you wish to show the limits of large operators as subscripts and superscripts in a displayed math environment.

The formula

$$\bigsqcup\nolimits_{\mathfrak{m}} X = a$$

is typed as

```
\[
   \bigsqcup\nolimits_{ \mathfrak{m} } X = a
\]
```

You can use the `\limits` command if you wish to show the limits of large operators below and above the operator symbol in an inline math environment. For example, $\bigsqcup\limits_{\mathfrak{m}} X = a$ is typed as

```
$\bigsqcup\limits_{ \mathfrak{m} } X = a$
```

Sums and products are very important constructs; these examples,

$$\frac{z^{d} - z_{0}^{d}}{z - z_{0}} = \sum_{k = 1}^{d} z_{0}^{k - 1} z^{d - k} \qquad (T^{n})'(x_{0}) = \prod_{k=0}^{n - 1} T'(x_{k})$$

are typed as

```
\[
   \frac{z^{d} - z_{0}^{d}}
        {z - z_{0}} =
   \sum_{k = 1}^{d} z_{0}^{k - 1} z^{d - k} \qquad
   (T^{n})'(x_{0}) = \prod_{k=0}^{n - 1} T'(x_{k})
\]
```

4.8.1 *Multiline subscripts and superscripts*

Large operators sometimes need multiline limits, which can be typeset with the `\substack` command provided by the amsmath package. Ⓐ

For instance,

$$\sum_{ \substack{ i < n\\ i \text{ even} } } x_{i}^{2}$$

is typed as

```
\[
   \sum_{ \substack{ i < n\\
                     i \text{ even} } }
    x_{i}^{2}
\]
```

There is only one rule to remember: Use the line separator command \\. You can use the \substack command wherever subscripts or superscripts are used.

The lines are centered by \substack; if you want them set flush left, as in

$$\sum_{\begin{subarray}{l} i<n\\ i \text{ even} \end{subarray}} x_i^2$$

then use the subarray environment with the argument l:

```
\[
   \sum_{ \begin{subarray}{l}
            i < n\\
            i \text{ even}
          \end{subarray} }
      x_{i}^{2}
\]
```

See Section 4.7.2 for another example.

4.9 Math accents

The accents used in text (see Section 2.4.7) cannot be used in math formulas; a separate set of commands is provided. All math accents are shown in Table 4.6 (see also Section A.8.1).

Double accents, such as

```
\[
   \hat{\hat{A}}
\]
```

Ⓐ which typesets as $\hat{\hat{A}}$, work fine if you use the amsmath package.

The two "wide" varieties, \widehat and \widetilde, expand to fit the symbols (their arguments) they cover: $\widehat{A}$, $\widehat{ab}$, $\widehat{iii}$, $\widehat{aiai}$, $\widehat{iiiii}$, and $\widetilde{A}$, $\widetilde{ab}$, $\widetilde{iii}$, $\widetilde{aiai}$, $\widetilde{iiiii}$ (the last example is typed as $\widetilde{iiiii}$). If the base is too wide, the accent is centered:

$$\widehat{ABCDE}$$

Ⓐ The "sp" commands, provided by the amsxtra package, are used for superscripts, as illustrated in Table 4.6. If you use a lot of accented characters, you will appreciate user-defined commands (see Section 9.1.1).

Notice the difference between $\bar{a}$ and $\overline{a}$, typed as

```
$\bar{a}$ $\overline{a}$
```

LaTeX		amsmath Ⓐ		amsxtra Ⓐ	
Type	Typeset	Type	Typeset	Type	Typeset
`\acute{a}`	$\acute{a}$				
`\bar{a}`	$\bar{a}$				
`\breve{a}`	$\breve{a}$			`\spbreve`	$\spbreve$
`\check{a}`	$\check{a}$			`\spcheck`	$\spcheck$
`\dot{a}`	$\dot{a}$			`\spdot`	$\spdot$
`\ddot{a}`	$\ddot{a}$			`\spddot`	$\spddot$
		`\dddot{a}`	$\dddot{a}$	`\spdddot`	$\spdddot$
		`\ddddot{a}`	$\ddddot{a}$		
`\grave{a}`	$\grave{a}$				
`\hat{a}`	$\hat{a}$				
`\widehat{a}`	$\widehat{a}$			`\sphat`	$\sphat$
`\mathring{a}`	$\mathring{a}$				
`\tilde{a}`	$\tilde{a}$				
`\widetilde{a}`	$\widetilde{a}$			`\sptilde`	$\sptilde$
`\vec{a}`	$\vec{a}$				

Table 4.6: Math accents.

For other examples of the `\overline` command, see Section 4.10.2.

To use an arbitrary symbol as an accent or to create "underaccents," use Javier Bezos' accents package, which you can find on CTAN (see Section 13.1) in the directory

```
/tex-archive/macros/latex/contrib/supported/bezos/
```

4.10 Stretchable horizontal lines

LaTeX provides three types of stretchable horizontal lines that appear above or below a formula: braces, bars, and arrows. There are also stretchable arrow math symbols. The amsmath package adds several more stretching arrows. 

4.10.1 Horizontal braces

The `\overbrace` command places a brace of variable size above its argument, as in

$$\overbrace{a + b + \cdots + z}$$

which is typed as

```
\[
   \overbrace{a + b + \cdots + z}
\]
```

A superscript adds a label to the brace, as in

$$\overbrace{a + a + \cdots + a}^{n}$$

typed as

```
\[
   \overbrace{a + a + \cdots + a}^{n}
\]
```

The `\underbrace` command works similarly, placing a brace below its argument. A subscript adds a label to the brace, as in

$$\underbrace{a + a + \cdots + a}_{n}$$

typed as

```
\[
   \underbrace{a + a + \cdots + a}_{n}
\]
```

The following example combines these two commands:

$$\underbrace{\overbrace{a + \cdots + a}^{(m-n)/2} + \underbrace{b + \cdots + b}_{n} + \overbrace{a + \cdots + a}^{(m-n)/2}}_{m}$$

This example is typed as

```
\[
   \underbrace{
      \overbrace{a + \cdots + a}^{(m - n)/2}
      + \underbrace{b + \cdots + b}_{n}
      + \overbrace{a + \cdots + a}^{(m - n)/2}
    }_{m}
\]
```

4.10.2 Overlines and underlines

You can draw lines above or below a formula with the `\overline` and `\underline` commands. For example,

$$\overline{\overline{X} \cup \overline{\overline{\overline{X}}}} = \overline{\overline{X}}$$

is typed as

```
\[
  \overline{ \overline{X} \cup \overline{ \overline{X} } } =
   \overline{ \overline{X} }
\]
```

Similarly, you can place arrows above and below an expression:

$$\begin{gather*}
\overleftarrow{a} \quad \overrightarrow{aa}\\
\overleftrightarrow{aaa} \quad \underleftarrow{aaaa} \quad
\underrightarrow{aaaaa} \quad \underleftrightarrow{aaaaaa}
\end{gather*}$$

typed as

```
\begin{gather*}
  \overleftarrow{a}         \quad \overrightarrow{aa}\\
  \overleftrightarrow{aaa} \quad \underleftarrow{aaaa}    \quad
  \underrightarrow{aaaaa}  \quad \underleftrightarrow{aaaaaa}
\end{gather*}
```

The commands used in the first line are standard LaTeX. The commands in the second and third lines are provided by the amsmath package. Ⓐ

4.10.3 *Stretchable arrow math symbols*

The amsmath package provides two stretchable arrow math symbols that extend to accommodate a formula above or below the arrows with the `\xleftarrow` and `\xrightarrow` commands. The formula on top is given as the argument (possibly empty) and the formula below is an optional argument. Ⓐ

$$A \xrightarrow{\text{1-1}} B \xleftarrow[\alpha \to \beta]{\text{onto}} C \xleftarrow[\gamma]{} D \xleftarrow{} E$$

is typed as

```
\[
  A \xrightarrow{\text{1-1}} B \xleftarrow[\alpha \to \beta]
   {\text{onto}} C \xleftarrow[\gamma]{} D \xleftarrow{} E
\]
```

There are similar commands described in Section 5.8, but they can only be used in commutative diagrams.

4.11 *Spacing of symbols*

LaTeX provides a large variety of math symbols: Greek characters (α), binary operations ($\circ$), binary relations ($\leq$), negated binary relations ($\nleq$), arrows ($\nearrow$), delimiters

(`{ }`), and so on. All the math symbols provided by LaTeX and the AMS packages are listed in the tables in Appendix A.

Consider the formula

$$A = \{\, x \in X \mid x\beta \geq x y > (x + 1)^{2} - \alpha \,\}$$

typed as

```
\[
   A = \{\, x \in X \mid x \beta \geq x y
     > (x + 1)^{2} - \alpha \,\}
\]
```

The spacing of the symbols in the formula varies. In $x\beta$, the two symbols are very close. In $x \in X$, there is some space around the $\in$, but in $x + 1$, there is somewhat less space around the $+$. There is a little space after $\{$ and before $\}$—not quite enough for this formula, which is why the thinspace commands (`\,`) were added.

4.11.1 *Classification*

LaTeX classifies symbols into several categories and spaces them accordingly. In the formula

$$A = \{\, x \in X \mid x\beta \geq x y > (x + 1)^{2} - \alpha \,\}$$

we find

- Ordinary math symbols: A, x, X, β, and so on
- Binary relations: $=$, $\in$, $|$, $\geq$, and $>$
- Binary operations: $+$ and $-$
- Delimiters: $\{$, $\}$, $($, and $)$

As a rule, you do not have to be concerned with whether or not a given symbol in a formula, say $\times$, is a binary operation in a formula. LaTeX will typeset the formula correctly.

4.11.2 *Three exceptions*

There are three symbols with more than one classification: $+$, $-$, and $|$.

$+$ or $-$ could be either a binary operation, $a - b$, or a sign, $-b$.

Rule ■ $+$ and $-$

$+$ (or $-$) is a binary operation if it is preceded and followed by a symbol or an empty group (`{ }`).

So, for instance, in

$$\begin{alignedat}{2}
(A + B C)x &+{} &C &y = 0,\\
Ex &+{} &(F + G)&y = 23.
\end{alignedat}$$

typed as (see the `alignat*` environment in Section 5.5.4)

```
\begin{alignat*}{2}
   (A + B C)x &+{} &C       &y = 0,\\
           Ex &+{} &(F + G)&y = 23.
\end{alignat*}
```

we use the empty group, `{}`, to tell LaTeX that `+` is a binary operation. If we leave out the empty group, and type

```
\begin{alignat*}{2}
   (A + B C)x &+ &C       &y = 0,\\
           Ex &+ &(F + G)&y = 23.
\end{alignat*}
```

instead, we get

$$\begin{alignedat}{2}
(A + B C)x &+ &C &y = 0,\\
Ex &+ &(F + G)&y = 23.
\end{alignedat}$$

Another illustration is given later in this section using the `\phantom` command. This problem often arises in split formulas: If the formula is split just before a $+$ or $-$, you should start the next line with `{}+` or `{}-` (see Section 5.3 for examples).

The | symbol can play several different roles in a math formula, so LaTeX provides separate commands to specify the symbol's meaning:

Rule ■ The four roles of the | symbol:

- `|` ordinary math symbol
- `\mid` binary relation
- `\left|` left delimiter
- `\right|` right delimiter

Note the differences between the spacing in $a|b$ (typed as `$a | b$`) and $a \mid b$ (typed as `$a \mid b$`).

4.11.3 Spacing commands

Ⓐ There are some situations where LaTeX cannot typeset a formula properly, and you will have to add spacing commands. Luckily, both LaTeX and the amsmath package provide a variety of spacing commands, listed in Table 4.7. Eight of them,

`\,` `\thinspace` `\!` `\:` `\;` `\quad` `\qquad` `\negthinspace`

are provided by LaTeX, the other five,

`\medspace` `\thickspace` `\negmedspace` `\negthickspace` `\mspace`

Ⓐ by the amsmath package. The `\neg` commands remove space ("reverse the print head").

The `\quad` and `\qquad` commands are normally used to adjust aligned formulas (see Chapter 5) or to add space before text in a math formula. The size of `\quad` (= 1 em) and `\qquad` (= 2 em) depends on the current font.

Ⓐ The `\,` and `\!` commands are the most useful for fine-tuning math formulas. The amsmath package provides you with even finer control by adding the `\mspace` command and the math unit *mu*; 18 mu = 1 em (defined in Section 2.8.3). For example, `\mspace{3mu}` adds a space that is 1/6 em long.

		LaTeX		amsmath Ⓐ	
Name	Width	Short	Long	Short	Long
Positive space					
1 mu (math unit)	ı				`\mspace{1mu}`
thinspace	␣	`\,`	`\thinspace`		
medspace	␣	`\:`			`\medspace`
thickspace	␣	`\;`			`\thickspace`
1 em	└┘		`\quad`		
2 em	└──┘		`\qquad`		
Negative space					
1 mu	ı				`\mspace{-1mu}`
thinspace	␣	`\!`	`\negthinspace`		
medspace	␣				`\negmedspace`
thickspace	␣				`\negthickspace`

Table 4.7: Math spacing commands.

4.11.4 *Examples*

The opening formula of this section shows the importance of fine-tuning: In set notation, when using `\mid` for "such that", thin spaces are inserted just inside the braces. Some more examples of fine-tuning follow. (See also the formula gallery in Section 1.5; one more example can be found in Section 4.12.1.)

Example 1 In Section 1.3, you typed the formula $\int_{0}^{\pi} \sin x \, dx = 2$ as

```
$\int_{0}^{\pi} \sin x \, dx = 2$
```

Notice the thinspace spacing command `\,` between `\sin x` and `dx`. Without the command, LaTeX would have crowded $\sin x$ and dx: $\int_{0}^{\pi} \sin x dx = 2$

Example 2 $| - f(x)|$ (typed as `$|-f(x)|$`) is spaced incorrectly; $-$ is a binary operation by the $+$ and $-$ rule. To get the correct spacing, as in $\left|-f(x)\right|$, you should type `$\left|-f(x)\right|$`; this form tells LaTeX that the first | is a left delimiter (by the | rule), and therefore $-$ is the unary minus sign, not the binary subtraction operation.

Example 3 In $\sqrt{5} \mbox{side}$, typed as

```
$\sqrt{5} \mbox{side}$
```

$\sqrt{5}$ is too close to side; so type it as

```
$\sqrt{5} \,\mbox{side}$
```

which typesets as $\sqrt{5} \,\mbox{side}$.

Example 4 In $\sin x / \log n$, the division symbol / is too far from $\log n$, so type

```
$\sin x / \! \log n$
```

which prints $\sin x / \! \log n$.

Example 5 In $f(1 / \sqrt{n})$, typed as

```
$f(1 / \sqrt{n})$
```

the square root almost touches the closing parenthesis. To correct it, type

```
$f(1 / \sqrt{n}\,)$
```

which typesets as $f(1 / \sqrt{n}\,)$.

There is one more symbol with special spacing: the `\colon` command; used for formulas such as $f \colon A \to B$ (typed as `$f \colon A \to B$`).

The colon (:) is a binary relation in math; `$f: A \to B$` typesets $f : A \to B$; as you can see, the spacing is awful.

See Section 4.12.3 on how to declare the type of a symbol.

4.11.5 *The* `\phantom` *command*

The `\phantom{`*argument*`}` command (introduced for text in Section 2.8.1) produces a space in a formula equivalent to the space that would be occupied by its typeset argument. This command is one of the most powerful tools available to us for fine-tuning alignments. Here are two simple illustrations (using the amsmath package):

$$A = \begin{pmatrix} 1 & 3 & 1\\ 2 & 1 & 1\\ -2 & 2 & -1 \end{pmatrix}$$

typed as

```
\[
   A = \begin{pmatrix}
          \phantom{-}1 & \phantom{-}3 & \phantom{-}1\\
          \phantom{-}2 & \phantom{-}1 & \phantom{-}1\\
                    -2 & \phantom{-}2 &            -1\\
       \end{pmatrix}
\]
```

and

$$\begin{aligned} a + b + c &+ d \phantom{ {}+e } = 0,\\ c &+ d + e = 5. \end{aligned}$$

typed as

```
\begin{align*}
     a + b + c & + d \phantom{ {}+e } = 0,\\
             c & + d + e              = 5.
   \end{align*}
```

Note that `\phantom{+e}` yields incorrect spacing (by the + and − rule):

$$\begin{aligned} a + b + c &+ d = 0,\\ c &+ d + e = 5. \end{aligned}$$

See Section 5.6.2 for an additional example.

4.12 *Building new symbols*

No matter how many math symbols LaTeX and the AMSFonts font set provide (see a complete listing in Appendix A), users always seem to need more. LaTeX and the amsmath package give you excellent tools to build new symbols from existing ones.

4.12.1 Stacking symbols

The LaTeX

```
\stackrel{top}{bottom}
```

command creates a new symbol by placing the symbol *top* (in superscript size) above the symbol *bottom*. For instance, $x \stackrel{?}{=} y$ is typed as `\stackrel{?}{=}`. Note that a symbol created with `\stackrel` is a binary relation, regardless of the type of *bottom*.

The amsmath package allows you place any symbol above, or below, any other. Ⓐ The `\overset` command takes two arguments; the first argument is set in a smaller size over the second argument. Unlike `\stackrel`, the spacing rules of the symbol in the second argument remain valid (i.e., the type remains the same). The `\underset` command is the same except that the first argument is set under the second argument. For example,

$$\overset{\alpha}{a} \qquad \underset{\boldsymbol{\cdot}}{X} \qquad \overset{\alpha}{ a_{i} } \qquad \overset{\alpha}{a}_{i}$$

are typed as

```
\[
  \overset{\alpha}{a}                 \qquad
  \underset{\boldsymbol{\cdot}}{X}  \qquad
  \overset{\alpha}{ a_{i} }           \qquad
  \overset{\alpha}{a}_{i}
\]
```

(For more information on the `\boldsymbol` command, see Section 4.13.3.) Note that in the third example, $\overset{\alpha}{a_i}$, the α seems to be sitting too far to the right; the fourth example corrects that.

You can also use these commands with binary relations, as in

$$f(x) \overset{\text{def}}{=} x^{2} - 1$$

typed as

```
\[
  f(x) \overset{ \text{def} }{=} x^{2} - 1
\]
```

Since $=$ is a binary relation, $\overset{\text{def}}{=}$ becomes a binary relation, as shown by the spacing on either side. Another example,

$$\frac{a}{b} \overset{u}{+} \frac{c}{d} \overset{l}{+} \frac{e}{f}$$

typed as

```
\[
   \frac{a}{b} \overset{u}{+} \frac{c}{d}
    \overset{l}{+} \frac{e}{f}
\]
```

Note that $\overset{u}{+}$ and $\overset{l}{+}$ are properly spaced as binary operations.

4.12.2 Negating and side-setting symbols

You can *negate* a symbol with the \not command; for instance, $a \not\in b$ and $a \not= b$ are typed as `$a \not\in b$` and `$a \not= b$`, respectively. It is preferable, however, to use the negated symbols $\notin$, typed as `$\notin$`, and $\ne$, typed as `$\ne$` (see the negated binary relations table in Section A.2.3). For instance, "a does not divide b", $a \nmid b$, should be typed as `$a \nmid b$` (an AMS symbol), not as `$a \not\mid b$`, which prints $a \not\mid b$. (In Section 4.12.3, you will learn how to improve $a \not\mid b$ to $a \mathrel{\not|} b$, typed as `$a \mathrel{\not|} b$`. However, `$a \nmid b$` is still best.)

The amsmath package provides the \sideset command to set symbols at the corners of a large operator. The \sideset command takes three arguments:

```
\sideset{ _{ll}^{ul} }{ _{lr}^{ur} }{large_op}
```

where *ll* stands for the symbol to be placed at the lower left, *ul* for upper left, *lr* for lower right, and *ur* for upper right; *large_op* is a large operator. Examples,

$$\sideset{}{_{*}^{*}}{\prod}\text{ and }\sideset{^{*}}{}{\prod}$$

typed as

```
\[
   \sideset{}{_{*}^{*}}{\prod}\text{ and }\sideset{^{*}}{}{\prod}
\]
```

Note that the first two arguments are compulsory, although they may be empty.

Here is a more meaningful example:

```
\[
   \sideset{}{'}{\sum}_{\substack{ i < 10\\ j < 10 } } x_{i}z_{j}
\]
```

is typeset as

$$\sideset{}{'}{\sum}_{\substack{ i < 10\\ j < 10 } } x_{i}z_{j}$$

In this example note that prime ($'$) is an automatically superscripted symbol (see Section 4.4.1), so you do not have to type `^'` in the second argument. Typing `\sum'` would not work, since LaTeX would place the prime above the sum symbol.

4.12.3 Changing a symbol's type

In Section 4.11, you have seen that some symbols are binary relations and some are binary operations. In fact, you can force any symbol to behave like either type.

The \mathbin command declares its argument to be a binary operation, for instance,

```
\mathbin{\alpha}
```

makes this instance of \alpha behave like a binary operation, as in $a \mathbin{\alpha} b$, typed as

```
$a \mathbin{\alpha} b$
```

You can use the \mathrel command to make a symbol behave like a binary relation, as in the formula $a \mathrel{\mbox{fine}} b$, typed as

```
$a \mathrel{ \mbox{fine} } b$
```

The \mathop command forces a symbol to behave like a simple math operator, as in the formula $\mathop{\mathrm{Trunc}} \alpha$, typed as

```
$\mathop{ \mathrm{Trunc} } \alpha$
```

If you use the amsmath package, then any symbol or string of characters can be declared as an operator or an operator with limits. For instance, to use Trunc as an operator, type (A)

```
$\operatorname{Trunc} f(x)$
```

which will typeset as $\operatorname{Trunc} f(x)$.

To use Trunc as an operator with limits, type

```
\[
   \operatorname*{Trunc}_{x \in X} A_{x}
\]
```

which typesets as

$$\operatorname*{Trunc}_{x \in X} A_{x}$$

Typesetting the same formula inline produces $\operatorname*{Trunc}_{x \in X} A_{x}$.

In Section 4.7.2, we discussed an alternate approach (also provided by the amsmath package), the \DeclareMathOperator command and its *-ed version. (A)

4.13 Math alphabets and symbols

The classification of math symbols in the context of spacing was discussed in Section 4.11. The symbols in a formula can also be classified as *characters from math alphabets* and *math symbols.* In the formula

$$A = \{x \in X \mid x\beta \geq xy > (x+1)^2 - \alpha\}$$

the following characters come from a math alphabet:

$$A \quad x \quad X \quad y \quad 1 \quad 2$$

whereas these characters are math symbols:

$$= \quad \{ \quad \in \quad | \quad \beta \quad \geq \quad > \quad (\quad + \quad) \quad - \quad \alpha \quad \}$$

4.13.1 *Math alphabets*

The letters and digits typed in a math formula come from a ***math alphabet***. LaTeX's default math alphabet—the one you get if you do not ask for something else—is Computer Modern math italic for *letters*. In the formula $x^2 \vee y_3 = \alpha$, x, and y come from this math alphabet. The default math alphabet for *digits* is Computer Modern roman; the 2 and 3 in this formula are typeset in Computer Modern roman.

LaTeX has a number of commands to switch to various math alphabets; the two most important commands select text fonts as math alphabets:

Command	Math alphabet	Produces
`\mathbf{a}`	math bold	$\mathbf{a}$
`\mathit{a}`	math italic	a

As a rule, any command that switches to a math alphabet should be used with *a single letter argument*. Some users make an exception, recommending that `\mathit` be used with word identifiers, as in the example below:

$$\mathit{credit} + \mathit{debit} = 0$$

typed as

```
\[
  \mathit{credit} + \mathit{debit} = 0
\]
```

But beware of the pitfalls. For instance, in `\mathit{left-side}` the hyphen will typeset as a minus: $\mathit{left-side}$.

There are four more commands that switch math alphabets:

Command	Math Alphabet	Produces
`\mathsf{a}`	math sans serif	a
`\mathrm{a}`	math roman	a
`\mathtt{a}`	math typewriter	$\mathtt{a}$
`\mathnormal{a}`	math italic	$\mathnormal{a}$

Math roman is used in formulas for operator names (such as sin in $\sin x$) and for text. For operator names, you should use the `\operatorname` command (see Section 4.12.3) or `\DeclareMathOperator` (or the *-ed version), which sets the name of the operator in roman, and also provides the proper spacing (see Section 4.12.3). For text, you should use the `\mbox` command (or the `\text` command if you use the amsmath package—see Section 4.5). Ⓐ

The `\mathnormal` command switches to the default math alphabet, but this command is seldom used in practice.

The Computer Modern fonts include a math bold italic alphabet, but neither LaTeX nor the amsmath package define a command to access it. Ⓐ

4.13.2 Math symbol alphabets

You may have noticed that α was not classified as belonging to an alphabet in the example at the beginning of this section. Indeed, α is treated by LaTeX as a math symbol rather than as a member of a math alphabet. You cannot italicize or slant it, nor is there a sans-serif version. There is a bold version (the AMSFonts even have it in smaller sizes) but you must use the `\boldsymbol` command in the amsbsy package (automatically loaded by amsmath and thus by all AMS document classes unless the `nomath` option is used) to produce it. Ⓐ

Two "alphabets of symbols" are built into LaTeX: the Greek alphabet (see Section A.1.2 for the symbol table) and calligraphic, an uppercase-only alphabet invoked with the `\mathcal` command; for example, $\mathcal{A}$, $\mathcal{C}$, and $\mathcal{E}$ are typed as

```
$\mathcal{A}$, $\mathcal{C}$, $\mathcal{E}$
```

The eucal package (see Section 8.6) provides the Euler Script alphabet as a substitute for the calligraphic alphabet. Type

```
\usepackage{eucal}
```

in the preamble of your document to *redefine* the `\mathcal` command. With this package loaded,

```
$\mathcal{A}$, $\mathcal{C}$, $\mathcal{E}$
```

now produce $\mathscr{A}$, $\mathscr{C}$, $\mathscr{E}$. To use both alphabets, you can invoke the eucal package in the form:

```
\usepackage[mathscr]{eucal}
```

The `\mathcal` command will continue to provide the standard calligraphic alphabet and the Euler Script alphabet can be used with the `\mathscr` command:

$\mathcal{A}$, $\mathcal{C}$, $\mathcal{E}$
$\mathscr{A}$, $\mathscr{C}$, $\mathscr{E}$

are typed as

```
$\mathcal{A}$, $\mathcal{C}$, $\mathcal{E}$

$\mathscr{A}$, $\mathscr{C}$, $\mathscr{E}$
```

The eufrak package (see Section 8.6), loaded with

```
\usepackage{eufrak}
```

in the preamble of your document, provides the `\mathfrak` command for typesetting both upper and lowercase letters in Euler Fraktur. The sample characters $\mathfrak{n}$, $\mathfrak{p}$, $\mathfrak{N}$, and $\mathfrak{P}$ are typed as

```
$\mathfrak{n}$, $\mathfrak{p}$, $\mathfrak{N}$, $\mathfrak{P}$
```

Ⓐ If you use the amsfonts package, you do not have to load the eufrak package to use Euler Fraktur.

Ⓐ The Blackboard bold math alphabet ($\mathbb{A}$, $\mathbb{B}$, $\mathbb{C}$), provided by the amsfonts package, is invoked with the `\mathbb` command. Blackboard bold is an uppercase-only math alphabet. The letters shown above were typed as

```
$\mathbb{A}$, $\mathbb{B}$, $\mathbb{C}$
```

4.13.3 *Bold math symbols*

In math, most of a font's characteristics are specified by LaTeX. One exception is boldface. To make a *letter* from a math alphabet within a formula bold, use the `\mathbf` command. For instance, in

let the vector $\mathbf{v}$ be chosen ...

$\mathbf{v}$ is produced by `$\mathbf{v}$`.

To obtain bold math *symbols*, use the `\boldsymbol` command provided by the Ⓐ amsbsy (AMS bold symbols) package, which is automatically loaded by the amsmath package and thus by all AMS document classes. For example, the bold symbols

$$\boldsymbol{5} \quad \boldsymbol{\alpha} \quad \boldsymbol{\Lambda} \quad \boldsymbol{\mathcal{A}} \quad \boldsymbol{\to} \quad \boldsymbol{A}$$

are typed as

```
\[
   \boldsymbol{5}       \quad \boldsymbol{\alpha}        \quad
   \boldsymbol{\Lambda} \quad \boldsymbol{ \mathcal{A} } \quad
   \boldsymbol{\to}     \quad \boldsymbol{A}
\]
```

Note that \boldsymbol{A} typesets as $\boldsymbol{A}$, a bold math italic A. If you do not have the AMSFonts installed, many of the bold symbols used in this book will not be available.

To make an entire formula bold, use the \mathversion{bold} command; as in

```
{\mathversion{bold} $a \equiv c \pmod{\theta}$}
```

which typesets as $\boldsymbol{a \equiv c \pmod{\theta}}$. Note that the \mathversion{bold} command is given *before the formula.*

To typeset $\boldsymbol{\mathcal{AMS}}$, type

```
$\boldsymbol{ \mathcal{A} } \boldsymbol{ \mathcal{M} }
   \boldsymbol{ \mathcal{S} }$
```

or

```
$\boldsymbol{ \mathcal{AMS} }$
```

or

```
{\mathversion{bold} $\mathcal{AMS}$}
```

Within the scope of \mathversion{bold}, you can undo its effect with

```
\mathversion{normal}
```

Not all symbols have bold variants; if you type

```
$\sum \quad \boldsymbol{\sum}$
```

you get $\sum \quad \sum$: the two symbols are identical. To obtain a bold version, use the *poor man's bold* invoked by the \pmb command (provided by the amsbsy package,  which is automatically loaded by the amsmath package and all the AMS document classes). This command typesets the symbol three times very close to each other producing a bold symbol of some quality; note that \pmb does destroy the type of the symbol: \pmb{\sum} is no longer spaced like a large operator. To make it into a large operator, declare it as

```
\mathop{\pmb{\sum}}
```

Compare the following three variants of sum:

$$\sum_{i=1}^{n} i^{2} \quad \textstyle\sum_{i=1}^{n} i^{2} \quad \displaystyle\mathop{\pmb{\sum}}_{i=1}^{n} i^{2}$$

The first sum is typed (in displayed math mode) as

```
\sum_{i = 1}^{n} i^{2}
```

The second uses poor man's bold, but does not declare the result to be a large operator:

```
\pmb{\sum}_{i = 1}^{n} i^{2}
```

The third uses poor man's bold and also declares the result to be a large operator:

```
\mathop{\pmb{\sum}}_{i = 1}^{n} i^{2}
```

4.13.4 *Size changes*

There are four math font sizes, invoked by the command declarations

- `\displaystyle`, normal size for displayed formulas
- `\textstyle`, normal size for inline formulas
- `\scriptstyle`, normal size for subscripted and superscripted symbols
- `\scriptscriptstyle`, normal size for doubly subscripted and superscripted symbols

These commands control a number of style parameters in addition to the size. Compare the two fractions

$$\frac{1}{\displaystyle 2 + \frac{1}{3}} \quad \frac{1}{ 2 + \frac{1}{3} }$$

which are typed as

```
\[
    \frac{1}{\displaystyle 2 + \frac{1}{3}} \quad
       \frac{1}{ 2 + \frac{1}{3} }
\]
```

4.13.5 *Continued fractions*

Ⓐ The amsmath package makes typesetting continued fractions easier by supplying the `\cfrac` command. The `\cfrac` command takes an optional argument `l` or `r`, to place the numerator on the left or on the right. For example,

$$\cfrac{1}{ 2 + \cfrac{1}{3 + \cdots} } \qquad \cfrac[l]{1}{2 + \cfrac[l]{1}{3 + \cdots}}$$

is typed as

```
\[
   \cfrac{1}{ 2 + \cfrac{1}{3 + \cdots} } \qquad
       \cfrac[l]{1}{2 + \cfrac[l]{1}{3 + \cdots}}
\]
```

4.14 *Vertical spacing*

As a rule, all horizontal and vertical spacing in a math formula is done by LaTeX. Nevertheless, you often need to adjust horizontal spacing (see Section 4.11). There is seldom a need to adjust vertical spacing, but there are a few exceptions.

The formula $\sqrt{a}+\sqrt{b}$ does not look quite right, because the square roots are not uniform in size. You can correct this with the `\mathstrut` commands, which insert an invisible vertical space:

```
$\sqrt{\mathstrut a} + \sqrt{\mathstrut b}$
```

typesets as $\sqrt{\mathstrut a}+\sqrt{\mathstrut b}$. See Section 2.9.4 for more information on struts.

Another way to handle this situation is with the vertical phantom command, `\vphantom`, which measures the height of its argument and places a math strut of that height into the formula. So

```
$\sqrt{\vphantom{b} a} + \sqrt{b}$
```

also prints uniform square roots, $\sqrt{\vphantom{b} a}+\sqrt{b}$, but is more versatile than the previous solution.

Here is a more complicated example from a recent research article:

$$\Theta_i = \bigcup \big(\, \Theta (\,\overline{a \wedge b}, \overline{\vphantom{b}a} \wedge \overline{b}) \mid a,\ b \in B_i \,\big) \vee \bigcup \big(\, \Theta(\,\overline{a \vee b}, \overline{\vphantom{b}a} \vee \overline{b} \,) \mid a,\ b \in B_i \,\big),$$

typed as

```
\[
   \Theta_i = \bigcup \big(\, \Theta (\,\overline{a \wedge b},
      \overline{\vphantom{b}a} \wedge \overline{b})
        \mid a,\ b \in B_i \,\big)
      \vee \bigcup \big(\, \Theta(\,\overline{a \vee b},
      \overline{\vphantom{b}a} \vee \overline{b} \,)
        \mid a,\ b \in B_i \,\big),
 \]
```

The `\smash` command directs LaTeX to pretend that its argument does not protrude above or below the line in which it is typeset.

For instance, the two lines of this admonition:

It is *very important* that you memorize the integral $\frac{1}{\int f(x)\,dx} = 2g(x) + C$, which will appear on the next test.

are too far apart because LaTeX had to make room for the fraction. However, in this instance, the extra vertical space is not necessary because the second line is very short. By placing the formula in the argument of a `\smash` command:

```
It is \emph{very important} that you memorize the integral
$\smash{\frac{1}{\int f(x) \, dx}} = 2 g(x) + C$, which will
appear on the next test.
```

LaTeX will produce the following:

It is *very important* that you memorize the integral $\frac{1}{\int f(x)\, dx} = 2g(x) + C$, which will appear on the next test.

Ⓐ The amsmath package adds an optional argument to the `\smash` command to control which part of the formula is ignored: `t` to smash the top, and `b` to smash the bottom.

4.15 Tagging and grouping

Ⓐ In addition to numbering, the amsmath package also allows you to attach a name to an equation using the `\tag` command. In the `equation` or `equation*` environments,

```
\tag{name}
```

attaches the tag *name* to the equation. The tag replaces the number.

Recall that the numbering of an equation is *relative;* that is, the number assigned to an equation is relative to the placement of the equation with respect to other equations in the document. An equation tag, on the other hand, is *absolute;* the tag remains the same even after the equation is moved. A numbered equation needs a `\label{name}` command, so that a `\ref{name}` command can reference the number generated by LaTeX. (An equation may contain both a tag and a label. The tag will be typeset; the label can be used for page reference with the `\pageref` command—see Section 6.4.2.)

Note that if there is a tag, the `equation` and the `equation*` environments are equivalent. For example,

$$\int_{-\infty}^{\infty} e^{-x^{2}} \, dx = \sqrt{\pi} \tag{Int}$$

may be typed as

```
\begin{equation*}
   \int_{-\infty}^{\infty} e^{-x^{2}} \, dx = \sqrt{\pi}\tag{Int}
\end{equation*}
```

or

```
\begin{equation}
   \int_{-\infty}^{\infty} e^{-x^{2}} \, dx = \sqrt{\pi}\tag{Int}
\end{equation}
```

The `\tag*` command (also provided by the amsmath package) is the same as `\tag` except that it does not automatically enclose the tag in parentheses. To get Ⓐ

$$\int_{-\infty}^{\infty} e^{-x^2}\,dx = \sqrt{\pi} \tag*{A–B}$$

you would type

```
\begin{equation}
  \int_{-\infty}^{\infty} e^{-x^{2}} \, dx = \sqrt{\pi}
   \tag*{A--B}
\end{equation}
```

Tagging allows numbered variants of equations. For instance, the equation

$$A^{[2]} \diamond B^{[2]} \cong (A \diamond B)^{[2]} \tag{1}$$

may need a variant:

$$A^{\langle 2\rangle} \diamond B^{\langle 2\rangle} \equiv (A \diamond B)^{\langle 2\rangle} \tag{1'}$$

If the label of the first equation is `E:first`, then the second equation may be typed as follows:

```
\begin{equation}\tag{\ref{E:first}$'$}
   A^{\langle 2 \rangle} \diamond B^{\langle 2\rangle}
   \equiv (A \diamond B)^{\langle 2 \rangle}
\end{equation}
```

Such a tag is not absolute; it changes with the referenced label, but will not change if the variant equation is moved.

In contrast, *grouping* (also provided by the amsmath package) applies to a group of *adjacent* equations. Suppose the last equation was numbered (2) and the next group of equations is to be referred to as (3), with individual equations numbered as (3a), (3b), and so on. Enclosing these equations in a `subequations` environment will accomplish this goal. For instance, Ⓐ

$$A^{[2]} \diamond B^{[2]} \cong (A \diamond B)^{[2]} \tag{2a}$$

and its variant

$$A^{\langle 2\rangle} \diamond B^{\langle 2\rangle} \equiv (A \diamond B)^{\langle 2\rangle} \tag{2b}$$

are typed as

```
\begin{subequations}\label{E:joint}
   \begin{equation}\label{E:original}
      A^{[2]} \diamond B^{[2]} \cong (A \diamond B)^{[2]}
   \end{equation}

   \begin{equation}\label{E:modified}
      A^{\langle 2 \rangle} \diamond B^{\langle 2 \rangle}
      \equiv (A \diamond B)^{\langle 2 \rangle}
   \end{equation}
\end{subequations}
```

Referring to these equations, you will find that

- `\eqref{E:joint}` resolves to (2)
- `\eqref{E:original}` resolves to (2a)
- `\eqref{E:modified}` resolves to (2b)

Note that in this example, references to the second and third labels produce numbers that also appear in the typeset version. The group label, `E:joint`, references the entire group.

A `subequations` environment can contain the multiline math constructs discussed in Chapter 5; see Section 5.4.3.

4.16 Generalized fractions

Ⓐ The amsmath package provides a generalized fraction command,

```
\genfrac{left-delim}{right-delim}{thickness}{mathstyle}
        {numerator}{denominator}
```

where

- *`left-delim`* is the left delimiter for the formula (default: none)
- *`right-delim`* is the right delimiter for the formula (default: none)
- *`thickness`* is the thickness of the fraction line, in the form x`pt` (default: the normal weight)
- *`mathstyle`* is one of
  - `0` for `\displaystyle`
  - `1` for `\textstyle`
  - `2` for `\scriptstyle`
  - `3` for `\scriptscriptstyle`
  - Default: Depends on the context; if the formula is being set in display style, then the default is `0`, and so on
- *`numerator`* is the numerator
- *`denominator`* is the denominator

All five arguments must be specified; the empty argument, `{}`, gives the default value.

4.16.1 *Examples*

1. `\frac{`*numerator*`}{`*denominator*`}`
   is the same as

   `\genfrac{}{}{}{}{`*numerator*`}{`*denominator*`}`

2. `\dfrac{`*numerator*`}{`*denominator*`}`
   is the same as

   `\genfrac{}{}{}{0}{`*numerator*`}{`*denominator*`}`

3. `\tfrac{`*numerator*`}{`*denominator*`}`
   is the same as

   `\genfrac{}{}{}{1}{`*numerator*`}{`*denominator*`}`

4. `\binom{`*numerator*`}{`*denominator*`}`
   is the same as

   `\genfrac{(}{)}{0pt}{}{`*numerator*`}{`*denominator*`}`

5. Here are some more examples:

$$\frac{a + b}{c} \quad \genfrac{}{}{1pt}{}{a + b}{c} \quad \genfrac{}{}{1.5pt}{}{a + b}{c} \quad \genfrac{}{}{2pt}{}{a + b}{c} \quad \genfrac{[}{]}{0pt}{}{a + b}{c} \quad \genfrac{]}{[}{0pt}{}{a + b}{c}$$

   typed as

```
\[
  \frac{a + b}{c} \quad
  \genfrac{}{}{1pt}{}{a + b}{c}   \quad
  \genfrac{}{}{1.5pt}{}{a + b}{c} \quad
  \genfrac{}{}{2pt}{}{a + b}{c}   \quad
  \genfrac{[}{]}{0pt}{}{a + b}{c} \quad
  \genfrac{]}{[}{0pt}{}{a + b}{c}
\]
```

   The delimiters you can choose from Table 4.1.

If a `\genfrac` construct is used repeatedly, you should name it; see Section 9.1 for user-defined commands.

4.17 *Boxed formulas*

The `\boxed` command puts its argument in a box, as in

$$\boxed{\int_{-\infty}^{\infty} e^{-x^2}\,dx = \sqrt{\pi}} \tag{3}$$

typed as

```
\begin{equation}
   \boxed{ \int_{-\infty}^{\infty} e^{-x^{2}}\, dx = \sqrt{\pi} }
\end{equation}
```

This command can also be used with a text argument.

CHAPTER

5

Multiline math displays

TEX and LATEX are about typesetting math. But they say very little about one crucial and difficult problem: How do you typeset multiline math formulas? This problem is addressed by the AMS packages; their solution is described in detail in this chapter.

For most mathematical documents, three constructs will suffice: *simple* and *annotated* alignments, which use the `align` environment; and the `cases` environment, which I first introduced in Section 1.6.2.

The AMS environments for typesetting multiline math formulas are introduced in Sections 5.2 through 5.7. To get an overview, start with the visual guide in Section 5.1.

Section 5.4 states some general rules that apply to all multiline math environments; it also discusses the numbering of groups of formulas.

Section 5.8 discusses a subsidiary math environment for typesetting simple commutative diagrams. Finally, Section 5.9 describes how to allow page breaks in multiline math environments.

Ⓐ All the constructs described in this chapter except the `array` and `eqnarray` environments require the amsmath package, so there will be no further reminders and the marginal warnings will be omitted. The document `multline.tpl` in the `samples` directory (see page 4) contains all the multiline formulas in this chapter.

The style parameters controlling these constructs are discussed in a number of publications:

- Section 8.9.2 of *The LaTeX Companion* [17][1]
- *User's guide for the* `amsmath` *package*, (*version* 2.0) [7] (in the AMS distribution; see Section 13.1)
- `amsmath.dtx` in the LaTeX distribution on CTAN (see Section 13.1), in the directory

  `/tex-archive/macros/latex/required/amslatex/math/`

Such parameters should be changed in a document class; that task goes beyond the mission statement of this book (see page xxxvi).

5.1 A visual guide

Multiline math formulas are displayed in columns, which are either *adjusted* (centered, or set flush left or right) or *aligned* (an alignment point is designated for each column in each line). The top half of Figure 5.1 shows thumbnail sketches of the adjusted environments, while the bottom half shows the aligned environments.

The first row of Figure 5.1 illustrates `gather`, a one-column, centered math environment—discussed in Section 5.2—which is used to display a number of formulas collected into one multiline formula; and `multline`, which displays a long formula with its first line set flush left, its last line set flush right, and the rest of the lines centered; see Section 5.3.

The `align` environment is one of the AMS's major contributions to LaTeX; as you saw in Section 1.6.2, it is used to create aligned formulas. The lower half of Figure 5.1 illustrates the `align` environment and two of its variants: `alignat` and `flalign`, discussed in Section 5.5.

While math environments like `gather`, `multline`, and `align` produce complete displays, subsidiary math environments create "large symbols" that can be used in math formulas. Three adjusted subsidiary math environments—`matrix`, `cases`, and `array`—are illustrated in the top half of Figure 5.1 and presented in Section 5.7.

The aligned subsidiary math environments `aligned` and `gathered` look just like the `align` and `gather` environments, so they are not illustrated in Figure 5.1; `aligned` and `gathered` are discussed in Section 5.6, along with the `split` environment.

[1] Chapter 8 of *The LaTeX Companion* [17] describes AMS-LaTeX, version 1.1. For an update, see the documents `ch8.ps` and `ch8.pdf` on CTAN—see Section 13.1—in the directory `/tex-archive/info/companion-rev/`

Adjusted environments

$$\begin{gather*} x_1x_2 + x_1^2x_2^2 + x_3 \\ x_1x_3 + x_1^2x_3^2 + x_2 \\ x_1x_2x_3 \end{gather*}$$

`gather`
one column, centered

$$\begin{multline*} (x_1x_2x_3x_4x_5x_6)^2 \\ + (x_1x_2x_3x_4x_5 + x_1x_3x_4x_5x_6 + x_1x_2x_4x_5x_6 + x_1x_2x_3x_5x_6)^2 \\ + (x_1x_2x_3x_4 + x_1x_2x_3x_5 + x_1x_2x_4x_5 + x_1x_3x_4x_5)^2 \end{multline*}$$

`multline`
flush left, centered, flush right

Adjusted subsidiary environments

$$\begin{pmatrix} 1 & 0 & \dots & 0 \\ 0 & 1 & \dots & 0 \\ \vdots & \vdots & \ddots & \vdots \\ 0 & 0 & \dots & 1 \end{pmatrix}$$

`matrix`
multicolumn, centered

$$f(x) = \begin{cases} -x^2, & \text{if } x < 0; \\ \alpha + x, & \text{if } 0 \leq x \leq 1; \\ x^2, & \text{otherwise.} \end{cases}$$

`cases`
columns flush left

$$\left(\begin{array}{cccr} a+b+c & uv & x-y & 27 \\ a+b & u+v & z & 134 \end{array} \right)$$

`array`
multicolumn
each column adjusted independently

Aligned environments

$$\begin{align*} f(x) &= x + yz & g(x) &= x + y + z \\ h(x) &= xy + xz + yz & k(x) &= (x + y)(x + z)(y + z) \end{align*}$$

`align`
multicolumn, aligned

$$\begin{flalign*} f(x) &= x + yz & g(x) &= x + y + z \\ h(x) &= xy + xz + yz & k(x) &= (x + y)(x + z)(y + z) \end{flalign*}$$

`flalign`
multicolumn, aligned

$$\begin{alignat}{4} a_{11}x_1 &+ a_{12}x_2 &&+ a_{13}x_3 && &&= y_1 \tag{17} \\ a_{21}x_1 &+ a_{22}x_2 && &&+ a_{24}x_4 &&= y_2 \tag{18} \\ a_{31}x_1 & &&+ a_{33}x_3 &&+ a_{34}x_4 &&= y_3 \tag{19} \end{alignat}$$

`alignat`
multicolumn, aligned

Aligned subsidiary environment

$$\begin{split} 0 &= \langle \dots, 0, \dots, \overset{i}{d}, \dots, 0, \dots \rangle \wedge \langle \dots, 0, \dots, \overset{j}{a}, \dots, 0, \dots \rangle \\ &\equiv \langle \dots, 0, \dots, \overset{j}{a}, \dots, 0, \dots \rangle \pmod{\Theta} \end{split} \tag{3.4}$$

`split`
one column, aligned

Figure 5.1: The AMS multiline formulas.

5.2 Gathering formulas

The gather environment groups a number of one-line formulas, each centered on a separate line:

$$x_1 x_2 + x_1^2 x_2^2 + x_3, \tag{1}$$
$$x_1 x_3 + x_1^2 x_3^2 + x_2, \tag{2}$$
$$x_1 x_2 x_3. \tag{3}$$

Formulas (1)–(3) are typed as follows:

```
\begin{gather}
   x_{1} x_{2} + x_{1}^{2} x_{2}^{2} + x_{3},\label{E:mm1.1}\\
   x_{1} x_{3} + x_{1}^{2} x_{3}^{2} + x_{2},\label{E:mm1.2}\\
   x_{1} x_{2} x_{3}.\label{E:mm1.3}
\end{gather}
```

Rule ■ gather environments

1. Lines are separated with \\. Do not type a \\ at the end of the last line!
2. Each line is numbered unless it has a \tag or \notag before the \\.
3. No blank lines are permitted within the environment.

The gather* environment is like gather, except that all lines are unnumbered (they can still be \tag-ged).

5.3 Splitting long formulas

The multline environment is used to split one very long formula into several lines; the first line is set flush left, the last line is set flush right, and the middle lines are centered:

$$\begin{multline} (x_1 x_2 x_3 x_4 x_5 x_6)^2 \\ + (y_1 y_2 y_3 y_4 y_5 + y_1 y_3 y_4 y_5 y_6 + y_1 y_2 y_4 y_5 y_6 + y_1 y_2 y_3 y_5 y_6)^2 \\ + (z_1 z_2 z_3 z_4 z_5 + z_1 z_3 z_4 z_5 z_6 + z_1 z_2 z_4 z_5 z_6 + z_1 z_2 z_3 z_5 z_6)^2 \\ + (u_1 u_2 u_3 u_4 + u_1 u_2 u_3 u_5 + u_1 u_2 u_4 u_5 + u_1 u_3 u_4 u_5)^2 \tag{4} \end{multline}$$

This formula is typed as:

```
\begin{multline}\label{E:mm2}
   (x_{1} x_{2} x_{3} x_{4} x_{5} x_{6})^{2}\\
   + (y_{1} y_{2} y_{3} y_{4} y_{5}
   +  y_{1} y_{3} y_{4} y_{5} y_{6}
```

```
   + y_{1} y_{2} y_{4} y_{5} y_{6}
   + y_{1} y_{2} y_{3} y_{5} y_{6})^{2}\\
   + (z_{1} z_{2} z_{3} z_{4} z_{5}
   + z_{1} z_{3} z_{4} z_{5} z_{6}
   + z_{1} z_{2} z_{4} z_{5} z_{6}
   + z_{1} z_{2} z_{3} z_{5} z_{6})^{2}\\
   + (u_{1} u_{2} u_{3} u_{4} + u_{1} u_{2} u_{3} u_{5}
   + u_{1} u_{2} u_{4} u_{5} + u_{1} u_{3} u_{4} u_{5})^{2}
\end{multline}
```

Rule ■ `multline` environments

1. Lines are separated with `\\`. Do not type a `\\` at the end of the last line!
2. The formula is numbered as a whole unless it is `\tag`-ged or numbering is suppressed with `\notag`.
3. No blank lines are permitted within the environment.

Subformulas have their own rules, which we will discuss in Section 5.4.1.

If you are very observant, you may have noticed that we failed to type `{}+` at the beginnings of the second to fourth lines of the formula; in Section 4.11.2, you were told that this omission would result in the second line being typeset as

$$+(y_1 y_2 y_3 y_4 y_5 + y_1 y_3 y_4 y_5 y_6 + y_1 y_2 y_4 y_5 y_6 + y_1 y_2 y_3 y_5 y_6)^2$$

The `multline` environment, however, knows that a long formula is being broken and so typesets `+` as a binary operation.

A common mistake is to write `multiline` for `multline`, resulting in the message:

```
! LaTeX Error: Environment multiline undefined.

1.5 \begin{multiline}
                          \label{E:mm2}
```

In the `multline*` environment, all lines are unnumbered (but can be jointly `\tag`-ged).

The indentation of the first and last lines is controlled by the `\multlinegap` length command (with a default of 10 points) unless there is a tag on one of those lines. You can adjust the indentation by enclosing the `multline` environment in a `setlength` environment, as in

```
\begin{multline*}
   (x_{1} x_{2} x_{3} x_{4} x_{5} x_{6})^{2}\\
   + (x_{1} x_{2} x_{3} x_{4} x_{5}
```

```
  + x_{1} x_{3} x_{4} x_{5} x_{6}
  + x_{1} x_{2} x_{4} x_{5} x_{6}
  + x_{1} x_{2} x_{3} x_{5} x_{6})^{2}\\
  + (x_{1} x_{2} x_{3} x_{4} + x_{1} x_{2} x_{3} x_{5}
  + x_{1} x_{2} x_{4} x_{5} + x_{1} x_{3} x_{4} x_{5})^{2}
\end{multline*}
\begin{setlength}{\multlinegap}{0pt}
  \begin{multline*}
    (x_{1} x_{2} x_{3} x_{4} x_{5} x_{6})^{2}\\
    + (x_{1} x_{2} x_{3} x_{4} x_{5}
    + x_{1} x_{3} x_{4} x_{5} x_{6}
    + x_{1} x_{2} x_{4} x_{5} x_{6}
    + x_{1} x_{2} x_{3} x_{5} x_{6})^{2}\\
    + (x_{1} x_{2} x_{3} x_{4} + x_{1} x_{2} x_{3} x_{5}
    + x_{1} x_{2} x_{4} x_{5} + x_{1} x_{3} x_{4} x_{5})^{2}
  \end{multline*}
\end{setlength}
```

which typesets as

$$\begin{multline*}
(x_{1} x_{2} x_{3} x_{4} x_{5} x_{6})^{2}\\
+ (x_{1} x_{2} x_{3} x_{4} x_{5} + x_{1} x_{3} x_{4} x_{5} x_{6} + x_{1} x_{2} x_{4} x_{5} x_{6} + x_{1} x_{2} x_{3} x_{5} x_{6})^{2}\\
+ (x_{1} x_{2} x_{3} x_{4} + x_{1} x_{2} x_{3} x_{5} + x_{1} x_{2} x_{4} x_{5} + x_{1} x_{3} x_{4} x_{5})^{2}
\end{multline*}$$

$$\begin{multline*}
(x_{1} x_{2} x_{3} x_{4} x_{5} x_{6})^{2}\\
+ (x_{1} x_{2} x_{3} x_{4} x_{5} + x_{1} x_{3} x_{4} x_{5} x_{6} + x_{1} x_{2} x_{4} x_{5} x_{6} + x_{1} x_{2} x_{3} x_{5} x_{6})^{2}\\
+ (x_{1} x_{2} x_{3} x_{4} + x_{1} x_{2} x_{3} x_{5} + x_{1} x_{2} x_{4} x_{5} + x_{1} x_{3} x_{4} x_{5})^{2}
\end{multline*}$$

Any line of a `multline` (or `multline*`) environment can be typeset flush left or right by making it the argument of a `\shoveleft` or `\shoveright` command, respectively. For instance, to typeset the second line of formula (4) flush left, as in

$$\begin{multline*}
(x_{1} x_{2} x_{3} x_{4} x_{5} x_{6})^{2}\\
\shoveleft{+ (x_{1} x_{2} x_{3} x_{4} x_{5} + x_{1} x_{3} x_{4} x_{5} x_{6} + x_{1} x_{2} x_{4} x_{5} x_{6} + x_{1} x_{2} x_{3} x_{5} x_{6})^{2}}\\
+ (x_{1} x_{2} x_{3} x_{4} + x_{1} x_{2} x_{3} x_{5} + x_{1} x_{2} x_{4} x_{5} + x_{1} x_{3} x_{4} x_{5})^{2}
\end{multline*}$$

type the formula as follows:

```
\begin{multline*}
  (x_{1} x_{2} x_{3} x_{4} x_{5} x_{6})^{2}\\
  \shoveleft{+ (x_{1} x_{2} x_{3} x_{4} x_{5}
    + x_{1} x_{3} x_{4} x_{5} x_{6}
```

```
        + x_{1} x_{2} x_{4} x_{5} x_{6}
        + x_{1} x_{2} x_{3} x_{5} x_{6})^{2}}\\
        + (x_{1} x_{2} x_{3} x_{4} + x_{1} x_{2} x_{3} x_{5}
        + x_{1} x_{2} x_{4} x_{5} + x_{1} x_{3} x_{4} x_{5})^{2}
\end{multline*}
```

Observe that the entire line is the argument of the `\shoveleft` command, which is followed by `\\` (unless it is the last line of the environment).

5.4 *Some general rules*

Even though you have only seen a few examples of multiline math environments, I should point out that the multiline math environments and subsidiary environments share a number of rules.

Rule ■ Multiline math environments

1. Lines are separated with `\\`. Do not type a `\\` at the end of the last line!
2. No blank lines are permitted within the environments.
3. If an environment contains more than one formula, then, as a rule, each formula is numbered separately. If you add a `\label` command to a line, then the equation number generated for that line can be cross-referenced.
4. You can suppress the numbering of a line by using a `\notag` command on the line.
5. You can also override numbering with the `\tag` command, which works just as it does for equations (see Section 4.15).
6. `\tag` and `\label` should always precede the line separator `\\` (except on the last line). The `\tag` command works for individual lines, not for the environment as a whole.
7. For cross-referencing, use `\label` and `\ref` the same way you would for an equation (see Section 6.4.2).
8. Each multiline math environment has a `*`-ed form, which suppresses numbering. (Individual formulas can still be `\tag`-ged).

A `\notag` command placed after the environment will be ignored, but a `\tag` command will give the error message

```
! Package amsmath Error: \tag not allowed here.
```

5.4.1 *Subformula rules*

A formula in the `multline` environment is split into a number of parts by `\\` commands; for instance, formula (4) is split into three parts:

```
1. (x_{1} x_{2} x_{3} x_{4} x_{5} x_{6})^{2}

2.    + (x_{1} x_{2} x_{3} x_{4} x_{5}
       + x_{1} x_{3} x_{4} x_{5} x_{6}
       + x_{1} x_{2} x_{4} x_{5} x_{6}
       + x_{1} x_{2} x_{3} x_{5} x_{6})^{2}

3.    + (x_{1} x_{2} x_{3} x_{4} + x_{1} x_{2} x_{3} x_{5} +
       x_{1} x_{2} x_{4} x_{5} + x_{1} x_{3} x_{4} x_{5})^{2}
```

Such parts of a formula are called *subformulas*.

The aligned formula $x = y + z$ (from the simple alignment example in Section 1.6.2), which is typed as

```
x &= y + z
```

is split up into two parts:

```
1.   x

2.        = y + z
```

In general, the first part is everything between the beginning of the formula and the first `&` symbol. There can then be any number of parts delimited by two consecutive `&` symbols. Finally, the last part is from the last `&` symbol to the end of the formula or the line separator `\\`. These parts are also called *subformulas*.

Here are the last of the general rules:

Rule ■ Subformulas

1. Each subformula must be a formula that LaTeX can typeset independently.
2. If a subformula starts with the binary operation + or −, type it as `{}+` or `{}-`.
3. If a subformula ends with the binary operation + or −, type it as `+{}` or `-{}`.

Suppose that you want to split the formula

$$x_1 + y_1 + \left(\sum_{i<5} \binom{5}{i} + a^2 \right)^2$$

just before the binomial coefficient. Try

```
\begin{multline}
   x_{1} + y_{1} + \left( \sum_{i < 5}\\
    \binom{4}{i} + a^{2} \right)^{2}
\end{multline}
```

When typesetting this formula, you will get the error message

```
! Missing \right. inserted.
<inserted text>
                \right .
...
l.11 \end{multline}
```

because the first subformula violates the first subformula rule:

```
x_{1} + y_{1} + \left( \sum_{i < 5}
```

cannot be typeset by LaTeX because the `\left(` command must be matched by the `\right` command and some delimiter.

Testing for the first subformula rule is easy: Split the formula into its subformulas, and try to typeset each subformula separately.

5.4.2 Breaking and aligning formulas

You do not have to know where and how to break inline math formulas because LaTeX does all the work for you.

Unfortunately, multiline formulas are different. The AMS packages give you excellent tools for displaying multiline math formulas, but they give you no advice on deciding where to break a long formula into lines. And that is how it should be: You, the author, are the only judge of where to break a long formula so that the result is aesthetically pleasing, mathematically informative, and follows the traditions of mathematical typesetting.

A strict set of rules is formulated in *Mathematics into Type* by Ellen Swanson, Arlene Ann O'Sean, and Antoinette Tingley Schleyer [58]. I will state only three:

Rule ■ Breaking displayed formulas

1. Try to break a long formula *before* a binary relation or binary operation.
2. If you break a formula before a `+` or `-`, start the next line with `{}+` or `{}-`.
3. If you break a formula within a bracket, indent the next line so that it begins *to the right of* the opening bracket

---

Formula (5) in Chapter 1 and formula (4) in this chapter illustrate the first rule. Here is an illustration of the third rule:

$$\begin{aligned} f(x,y,z,u) = [&(x+y+z) \times (x^2+y^2+z^2-1) \times (x^3+y^3+z^3-u) \\ &\times (x^4+y^4+z^4+u)]^2 \end{aligned}$$

The rules for aligning columns are similar.

Rule ■ Aligning columns

1. Try to align columns at a binary relation or a binary operation.
2. If you align a column at a binary relation, put the `&` symbol immediately to the left of the binary relation.
3. If you align a column at the binary operation + or -, put the `&` symbol to the left of the binary operation and `{}` between the `&` and the operation: `&{}+` or `&{}-`.

5.4.3 *Numbering groups of formulas*

With most constructs in this chapter, you will have a number of equations typeset together, arranged in some way (aligned or adjusted). Each equation is numbered separately, unless `\tag`-ged or `\notag`-ged. Often, you may want the equations to share a common number, but still be able to reference each equation separately.

You can change the numbering of the equations on page 206 in formulas (1)–(3) to (1), (1a), and (1b) as follows:

```
\begin{gather}
   x_{1} x_{2} + x_{1}^{2} x_{2}^{2} + x_{3},\label{E:mm1}\\
   x_{1} x_{3} + x_{1}^{2} x_{3}^{2} + x_{2},\tag{\ref{E:mm1}a}\\
   x_{1} x_{2} x_{3};\tag{\ref{E:mm1}b}
\end{gather}
```

produces the desired result

$$x_1x_2 + x_1^2x_2^2 + x_3, \tag{1}$$

$$x_1x_3 + x_1^2x_3^2 + x_2, \tag{1a}$$

$$x_1x_2x_3; \tag{1b}$$

To obtain (1′) or (1’) type

```
\tag{\ref{E:mm1}$'$}
```

or

```
\tag{(1\textquoteright)}
```

and for (1_{a}), type

```
\tag{\ref{E:mm1}${}_{\text{a}}$}
```

Alternatively, you may include the gather environment in a subequations environment (see Section 4.15):

$$x_1x_2 + x_1^2x_2^2 + x_3, \tag{5a}$$

$$x_1x_3 + x_1^2x_3^2 + x_2, \tag{5b}$$

$$x_1x_2x_3, \tag{5c}$$

typed as

```
\begin{subequations}\label{E:gp}
   \begin{gather}
      x_{1} x_{2} + x_{1}^{2} x_{2}^{2} + x_{3},\label{E:gp1}\\
      x_{1} x_{3} + x_{1}^{2} x_{3}^{2} + x_{2},\label{E:gp2}\\
      x_{1} x_{2} x_{3},\label{E:gp3}
   \end{gather}
\end{subequations}
```

Then `\eqref{E:gp}` references the whole group of equations as (5), while

`\eqref{E:gp1}`, `\eqref{E:gp2}`, and `\eqref{E:gp3}`

reference the individual formulas as (5a), (5b), and (5c).

5.5 *Aligned columns*

The lines of many multiline formulas are naturally divided into columns. In this section, we will discuss how to typeset such formulas with *aligned columns.* All of these constructs are implemented with the align math environment and its variants.

In Section 1.6.2, you saw two simple, one-column examples of aligned columns (which we called *simple alignment*) and a special case of aligned columns (which we called *annotated alignment*).

The align environment can also create multiple aligned columns; the number of columns is restricted only by the width of the page. In the following example, there are two aligned columns,

$$\begin{aligned} f(x) &= x + yz & g(x) &= x + y + z\\ h(x) &= xy + xz + yz & k(x) &= (x + y)(x + z)(y + z) \end{aligned} \tag{6}$$

typed as

```
\begin{align}\label{E:mm3}
   f(x) &= x + yz         & g(x) &= x + y + z\\
   h(x) &= xy + xz + yz   & k(x) &= (x + y)(x + z)(y + z)
    \notag
\end{align}
```

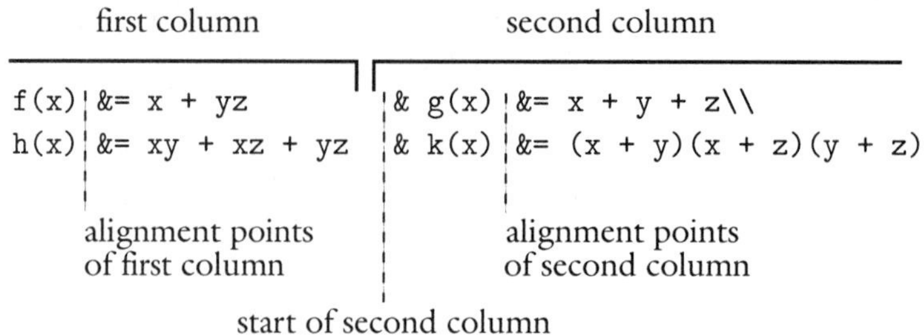

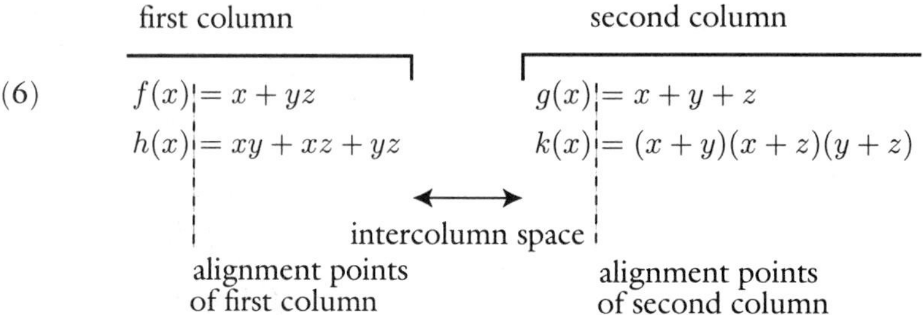

Figure 5.2: Two aligned columns: source and typeset.

Use Figure 5.2 to visualize how the alignment points in the source turn into alignment points in the typeset formula and the role played by the intercolumn space.

In a multicolumn `align` environment, the ampersand (`&`) doubles as a mark for the *alignment point* and as a *column separator*. In the first line of this formula,

```
f(x) &= x + yz        & g(x) &= x + y + z
```

the two columns are

```
f(x) &= x + yz
```

and

```
                      g(x) &= x + y + z
```

In each column, we use a single ampersand to mark the alignment point. Of the three `&` symbols in the previous example,

- The first `&` marks the *alignment point* of the first column
- The second `&` is a *column separator;* it separates the first and second columns
- The third `&` marks the *alignment point* of the second column

I use the convention of typing a space on the left of an alignment point `&` and no space on the right, and of putting spaces on both sides of `&` as a column separator.

If the number of columns is three, then there should be five &s in each line. The two even-numbered &s are column separators and the three odd-numbered &s are alignment marks.

Rule ■ If there are n aligned columns, then each line should have at most $2n - 1$ ampersands: the even-numbered &s are column separators; odd-numbered &s mark the alignment points.

5.5.1 *An* `align` *variant*

A variant of `align` is the flush alignment environment `flalign`, which moves the leftmost column as far left and the rightmost column as far right as space allows, making more room for the formula. Here is formula (6) again, followed by the `flalign` variant:

$$\begin{aligned} f(x) &= x + yz & g(x) &= x + y + z \\ h(x) &= xy + xz + yz & k(x) &= (x + y)(x + z)(y + z) \end{aligned} \tag{6}$$

$$\begin{aligned} f(x) &= x + yz & g(x) &= x + y + z \\ h(x) &= xy + xz + yz & k(x) &= (x + y)(x + z)(y + z) \end{aligned} \tag{7}$$

The variant is typed as follows:

```
\begin{flalign}\label{E:mm3fl}
   f(x) &= x + yz        & g(x) &= x + y + z\\
   h(x) &= xy + xz + yz & k(x) &= (x + y)(x + z)(y + z)
    \notag
\end{flalign}
```

5.5.2 `eqnarray`*, the ancestor of* `align`

For historical reasons, it is appropriate to mention the ancestor of `align`, LATEX's `eqnarray` math environment. Here is an example:

```
\begin{eqnarray}
   x & = & 17y\\
   y & > & a + b + c
\end{eqnarray}
```

which typeset as

$$x \quad = \quad 17y \tag{8}$$

$$y \quad > \quad a + b + c \tag{9}$$

You can type the same formulas with `align`:

```
\begin{align}
   x  & =  17y\\
   y  & >  a + b + c
\end{align}
```

which typesets as

$$x = 17y \tag{10}$$
$$y > a + b + c \tag{11}$$

As you can see, with `eqnarray`, the spaces around the $=$ and $>$ come out too wide by default. In the `eqnarray` environment; the spacing is based on the spacing of the columns rather than on the spacing requirements of the symbols.

5.5.3 *The subformula rule revisited*

Suppose that you want to align the formula

$$x_1 + y_1 + \left(\sum_{i<5} \binom{5}{i} + a^2 \right)^2$$

with

$$\left(\sum_{i<5} \binom{5}{i} + \alpha^2 \right)^2$$

such that the $+a^2$ in the first formula aligns with the $+\alpha^2$ in the second formula. You might try typing

```
\begin{align}
   x_{1} + y_{1} + \left( \sum_{i < 5} \binom{5}{i}
            &+ a^{2} \right)^{2}\\
    \left( \sum_{i < 5} \binom{5}{i} + \alpha^{2} \right)^{2}
\end{align}
```

But when you typeset this formula, you will get the error message

```
! Extra }, or forgotten \right.
<template> }
            $}\ifmeasuring@ \savefieldlength@ \fi \set@field ...
...
l.12 \end{align}
```

This alignment structure violates the subformula rule because

```
 x_{1} + y_{1} + \left( \sum_{i < 5} \binom{5}{i}
```

is a subformula that LaTeX cannot typeset.

As another simple example, try to align the + in $\binom{a+b}{2}$ with the + in $x + y$:

```
\begin{align}
  \binom{a &+ b}{2}\\
    x &+ y
\end{align}
```

When typesetting this formula, you get the error message

```
! Missing } inserted.
<inserted text>
                }
```

Again, LaTeX cannot typeset the subformula `\binom{a`.

To align the two formulas in the first example, add a `\phantom` command to push the second line to the right:

```
\begin{align*}
   &x_{1} + y_{1} + \left( \sum_{i < 5} \binom{5}{i}
      + a^{2} \right)^{2}\\
   &\phantom{x_{1} + y_{1} + {}}
      \left( \sum_{i < 5} \binom{5}{i} + \alpha^{2} \right)^{2}
\end{align*}
```

yielding

$$\begin{aligned}
&x_{1} + y_{1} + \left(\sum_{i < 5} \binom{5}{i} + a^{2} \right)^{2}\\
&\phantom{x_{1} + y_{1} + {}}\left(\sum_{i < 5} \binom{5}{i} + \alpha^{2} \right)^{2}
\end{aligned}$$

5.5.4 *The* alignat *environment*

Another variant of the `align` environment is the `alignat` environment, which is one of the most important aligned environments. While the `align` environment calculates how much space to put between the columns, the `alignat` environment leaves spacing up to the user. It is important to note that the `alignat` environment has a required argument, the number of columns.

Here is formula (6) typed with the `alignat` environment:

```
\begin{alignat}{2}\label{E:mm3A}
   f(x) &= x + yz          & g(x) &= x + y + z\\
   h(x) &= xy + xz + yz & k(x) &= (x + y)(x + z)(y + z)
```

```
   \notag
\end{alignat}
```

when typeset, you get

$$f(x) = x + yz \qquad g(x) = x + y + z \tag{12}$$
$$h(x) = xy + xz + yzk(x) = (x + y)(x + z)(y + z)$$

This attempt did not work very well: `alignat` did not separate the two formulas in the second line. So you must provide the intercolumn spacing. For instance, if you want a \qquad space between the columns, as in

$$\begin{aligned} f(x) &= x + yz & g(x) &= x + y + z \\ h(x) &= xy + xz + yz \qquad & k(x) &= (x + y)(x + z)(y + z) \end{aligned} \tag{13}$$

then type the formula as

```
\begin{alignat}{2}\label{E:mm3B}
   f(x) &= x + yz                 & g(x) &= x + y + z\\
   h(x) &= xy + xz + yz \qquad & k(x) &= (x + y)(x + z)(y + z)
    \notag
\end{alignat}
```

The `alignat` environment is especially appropriate when annotating formulas; you would normally want a \quad between the formula and the text. To obtain

$$\begin{aligned} x &= x \wedge (y \vee z) & &\quad\text{(by distributivity)} \\ &= (x \wedge y) \vee (x \wedge z) & &\quad\text{(by condition (M))} \\ &= y \vee z \end{aligned} \tag{14}$$

type

```
\begin{alignat}{2}\label{E:mm4}
   x &= x \wedge (y \vee z) & &\quad\text{(by distributivity)}\\
     &= (x \wedge y) \vee (x \wedge z) & &
      \quad\text{(by condition (M))}\notag\\
     &= y \vee z \notag
\end{alignat}
```

`alignat` is very important for typing systems of equations such as

$$(A + BC)x + \qquad Cy = 0, \tag{15}$$
$$Ex + (F + G)y = 23. \tag{16}$$

typed as follows:

```
\begin{alignat}{2}
   (A + B C)x &+{} &C       &y = 0,\\
           Ex &+{} &(F + G)&y = 23.
\end{alignat}
```

(Note again +{}; see Rule 2 in Section 5.4.1.)

As a last example, consider

$$\begin{alignat}{4} a_{11}x_1 &+ a_{12}x_2 &&+ a_{13}x_3 && &&= y_1, \tag{17}\\ a_{21}x_1 &+ a_{22}x_2 && &&+ a_{24}x_4 &&= y_2, \tag{18}\\ a_{31}x_1 & &&+ a_{33}x_3 &&+ a_{34}x_4 &&= y_3. \tag{19} \end{alignat}$$

typed as

```
\begin{alignat}{4}
  a_{11}x_1 &+ a_{12}x_2 &&+ a_{13}x_3 &&             &&= y_1,\\
  a_{21}x_1 &+ a_{22}x_2 &&             &&+ a_{24}x_4 &&= y_2,\\
  a_{31}x_1 &            &&+ a_{33}x_3 &&+ a_{34}x_4 &&= y_3.
\end{alignat}
```

Note that the argument of `alignat` does not have to be precise: If you want two columns, it can be 2, or 3, or any larger number. If you want to, you can simply type `10` and just ignore the argument; you may define a new environment (see Section 9.2.1) that does just that.

5.5.5 *Inserting text*

The `\intertext` command places one or more lines of text in the middle of an aligned environment. For instance, to obtain

$$h(x) = \int \left(\frac{f(x) + g(x)}{1 + f^2(x)} + \frac{1 + f(x)g(x)}{\sqrt{1 - \sin x}} \right) dx \tag{20}$$

The reader may find the following form easier to read:

$$= \int \frac{1 + f(x)}{1 + g(x)}\, dx - 2\arctan(x - 2)$$

you would type

```
\begin{align}\label{E:mm5}
      h(x) &= \int \left(
                          \frac{ f(x) + g(x) }
                               {1 + f^{2}(x)} +
                          \frac{1 + f(x)g(x)}
```

```
                                { \sqrt{1 - \sin x} }
                        \right) \, dx\\
   \intertext{The reader may find the following form easier to
    read:}
      &= \int \frac{1 + f(x)}
                        {1 + g(x)}
         \, dx - 2 \arctan(x - 2) \notag
\end{align}
```

Notice how the equal sign in the first formula is aligned with the equal sign in the second formula even though a line of text separates the two.

Here is another example, this one using `align*`:

$$f(x) = x + yz \qquad\qquad g(x) = x + y + z$$

The reader may also find the following polynomials useful:

$$h(x) = xy + xz + yz \qquad\qquad k(x) = (x + y)(x + z)(y + z)$$

is typed as

```
\begin{align*}
   f(x) &= x + yz & \qquad g(x) &= x + y + z\\
   \intertext{The reader may also find the following
    polynomials useful:}
   h(x) &= xy + xz + yz
                  & \qquad k(x) &= (x + y)(x + z)(y + z)
\end{align*}
```

The `\intertext` command must follow a line separator command, `\\` or `\\*`; see Section 5.9. If you violate this rule, you will get the error message

```
! Misplaced \noalign.
\intertext #1->\noalign
                         {\penalty \postdisplaypenalty \vskip ...
l.11 \end{align*}
```

The text in `\intertext` can be centered using a `center` environment or with the `\centering` command declaration (see Section 3.8).

5.6 Aligned subsidiary math environments

A *subsidiary math environment* is a math environment that can only be used inside another math environment; think of it as creating a "large math symbol."

In this section, we will discuss aligned subsidiary math environments. We will discuss adjusted subsidiary math environments (including `cases`) in Section 5.7.

5.6.1 Subsidiary variants

The `align` (see Section 5.5) and `gather` (see Section 5.2) environments have subsidiary versions: `aligned`, `alignedat`, and `gathered`.

To obtain

$$\begin{aligned} x &= 3 + \mathbf{p} + \alpha\\ y &= 4 + \mathbf{q}\\ z &= 5 + \mathbf{r}\\ u &=6 + \mathbf{s} \end{aligned} \text{\qquad using\qquad} \begin{gathered} \mathbf{p} = 5 + a + \alpha\\ \mathbf{q} = 12\\ \mathbf{r} = 13\\ \mathbf{s} = 11 + d \end{gathered}$$

type

```
\[
   \begin{aligned}
      x &= 3 + \mathbf{p} + \alpha\\
      y &= 4 + \mathbf{q}\\
      z &= 5 + \mathbf{r}\\
      u &=6 + \mathbf{s}
   \end{aligned}
   \text{\qquad using\qquad}
   \begin{gathered}
      \mathbf{p} = 5 + a + \alpha\\
      \mathbf{q} = 12\\
      \mathbf{r} = 13\\
      \mathbf{s} = 11 + d
   \end{gathered}
\]
```

Note how the list of aligned formulas

$$\begin{aligned} x &= 3 + p + \alpha\\ y &= 4 + \mathbf{q}\\ z &= 5 + \mathbf{r}\\ u &= 6 + \mathbf{s} \end{aligned}$$

and the list of centered formulas

$$\begin{gathered} \mathbf{p} = 5 + a + \alpha\\ \mathbf{q} = 12\\ \mathbf{r} = 13\\ \mathbf{s} = 11 + d \end{gathered}$$

are treated as individual large symbols.

The aligned, alignedat, and gathered subsidiary math environments follow the same rules as align and gather. The aligned subsidiary environment allows any number of columns, but you must specify the intercolumn spacing as in the alignat environment.

You can use the aligned subsidiary math environment to rewrite formula (5) from Section 1.6.2 so that the formula number is centered between the two lines:

$$\begin{aligned} h(x) &= \int \left(\frac{f(x)+g(x)}{1+f^{2}(x)} + \frac{1+f(x)g(x)}{\sqrt{1-\sin x}} \right) \, dx\\ &= \int \frac{1+f(x)}{1+g(x)} \, dx - 2\arctan(x-2) \end{aligned} \tag{21}$$

is typed as

```
\begin{equation}\label{E:mm6}
   \begin{aligned}
      h(x) &= \int \left(
                      \frac{ f(x) + g(x) }
                           { 1 + f^{2}(x) } +
                      \frac{ 1 + f(x)g(x) }
                           { \sqrt{1 - \sin x} }
                 \right) \, dx\\
           &= \int \frac{ 1 + f(x) }
                     { 1 + g(x) } \, dx - 2 \arctan (x - 2)
   \end{aligned}
\end{equation}
```

See Section 5.6.2 for a better way to split a long formula.

Symbols, as a rule, are centrally aligned. This is not normally an issue with math symbols, but it may be important with large symbols created by subsidiary math environments. Some subsidiary math environments (aligned, gathered, and array) take c, t, or b as an optional argument to force centered, top, or bottom alignment, respectively. The default is c (centered). To obtain

$$\begin{aligned}[b] x &= 3 + \mathbf{p} + \alpha\\ y &= 4 + \mathbf{q}\\ z &= 5 + \mathbf{r}\\ u &= 6 + \mathbf{s} \end{aligned} \text{ using } \begin{gathered}[b] \mathbf{p} = 5 + a + \alpha\\ \mathbf{q} = 12\\ \mathbf{r} = 13\\ \mathbf{s} = 11 + d \end{gathered}$$

for example, you would type

```
\[
   \begin{aligned}[b]
      x &= 3 + \mathbf{p} + \alpha\\
      y &= 4 + \mathbf{q}\\
```

```
        z &= 5 + \mathbf{r}\\
        u &=6 + \mathbf{s}
    \end{aligned}
    \text{\qquad using\qquad}
    \begin{gathered}[b]
        \mathbf{p} = 5 + a + \alpha\\
        \mathbf{q} = 12\\
        \mathbf{r} = 13\\
        \mathbf{s} = 11 + d
    \end{gathered}
\]
```

There is no numbering or `\tag`-ing allowed in subsidiary environments; LaTeX will not number or tag what it considers to be a single symbol.

5.6.2 *Split*

The `split` subsidiary math environment is used to split a (very long) formula into aligned parts. There are two major reasons to use `split`:

1. The math environment that contains it considers the `split` environment to be a single equation, so it generates only one number for it.
2. If a `split` environment appears inside an `align` environment, the alignment point of the `split` environment is recognized by `align` and is used in aligning all the formulas in the `align` environment.

To illustrate the first reason, consider

$$\begin{split}(x_{1}x_{2}&x_{3}x_{4}x_{5}x_{6})^{2}\\ &+ (x_{1}x_{2}x_{3}x_{4}x_{5} + x_{1}x_{3}x_{4}x_{5}x_{6} + x_{1}x_{2}x_{4}x_{5}x_{6} + x_{1}x_{2}x_{3}x_{5}x_{6})^{2}\end{split} \tag{22}$$

typed as

```
\begin{equation}\label{E:mm7}
    \begin{split}
        (x_{1}x_{2}&x_{3}x_{4}x_{5}x_{6})^{2}\\
                    &+ (x_{1}x_{2}x_{3}x_{4}x_{5}
                     + x_{1}x_{3}x_{4}x_{5}x_{6}
                     + x_{1}x_{2}x_{4}x_{5}x_{6}
                     + x_{1}x_{2}x_{3}x_{5}x_{6})^{2}
    \end{split}
\end{equation}
```

See also the two examples of `split` in the `sampart.tex` sample article in Section 8.3 (and in the `samples` directory; see page 4).

To illustrate the second, here is an example of a `split` subsidiary math environment within an `align` environment:

$$\begin{aligned} f &= (x_1 x_2 x_3 x_4 x_5 x_6)^2 \\ &= (x_1 x_2 x_3 x_4 x_5 + x_1 x_3 x_4 x_5 x_6 + x_1 x_2 x_4 x_5 x_6 + x_1 x_2 x_3 x_5 x_6)^2, \end{aligned} \tag{23}$$

$$g = y_1 y_2 y_3. \tag{24}$$

which is typed as

```
\begin{align}\label{E:mm8}
   \begin{split}
      f &= (x_{1} x_{2} x_{3} x_{4} x_{5} x_{6})^{2}\\
        &= (x_{1} x_{2} x_{3} x_{4} x_{5}
          + x_{1} x_{3} x_{4} x_{5} x_{6}
          + x_{1} x_{2} x_{4} x_{5} x_{6}
          + x_{1} x_{2} x_{3} x_{5} x_{6})^{2},
   \end{split}\\
      g &= y_{1} y_{2} y_{3}.\label{E:mm9}
\end{align}
```

Notice the `\\` command following `\end{split}` to separate the lines for `align`.

Rule ■ `split` subsidiary math environment

1. `split` can only be used inside another math environment, such as

   `displaymath`, `equation`, `align`, `gather`, `flalign`, `gathered`

   and their ∗-ed variants.
2. A `split` formula has only one number (automatically generated) or tag (from a `\tag` command). Use the `\notag` command to suppress numbering.
3. The `\label`, `\tag`, or `\notag` command must precede `\begin{split}` or follow `\end{split}`.

Here is an example of `split` inside a `gather` environment:

```
\begin{gather}\label{E:mm10}
   \begin{split}
      f &= (x_{1} x_{2} x_{3} x_{4} x_{5} x_{6})^{2}\\
        &= (x_{1} x_{2} x_{3} x_{4} x_{5}
           + x_{1} x_{3} x_{4} x_{5} x_{6}
           + x_{1} x_{2} x_{4} x_{5} x_{6}
           + x_{1} x_{2} x_{3} x_{5} x_{6})^{2}\\
        &= (x_{1} x_{2} x_{3} x_{4}
```

```
            + x_{1} x_{2} x_{3} x_{5}
            + x_{1} x_{2} x_{4} x_{5}
            + x_{1} x_{3} x_{4} x_{5})^{2}
   \end{split}\\
   \begin{align*}
      g &= y_{1} y_{2} y_{3}\\
      h &= z_{1}^{2} z_{2}^{2} z_{3}^{2} z_{4}^{2}
   \end{align*}
\end{gather}
```

which produces

$$\begin{split} f &= (x_1x_2x_3x_4x_5x_6)^2\\ &= (x_1x_2x_3x_4x_5 + x_1x_3x_4x_5x_6 + x_1x_2x_4x_5x_6 + x_1x_2x_3x_5x_6)^2\\ &= (x_1x_2x_3x_4 + x_1x_2x_3x_5 + x_1x_2x_4x_5 + x_1x_3x_4x_5)^2 \end{split} \tag{25}$$

$$g = y_1y_2y_3$$
$$h = z_1^2z_2^2z_3^2z_4^2$$

If you try to use split outside a displayed math environment, you will get the error message

```
! Package amsmath Error: \begin{split} won't work here.
 ...

l.7     \begin{split}
```

You may want to read the discussion of AMS document class and amsmath package options in Section 8.5 that modify the placement of equation numbers.

5.7 Adjusted columns

In an *adjusted* multiline math environment, the columns are adjusted so that they are displayed centered, flush left, or flush right, instead of aligned (as in Section 5.5).

In Sections 5.2 and 5.3, we discussed two adjusted (one-column) math environments, gather and multline. All the other adjusted constructs are subsidiary math environments. For example, a matrix environment (see Section 5.7.1) produces a multicolumn centered display:

$$\begin{pmatrix} a+b+c & uv & x-y & 27\\ a+b & u+v & z & 1340 \end{pmatrix} = \begin{pmatrix} 1 & 100 & 115 & 27\\ 201 & 0 & 1 & 1340 \end{pmatrix}$$

The array environment (see Section 5.7.2) produces a multicolumn adjusted display (centered, flush left, or flush right):

$$\left(\begin{array}{cccr} a+b+c & uv & x-y & 27\\ a+b & u+v & z & 1340 \end{array} \right) = \left(\begin{array}{rrrr} 1 & 100 & 115 & 27\\ 201 & 0 & 1 & 1340 \end{array} \right)$$

In this example, the first matrix has three centered columns and one flush right column, while the second matrix has four flush right columns. A variant, cases (see Section 5.7.3), produces two columns set flush left:

$$f(x) = \begin{cases} -x^2, & \text{if } x < 0;\\ \alpha + x, & \text{if } 0 \leq x \leq 1;\\ x^2, & \text{otherwise.} \end{cases} \tag{26}$$

5.7.1 *Matrices*

Use the matrix subsidiary math environment to typeset matrices. For example,

```
\begin{equation*}
   \left(
   \begin{matrix}
      a + b + c & uv    & x - y & 27\\
      a + b     & u + v & z     & 1340
   \end{matrix}
   \right) =
   \left(
   \begin{matrix}
      1   & 100 & 115 & 27\\
      201 & 0   & 1   & 1340
   \end{matrix}
   \right)
\end{equation*}
```

which produces

$$\left(\begin{matrix} a + b + c & uv & x - y & 27\\ a + b & u + v & z & 1340 \end{matrix} \right) = \left(\begin{matrix} 1 & 100 & 115 & 27\\ 201 & 0 & 1 & 1340 \end{matrix} \right)$$

If you use matrix on its own (i.e., outside a math environment),

```
\begin{matrix}
   a + b + c & uv    & x - y & 27\\
   a + b     & u + v & z     & 134
\end{matrix}
```

you will get the error message

```
! Missing $ inserted.
<inserted text>
                $
l.5 \begin{matrix}
```

reminding you that `matrix` is a subsidiary math environment.

The `matrix` subsidiary math environment provides a matrix of up to 10 centered columns. If you need more columns, you have to ask for them. The following example sets the number of columns to 12:

```
\begin{equation}\label{E:mm12}
   \setcounter{MaxMatrixCols}{12}
   \begin{matrix}
      1 & 2 & 3 & 4 & 5 & 6 & 7 & 8 & 9 & 10 & 11 & 12\\
      1 & 2 & 3 & \hdotsfor{7}                & 11 & 12
   \end{matrix}
\end{equation}
```

which produces

$$\begin{matrix} 1 & 2 & 3 & 4 & 5 & 6 & 7 & 8 & 9 & 10 & 11 & 12\\ 1 & 2 & 3 & \hdotsfor{7} & 11 & 12 \end{matrix} \tag{27}$$

We discuss `\setcounter` and counters further in Section 9.5.1.

You can have dots span any number of columns with the `\hdotsfor` command; the argument specifies the number of columns to fill (which is one more than the number of `&`s the command replaces). The `\hdotsfor` command must either appear at the beginning of a row or immediately following an ampersand (`&`). If you violate this rule, you will get the error message

```
! Misplaced \omit.
\multispan #1->\omit
                      \mscount #1\relax \loop \ifnum \mscount ...
l.12 \end{equation}
```

The `\hdotsfor` command also takes an optional argument, a number that multiplies the spacing between the dots; the default is `1`. For instance, if we replace `\hdotsfor{7}` in the previous example by `\hdotsfor[3]{7}`, then we get

$$\begin{matrix} 1 & 2 & 3 & 4 & 5 & 6 & 7 & 8 & 9 & 10 & 11 & 12\\ 1 & 2 & 3 & \hdotsfor[3]{7} & 11 & 12 \end{matrix} \tag{28}$$

Matrix variants

Using delimiters (see Section 4.6.1), a matrix may be enclosed in a number of different ways:

$$\begin{matrix} a+b+c & uv\\ a+b & c+d \end{matrix} \qquad \begin{pmatrix} a+b+c & uv\\ a+b & c+d \end{pmatrix} \qquad \begin{bmatrix} a+b+c & uv\\ a+b & c+d \end{bmatrix}$$

$$\begin{vmatrix} a+b+c & uv\\ a+b & c+d \end{vmatrix} \qquad \begin{Vmatrix} a+b+c & uv\\ a+b & c+d \end{Vmatrix} \qquad \begin{Bmatrix} a+b+c & uv\\ a+b & c+d \end{Bmatrix}$$

The first matrix is typed as follows:

```
\begin{matrix}
   a + b + c & uv\\
   a + b     & c + d
\end{matrix}
```

The others are the same, except that they use the pmatrix, bmatrix, vmatrix, Vmatrix, and Bmatrix environments, respectively. We can also use any other pair of delimiters, as in

```
\begin{equation*}
   \left(
   \begin{matrix}
      1      &     0   & \dots    & 0\\
      0      &     1   & \dots    & 0\\
      \vdots & \vdots & \ddots   & \vdots\\
      0      &     0   & \dots    & 1
   \end{matrix}
   \right]
\end{equation*}
```

which produces

$$\left(\begin{matrix} 1 & 0 & \dots & 0\\ 0 & 1 & \dots & 0\\ \vdots & \vdots & \ddots & \vdots\\ 0 & 0 & \dots & 1 \end{matrix}\right]$$

This example also uses *vertical dots* provided by the \vdots commands and *diagonal dots* provided by the \ddots commands, first mentioned in Section 4.4.3.

Small matrix

If you put a matrix in an inline math formula, it may be too large; instead, use the smallmatrix environment. Compare $\begin{pmatrix} a + b + c & uv\\ a + b & c + d \end{pmatrix}$, typed as

```
$\begin{pmatrix}
   a + b + c & uv\\
   a + b     & c + d
\end{pmatrix}$
```

with the small matrix $\left(\begin{smallmatrix} a + b + c & uv\\ a + b & c + d \end{smallmatrix}\right)$, typed as

```
$\left(
\begin{smallmatrix}
```

```
   a + b + c & uv\\
   a + b     & c + d
\end{smallmatrix}
\right)$
```

There are no delimited variants of `smallmatrix` similar to those of `matrix`; instead, use the `\left` and `\right` commands with delimiters to enclose a small matrix. Also, the `\hdotsfor` command does not work in a small matrix.

5.7.2 *Arrays*

The `matrix` subsidiary math environment provided by the amsmath package is similar to LaTeX's `array` subsidiary math environment.

The first matrix in the introduction to Section 5.7 would be typed as follows using the `array` subsidiary math environment:

```
\begin{equation*}
   \left(
   \begin{array}{cccc}
      a + b + c & uv    & x - y & 27\\
      a + b     & u + v & z     & 134
   \end{array}
   \right)
\end{equation*}
```

which produces

$$\left(\begin{array}{cccc} a+b+c & uv & x-y & 27\\ a+b & u+v & z & 134 \end{array}\right)$$

Rule ■ `array` subsidiary math environments

1. Adjacent columns are separated by an ampersand (`&`).
2. The argument of `\begin{array}` is mandatory. The argument is a series of the letters `l`, `r`, or `c`, signifying that the corresponding column in the array should be set flush left, flush right, or centered, respectively.

The matrix

$$\left(\begin{array}{cccr} a+b+c & uv & x-y & 27\\ a+b & u+v & z & 134 \end{array}\right)$$

could not have been typeset with `matrix` since the last column is set flush right. (Of course, this is not quite true: In a `matrix` environment, `\hfill 27` would force the number 27 to be set flush right—see Section 2.8.4.)

If the argument of `\begin{array}` is missing, as in

```
\begin{equation}
   \begin{array}
      a + b + c & uv      & x - y & 27\\
      a + b     & u + v   & z     & 134
   \end{array}
\end{equation}
```

LaTeX will generate the error message

```
! LaTeX Error: Illegal character in array arg.

l.7 a
      + b + c & uv      & x - y & 27\\
```

If the amsmath package is loaded, then the error message will be

```
! Extra alignment tab has been changed to \cr.
<recently read> \endtemplate

l.14  \end{equation}
```

If you change the first entry of the matrix to `c + b + a`, then the LaTeX error message will be

```
! Extra alignment tab has been changed to \cr.
<recently read> \endtemplate

l.5        c + b + a &
                      uv      & x - y & 27\\
```

and amsmath would produce the error message

```
Runaway argument?

! Paragraph ended before \equation was complete.
<to be read again>
                   \par
l.8
```

Note that the first character in `c + b + a` is not an

```
Illegal character in array arg.
```

because `c` is one possible argument of `\begin{array}`.

If the closing brace of the argument of `\begin{array}` is missing, as in

```
\begin{equation}
   \begin{array}{cccc
      a + b + c & uv    & x - y & 27\\
      a + b     & u + v & z     & 134
   \end{array}
\end{equation}
```

you will get the error message

```
Runaway argument?
{cccc a + b + c & uv    & x - y & 27\\ a + b     & u + v \ETC.
! Paragraph ended before \@array was complete.
<to be read again>
                   \par
```

In fact, the argument of array can be more complex than stated in the rule; the array subsidiary math environment can take any argument that the tabular environment can take (see Section 3.7).

5.7.3 *Cases*

The cases environment is also a subsidiary math environment. Here is the example from the introduction to this section:

$$f(x) = \begin{cases} -x^{2}, & \text{if } x < 0; \\ \alpha + x, & \text{if } 0 \leq x \leq 1; \\ x^{2}, & \text{otherwise.} \end{cases}$$

It is typed as

```
\begin{equation}
   f(x)=
   \begin{cases}
      -x^{2},        &\text{if $x < 0$;}\\
      \alpha + x,    &\text{if $0 \leq x \leq 1$;}\\
      x^{2},         &\text{otherwise.}
   \end{cases}
\end{equation}
```

It would be easy to code the cases environment as a special case of the array environment.

5.8 *Commutative diagrams*

The amscd package provides the CD subsidiary math environment for typesetting simple commutative diagrams. For instance, to obtain

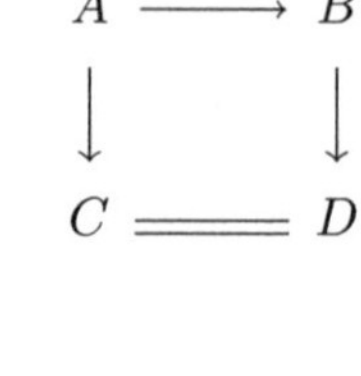

type

```
\[
   \begin{CD}
      A        @>>>        B\\
      @VVV                 @VVV\\
      C        @=          D
   \end{CD}
\]
```

A commutative diagram is a matrix made up of two kinds of rows: *horizontal rows,* that is, rows with horizontal arrows; and *vertical rows,* rows with vertical arrows. For example,

```
A          @>>>       B
```

is a typical horizontal row. It defines two columns and a connecting horizontal arrow @>>>. There may also be more than two columns, as in

```
A  @>>>  B  @>>>  C  @=  D  @<<<  E  @<<<  F
```

The connecting pieces can be

- Stretchable right arrows, @>>>
- Stretchable left arrows, @<<<
- Stretchable equal signs, @=
- Blanks, @.

The label above a stretchable arrow should be typed between the first and second > (or <) symbols, whereas the label below should be typed between the second and third > (or <) symbols; you can have both.

The following is a typical vertical row containing vertical arrows:

```
@VVV         @VVV         @AAA
```

The vertical pieces could be

- Stretchable down arrows, @VVV
- Stretchable up arrows, @AAA

- Blanks, `@.`
- Double vertical lines, `@|` or `@\vert`

The vertical arrows are placed starting with the first column.

The label to the left of a stretchable vertical arrow should be typed between the first and second `V` or `A`, whereas the label on the right should be typed between the second and third `V` or `A` symbols; you can have both.

These constructs are also illustrated in

$$
\begin{CD}
\mathbb{C} @>H_{1}>> \mathbb{C} @>H_{2}>> \mathbb{C}\\
@VP_{c,3}VV @VP_{\bar{c},3}VV @VVP_{-c,3}V\\
\mathbb{C} @>H_{1}>> \mathbb{C} @>H_{2}>> \mathbb{C}
\end{CD}
$$

typed as

```
\[
  \begin{CD}
    \mathbb{C} @>H_{1}>> \mathbb{C} @>H_{2}>> \mathbb{C}\\
    @VP_{c,3}VV  @VP_{\bar{c},3}VV  @VVP_{-c,3}V\\
    \mathbb{C} @>H_{1}>> \mathbb{C} @>H_{2}>> \mathbb{C}
  \end{CD}
\]
```

Here is a more complicated example containing all the commands for commutative diagrams as well as the `\text` command from the amstext package, followed by its source:

$$
\begin{CD}
A @>\log>> B @>>\text{bottom}> C @= D @<<< E @<<< F\\
@V\text{one-one}VV @. @AA\text{onto}A @|\\
X @= Y @>>> Z @>>> U\\
@A\beta AA @AA\gamma A @VVV @VVV\\
D @>\alpha>> E @>>> H @. I
\end{CD}
$$

```
\[
  \begin{CD}
    A         @>\log>>      B       @>>\text{bottom}>       C
              @=            D       @<<<                    E
              @<<<          F\\
    @V\text{one-one}VV      @.      @AA\text{onto}A         @|\\
    X         @=            Y       @>>>                    Z
              @>>>          U\\
```

```
      @A\beta AA          @AA\gamma A       @VVV            @VVV\\
      D         @>\alpha>>   E         @>>>                  H
                @.           I\\
   \end{CD}
\]
```

Diagrams requiring more advanced commands should be done with a drawing (or drafting) application or with specialized packages.

For a survey of commutative-diagram packages, see Gabriel Valiente Feruglio, *Typesetting commutative diagrams* [60]. See the CTAN subdirectory

```
/tex-archive/macros/generic/diagrams/
```

for a collection of diagramming packages and Section 13.1 for information on how to get them.

5.9 Page breaks

By default, the math environments described in this chapter do not allow page breaks. While a page break in a `cases` environment is obviously not desirable, it may be acceptable in an `align` or `gather` environment. You can allow page breaks by using the

```
\allowdisplaybreaks
```

command. It will allow page breaks in a multiline math environment within its scope. For instance,

```
{\allowdisplaybreaks
\begin{align}\label{E:mm13}
   a &= b + c,\\
   d &= e + f,\\
   x &= y + z,\\
   u &= v + w.
\end{align}
}% end of \allowdisplaybreaks
```

allows a page break after any one of the first three lines.

Within the scope of an `\allowdisplaybreaks` command, use the `\\*` command to prohibit a break after that line. The line separators `\\` and `\\*` can also be modified to add some additional interline space, as discussed in Section 2.7.2.

Just before the line separator command (`\\`), include a `\displaybreak` command to force a break, or a

```
\displaybreak[0]
```

command to allow one. `\displaybreak[`*n*`]`, where n is 1, 2, or 3, specifies the intermediate steps between allowing and forcing a break. `\displaybreak[4]` is the same as `\displaybreak`. You can easily visualize these rules:

allow display break =
`\displaybreak[0] \displaybreak[1] ... \displaybreak[4]`
= `\displaybreak`
= force display break

Note the similarity between the displaybreak sequence and the pagebreak sequence in Section 2.7.3.

If you want to allow page breaks in all multiline math environments in your document, place the `\allowdisplaybreaks[1]` command in the preamble of your document.

Note that neither the `\displaybreak` nor the `\allowdisplaybreaks` command will have any effect on the subsidiary math environments `split`, `aligned`, `gathered`, and `alignedat`.

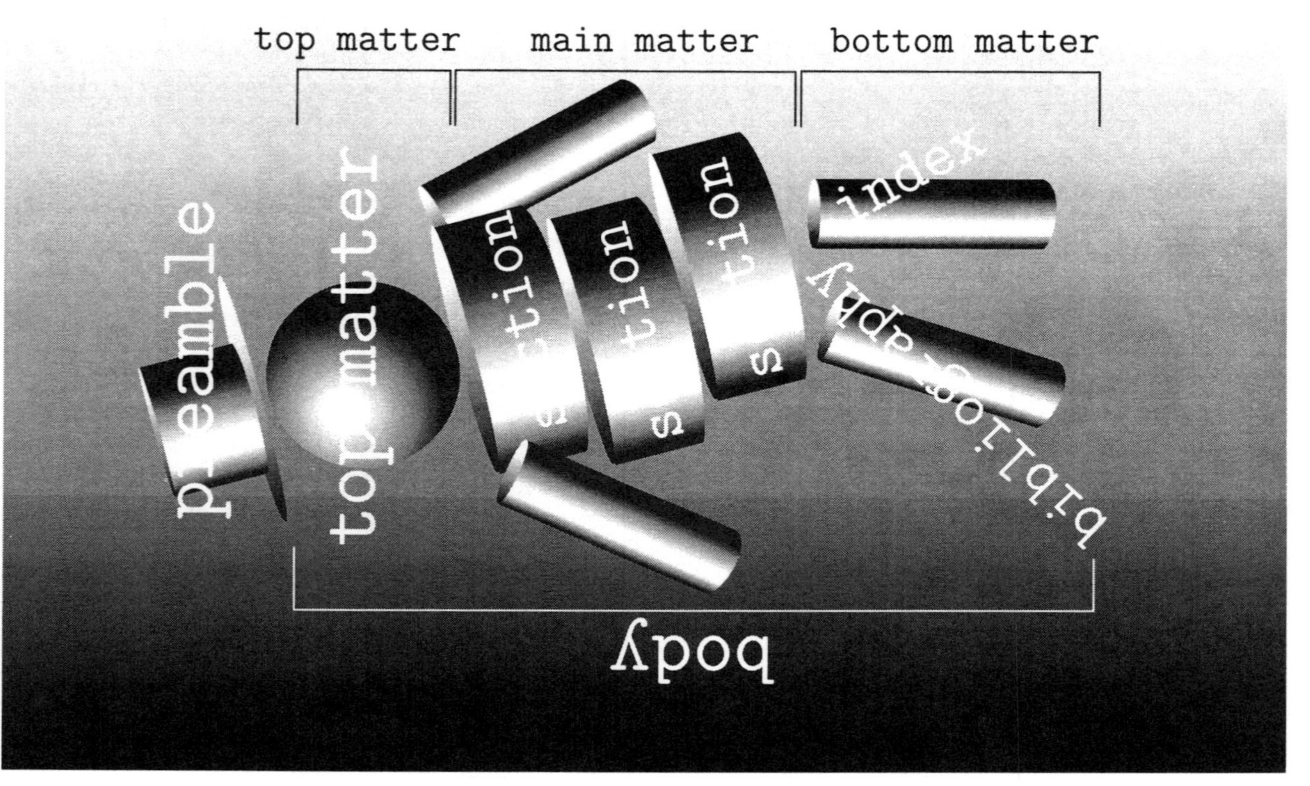
top matter
main matter
bottom matter
index
body

PART III

Document structure

CHAPTER

6

LaTeX documents

In this chapter, we take up the organization of shorter documents; longer documents and books will be discussed in Part V. Section 6.1 discusses document structure in general; Section 6.2 presents the preamble. Section 6.3 discusses the front matter, including the `abstract` environment and the table of contents. Section 6.4 presents the main matter, including sectioning, cross-referencing, tables, and figures. Section 6.5 covers the back matter, including the bibliography and index.

These sections discuss the logical design of a LaTeX document. The visual design is largely left to the document class. In Section 6.6, however, we briefly discuss one frequently adjusted aspect of visual design: page style.

If you are writing a simple article, you may safely ignore much of the material discussed in this chapter; start your article with a template that includes a preamble, the top matter, and proclamation definitions, and you will not have to worry about most of the subject matter of this chapter. In Section 1.8, you created such a template for the `article` document class; Section 8.4 describes how to do the same for the more detailed `amsart` document class.

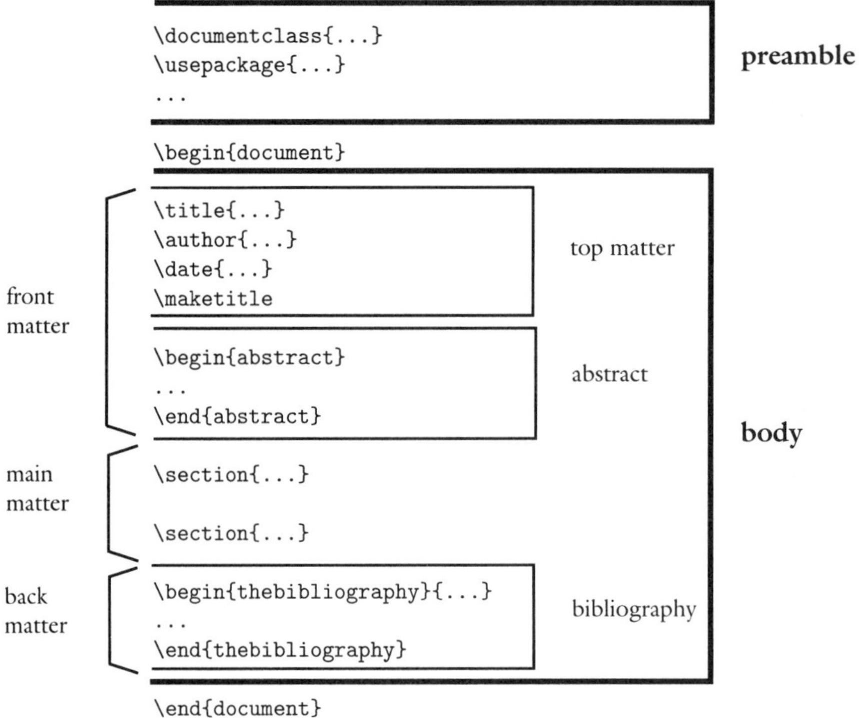

Figure 6.1: The structure of a LaTeX document.

6.1 *The structure of a document*

The source file of a LaTeX document is divided into two main parts: the preamble and the body (see Figure 6.1).

Preamble The portion of the source file before the

```
\begin{document}
```

command. It contains definitions and instructions that affect the entire document.

Body The `document` environment itself. It contains all the material that will be typeset.

These statements oversimplify the situation somewhat. For instance, you can define a command in the preamble that typesets some text; the command is used in the body, but the text that will be typeset actually appears in the preamble. Nevertheless, I hope the division between the preamble and the body is clear.

The body is further divided into three parts:

Front matter Includes, for the most part, the material that is typeset at the beginning of the document. In a typical document, this material includes the top matter from which the title page is constructed and an optional abstract. See Chapter 12 for more information about additional components that can be used in longer documents and books.

Main matter The main part of the document, including any optional appendices.

Back matter Material that is typeset at the end of the document. For a typical shorter document, the back matter is just the bibliography. See Chapter 12 for more information about additional components that are often used in longer documents and books.

6.2 *The preamble*

You were introduced to the preamble of a document in Section 1.7. As you will recall, the preamble contains the crucial `\documentclass` line, specifying the document class and the options that modify its behavior. For instance,

```
\documentclass[draft,twocolumn]{article}
```

loads the document class `article` with the `draft` option, which paints a slug in the margin indicating lines that are too wide (see Section 2.7.1); and the `twocolumn` option, which typesets the document in two-column format (see Section 7.1.1).

The `\documentclass` command is usually followed by the `\usepackage` commands, which load LaTeX enhancements called *packages*. For instance,

```
\usepackage{latexsym}
```

loads a package that defines some additional LaTeX symbol names (see Section 7.3), whereas

```
\usepackage[reqno]{amsmath}
```

Ⓐ loads the amsmath package with the `reqno` option to place equation numbers on the right (see Section 8.5). Document class options are also passed on to the packages as possible options, so

```
\documentclass[reqno]{amsart}
```

would also load the amsmath package with the `reqno` option. (Document class options not relevant for a package are ignored.) `\usepackage` commands can also be combined:

```
\usepackage{amssymb,latexsym}
```

is the same as

```
\usepackage{amssymb}
\usepackage{latexsym}
```

Document class files have a `cls` extension, whereas package files are denoted by an `sty` extension; the document class `article` is defined in the `article.cls` file, the amsmath package is defined in the `amsmath.sty` file. You may define your own packages, such as the lattice package described in Section 9.3.

The preamble normally contains any user-defined commands (see Chapter 9) and the proclamation definitions (see Section 3.4).

There are a few commands that *must* be placed in the preamble. Two such commands are the `\DeclareMathOperator` command (see Section 4.7.2) and the `\numberwithin` command (see Section 4.3), both from the amsmath package. 

There is one important command that may only be placed *before* the

```
\documentclass{...}
```

line:

```
\NeedsTeXFormat{LaTeX2e}[1995/12/01]
```

This command checks the version of LaTeX being used to typeset the document and issues a warning if it is older than December 1, 1995. Use this optional date argument if your document contains a feature that was introduced on or after the date specified or if an earlier version had a bug that would materially affect the typesetting of your document. For instance, if you use the `\textbackslash` command (which typesets \), introduced in the December 1, 1995, release, then you could use the `\NeedsTeXFormat` line shown above.

Finally, there is one environment that may only appear in the preamble, also preceding the `\documentclass` command: the `filecontents` environment (see Section 12.3.3).

6.3 Front matter

The front matter of an article, as a rule, contains the top matter used to create the title page and, optionally, an abstract.

Discussion of the top matter should take place in the context of a particular document class. We discussed the top matter of the `article` document class in Section 1.9; the `amsart` document class top matter is covered in Section 8.2.

Long documents, such as books, have rather complicated front matter such as tables of contents; see the discussion in Chapter 12. In this section, we will only discuss the abstract.

6.3.1 Abstract

Most standard document classes (except those for letters and books) make provisions for an abstract, typed in an abstract environment.

The document class formats the heading as ABSTRACT (or some variant) and, as a rule, typesets the text of the abstract in smaller type with wider margins.

Tip Do not insert an abstract environment and postpone typing it until later because the abstract environment cannot be empty.

If the abstract environment is empty, you will get the error message

```
! LaTeX Error: Something's wrong--perhaps a missing \item.
```

Either comment out the abstract environment, or insert something temporary, such as Yet to do!

Ⓐ The AMS document classes require you to place the abstract environment *before* the \maketitle command; see, for example, the abstract in the sampart.tex sample article on page 290. If you forget, you will get the warning

```
Class amsart Warning: Abstract should precede \maketitle in
\AMS documentclasses; reported on input line 21.
```

6.4 Main matter

The main matter contains most of the essential parts of the document, including the appendices.

We discuss sectioning in Section 6.4.1, cross-referencing in Section 6.4.2, and tables and figures in Section 6.4.3. Cross-referencing is typically used only in the main matter, although it could also be used elsewhere.

6.4.1 Sectioning

The main matter of a typical shorter document is divided into *sections.* See Section 12.1.1 for a discussion on sectioning longer documents.

Sections

LaTeX is instructed to start a section with the \section command, which takes the title of the section as its argument. This argument may also be used for the running head and table of contents (see Section 12.2), which means that you need to protect fragile commands with the \protect command; see Section 2.3.3. LaTeX will automatically assign a section number and typeset the number followed by the section title.

Of course, any \section command may be followed by a \label command, so that you can refer to the number generated by LaTeX. For example,

```
\section{Introduction}\label{S:intro}
```

The command \ref{S:intro} refers to the number of the section.

Other sectioning commands

A section may be subdivided into *subsections*, which may themselves be divided into *subsubsections*, *paragraphs*, and *subparagraphs*. Subsections are numbered within a section (in Section 1, they are numbered 1.1, 1.2, and so on). Here is the whole hierarchy:

```
\section
   \subsection
      \subsubsection
         \paragraph
            \subparagraph
```

It is important to understand that the five levels of sectioning are not just five different styles for typesetting section headers; they form a hierarchy: You should never have a subsection outside a section, a subsubsection outside a subsection, and so on. For instance, if the first sectioning command in your document is \subsection, the subsection will be numbered 0.1 or if in the first section of your document the first sectioning command is \subsubsection, the subsubsection will be numbered 1.0.1; both are clearly undesirable.

There are two additional sectioning commands provided by the report and book document classes: \chapter and \part; see Section 12.1.1.

All of the sectioning commands may be followed by a \label command so that you can refer to the number generated by LaTeX and the page on which they appear; see Section 6.4.2.

The form of sectioning commands

All sectioning commands take one of the following three forms, illustrated below with the \section command:

Form 1 The simplest form is

```
\section{title}
```

where *title* is the section title, of course. You will need to protect any fragile commands in *title* with the \protect command; see Section 2.3.3.

Form 2 The sectioning command may have an optional argument:

```
\section[short_title]{title}
```

The optional `short_title` argument is used in the running head and table of contents. Protect any fragile commands in `short_title` with the `\protect` command; see Section 2.3.3.

Form 3 Finally, the ∗-ed version:

```
\section*{title}
```

There are no section numbers printed and the `title` is not included in either the running heads or in the table of contents. Remember that if you ∗ a section, all subsections, and so on, must also be ∗-ed to avoid having strange section numbers.

Sectioning commands typeset

The document class determines the styles in which the titles of sections, subsections, and so on are typeset, and which of them are numbered. Consider the following text:

```
\section{Introduction}\label{S:Intro}
We shall discuss the main contributors of this era.
\subsection{Birkhoff's contributions}\label{SS:contrib}
Of course, Garrett Birkhoff is the first in line.
\subsubsection{The years 1935--1945}\label{SSS:1935}
Going to Oxford was a major step.
\paragraph{The first paper}
What should be the definition of a universal algebra?
\subparagraph{The idea}
One should read Whitehead very carefully.
```

Figure 6.2 shows how this text is typeset with the `article` document class, Ⓐ while Figure 6.3 shows the same section with the `amsart` document class. Notice that paragraphs and subparagraphs are unnumbered in both document classes.

Section 9.5.1 discusses how you can change the format of the section numbers, and how to specify which sectioning levels will be numbered.

Sections 2.3.1 and 2.3.2 of *The LaTeX Companion* [17] explain how to change the layout of section headings.

Appendix

In the main matter, the `\appendix` command marks the beginning of the appendices. The highest level of sectioning command available in the document class defines an appendix. For example, in the `article` document class,

1 Introduction

We shall discuss the main contributors of this era.

1.1 Birkhoff's contributions

Of course, Garrett Birkhoff is the first in line.

1.1.1 The years 1935–1945

Going to Oxford was a major step.

The first paper What should be the definition of a universal algebra?

The idea One should read Whitehead very carefully.

Figure 6.2: Sectioning commands in the `article` document class.

1. INTRODUCTION

We shall discuss the main contributors of this era.

1.1. Birkhoff's contributions. Of course, Garrett Birkhoff is the first in line.

1.1.1. *The years 1935–1945.* Going to Oxford was a major step.
The first paper. What should be the definition of a universal algebra?
The idea. One should read Whitehead very carefully.

Figure 6.3: Sectioning commands in the `amsart` document class.

```
\appendix
\section{A geometric proof of the Main Theorem}\label{S:geom}
```

produces an appendix with the given title.

Note that appendices may be labeled and cross-referenced like any other section. In an appendix, subsections are numbered A.1, A.2, and so on; subsubsections within A.1 are numbered A.1.1, A.1.2, and so on; the precise form, of course, depends on the document class.

6.4.2 *Cross-referencing*

There are three types of cross-referencing available in LaTeX:

1. Symbolic referencing with `\ref`
2. Page referencing with `\pageref`
3. Bibliographic referencing with `\cite`

In this section, we discuss the first two; bibliographies are discussed in Section 6.5.1 (see also Chapter 10).

Symbolic referencing

Wherever LaTeX (automatically) generates a number in your document, you can place a `\label` command:

```
\label{symbol}
```

Then at any place in your document you can use the `\ref` command,

```
\ref{symbol}
```

to place that number in the document. We call `symbol` the *label*.

You can use labels for sectioning units, equations, figures, tables, items in an enumerated list environment (see Section 3.1.1), as well as for theorems and other proclamations.

If the equation labeled `E:int` is the fifth equation in an article, then the label `E:int` will store the number 5, and `\ref{E:int}` will produce the number 5. If equations are numbered within sections (see Section 4.3), and an equation is the third equation in Section 2, then the label `E:int` will store the number 2.3 and `\ref{E:int}` will produce the number 2.3.

Example 1 The present section starts with the command

```
\section{Main matter}\label{S:MainMatter}
```

So `\ref{S:MainMatter}` will produce the number 6.4.

Example 2

```
\begin{equation}\label{E:int}
   \int_{0}^{\pi} \sin x \, dx = 2.
\end{equation}
```

In this case, `\ref{E:int}` produces the number of the equation. If parentheses are required, you must type

```
(\ref{E:int})
```

Ⓐ or use the `\eqref` command from the amsmath package, which supplies the parentheses automatically. In fact, `\eqref` does somewhat more: even when the surrounding text is emphasized (e.g., as in plain style theorems), the parentheses and the number will be set upright.

Example 3

```
\begin{theorem}\label{T:fund}
   Statement of theorem.
\end{theorem}
```

The reference `\ref{T:fund}` produces the number of the theorem.

Tip Typeset a document twice to see a change in a cross-reference.

See Section C.2.4 for a discussion of how LaTeX stores these numbers and why you have to typeset twice. If you typeset only once, and LaTeX suspects that the cross-references have not been updated, you will get a warning:

```
LaTeX Warning: Label(s) may have changed.
Rerun to get cross-references right.
```

Rule ■ `\label` commands
The argument of the `\label` command is a string of letters, punctuation marks, and digits. It is case sensitive, so `S:intro` is different from `S:Intro`.

Tip Place a `\label` command immediately after the command that generates the number.

Tip Use the tie (nonbreakable space, ~) when referencing:

```
see Section~\ref{S:Intro}
proved in Theorem~\ref{T:main}
```

It is difficult to overemphasize how useful automatic cross-referencing can be when writing a document. There are three simple ways to make cross-referencing even more useful:

Tip

1. Utilize user-defined commands to minimize the typing necessary for referencing (see Section 9.1.1).

2. Systematize your labels. For example, start the label for a section with `S:`, subsection with `SS:`, subsubsection with `SSS:`, theorem with `T:`, lemma with `L:`, definition with `D:`, and so on.
3. Make your labels meaningful.

When you are cross-referencing, even if you follow these tips, it may not be easy to remember a label. David Carlisle's showkeys package may help you out (it is part of the tools distribution—see Section 7.3.1 and Chapter 13). Include the line:

```
\usepackage{showkeys}
```

in the preamble of your document. This package shows all symbolic references in the margin of the typeset document. With the `notcite` option (my preference),

```
\usepackage[notcite]{showkeys}
```

showkeys will not show the labels for bibliographic references. When the document is ready for final typesetting, comment out this line.

Section 2.5 of *The LaTeX Companion* [17] describes the varioref package, which package extends the power of `\ref`; and the xr package for referencing other documents.

Page referencing

The command

```
\pageref{symbol}
```

produces the number of the typeset page corresponding to the location of the command `\label{symbol}`. For example, if the following text is typeset on page 5:

```
There may be three types of problems with the
construction of such lattices.\label{problem}
```

And you type

```
Because of the problems associated with
the construction (see page~\pageref{problem})
```

somewhere else, LaTeX produces

Because of the problems associated with the construction (see page 5)

Because of the way LaTeX typesets a page, page references may be off by one. See the discussion in Section 12.5 on how to guarantee that the page number will be correct.

6.4.3 Tables and figures

Many documents contain tables and figures (graphics). These must be treated in a special way since they cannot be broken across pages. If necessary, LATEX moves—floats—a table or a figure to the top or bottom of the current or the next page if possible; further away if not.

LATEX provides the `table` and `figure` environments for typesetting floats. The two are essentially identical except that the `figure` environments are named Figure 1, Figure 2, and so on, whereas the `table` environments are numbered as Table 1, Table 2, and so on.

Tables

A `table` environment is set up as follows:

```
\begin{table}
    Place the table here
   \caption{title}\label{Ta:xxx}
\end{table}
```

The `\caption` command is optional and may also precede the table. The optional `\label` command must be placed between the `\caption` command and `\end{table}`. The label is used to reference the table's number. A table can have more than one caption.

The `table` environment is primarily used for tables made with the `tabular` or similar environment (see Section 3.7). There are many examples of tables in this book; for instance, Section 2.4.7 has three.

If your document uses the `twocolumn` document class option, the `table` environment will produce tables that span only one column; the `table*` environment produces tables that span both columns—these tables can only be placed at the top of a page.

Figures

Graphics (drawings, scanned images, digitized photos, and so on) can be inserted with a `figure` environment:

```
\begin{figure}
    Place the graphics here
   \caption{title}\label{Fi:xxx}
\end{figure}
```

The above discussion of captions and labels for tables also applies to figures. Also, if your document uses the `twocolumn` document class option, the `figure` environment will produce figures that span only one column; the `figure*` environment produces figures that span both columns—these figures can only be placed at the top of a page.

The standard way of including a graphics file is with the commands provided by the graphics package by David Carlisle and Sebastian Rahtz, which is part of the LaTeX distribution (see Section 7.3). Save your graphics in EPS (Encapsulated PostScript) format. (Your graphics can also be made within a `picture` environment, an approach that is not discussed in this book.)

Using the graphics package, a typical `figure` is specified as follows:

```
\begin{figure}
   \includegraphics{file}
   \caption{title}\label{Fi:xxx}
\end{figure}
```

The graphics file must be in a form that your printer driver can handle, and *file* must contain the information about its size (EPS graphics do). If you have to scale the graphics image, say to 68% of its original size, use the command

```
\scalebox{.68}{\includegraphics{file}}
```

For instance, the figure on page 57 is included with the commands

```
\begin{figure}
   \scalebox{.80}{\includegraphics{fig1.eps}}
   \caption{The structure of \protect\LaTeX.}\label{Fi:StrucLaT}
\end{figure}
```

The `\scalebox` command (provided by the graphics package) can also be used to scale typeset text or math. For instance,

```
\scalebox{0.8}{\parbox{\textwidth}{%
\begin{gather*}
   x_{1} x_{2} + x_{1}^{2} x_{2}^{2} + x_{3},\\
   x_{1} x_{3} + x_{1}^{2} x_{3}^{2} + x_{2},\\
   x_{1} x_{2} x_{3}.
 \end{gather*}
}}
```

provides a thumbnail sketch of this multiline math formula:

$$\begin{gathered} x_1 x_2 + x_1^2 x_2^2 + x_3, \\ x_1 x_3 + x_1^2 x_3^2 + x_2, \\ x_1 x_2 x_3. \end{gathered}$$

Float control

The `table` and `figure` environments may have an optional argument, with which you can influence LaTeX's placement of the typeset table. The optional argument consists of one to four letters:

- `b`, the bottom of the page
- `h`, here (where the environment appears in the text)

- t, the top of the page
- p, a separate page

For instance,

```
\begin{table}[ht]
```

requests LaTeX to place the table "here" or at the "top" of a page. The default is [tbp] and the order of the optional arguments is immaterial: [th] is the same as [ht]. If h is specified, it takes precedence, followed by t and b.

LaTeX has more than a dozen internal parameters that control a complicated algorithm that determines the placement of tables and figures. If you want to override these parameters *for one table or figure only*, add an exclamation mark (!) to the optional argument. For instance, [!h] requests that this table or figure be placed where it is in the source file even if this placement violates the rules as set by some of the parameters. For a detailed discussion of the float mechanism, see Chapter 6 of *The LaTeX Companion* [17].

The \suppressfloats command stops LaTeX from placing any more tables or figures on the page it appears on. An optional argument t or b (but not both) prohibits placement of floats at the top or bottom of the current page. The table or figure that is "suppressed" will appear on the next page or later in the document, if necessary.

Your demands and LaTeX's float mechanism may conflict with one another: LaTeX may run out of memory or place material where you do not want it. Combining two tables or figures into one sometimes helps. The \clearpage command will not only start a new page with the \newpage command, but also forces LaTeX to print all the tables and figures it has accumulated but not yet placed in the typeset document. See also some related commands discussed in Section 2.7.3.

For more information on graphics, see Chapters 10 and 11 of *The LaTeX Companion* [17] and Chapter 2 of *The LaTeX Graphics Companion* [18]; see also the documentation for the graphics package in the LaTeX distribution.

6.5 Back matter

The back matter of an article is very simple, as a rule. It is either empty, or consists of only a bibliography. A long document, such as a book, may have more complicated back matter (see Chapter 12). In this section, we will only discuss the *bibliography* and *index*.

6.5.1 Bibliographies in articles

The simplest way to typeset a bibliography is to type it directly into the article. For an example, see the bibliography in the intrart.tex introductory sample article (on page 45). A more complete example is shown typeset on page 254. This sample bibliography contains two examples (one short and one long) of each of the seven most frequently used kinds of items.

You type the text of a bibliography in a `thebibliography` environment, as shown in the following examples (you can find these entries in `inbibl.tpl`—see page 4; the templates for these entries are also reproduced in `article.tpl` following the line `\end{document}`):

```
\begin{thebibliography}{99}
\bibitem{hA70}
   Henry~H. Albert,
   \emph{Free torsoids},
   Current Trends in Lattice Theory, D.~Van Nostrand, 1970.
\bibitem{hA70a}
   Henry~H. Albert,
   \emph{Free torsoids},
   Current Trends in Lattice Theory (G.~H. Birnbaum, ed.),
    vol.~7, D.~Van Nostrand, Princeton, January, 1970,
   no translation available, pp.~173--215 (German).
\bibitem{sF90}
   Soo-Key Foo,
   \emph{Lattice Constructions},
   Ph.D. thesis, University of Winnebago, 1990.
\bibitem{sF90a}
   Soo-Key Foo,
   \emph{Lattice Constructions},
   Ph.D. thesis, University of Winnebago, Winnebago, MN,
   December 1990, final revision not yet available.
\bibitem{gF86}
   Grant~H. Foster,
   \emph{Computational complexity in lattice theory},
   tech. report, Carnegie Mellon University, 1986.
\bibitem{gF86a}
   Grant~H. Foster,
   \emph{Computational complexity in lattice theory},
   Research Note 128A, Carnegie Mellon University,
   Pittsburgh, PA, December, 1986,
   research article in preparation.
\bibitem{pK69}
   Peter Konig,
   \emph{Composition of functions},
   Proceedings of the Conference on Universal Algebra
   (Kingston, 1969).
```

References

[1] Henry H. Albert, *Free torsoids*, Current Trends in Lattice Theory, D. Van Nostrand, 1970.

[2] Henry H. Albert, *Free torsoids*, Current Trends in Lattice Theory (G. H. Birnbaum, ed.), vol. 7, D. Van Nostrand, Princeton, January, 1970, no translation available, pp. 173–215 (German).

[3] Soo-Key Foo, *Lattice Constructions*, Ph.D. thesis, University of Winnebago, 1990.

[4] Soo-Key Foo, *Lattice Constructions*, Ph.D. thesis, University of Winnebago, Winnebago, MN, December 1990, final revision not yet available.

[5] Grant H. Foster, *Computational complexity in lattice theory*, tech. report, Carnegie Mellon University, 1986.

[6] Grant H. Foster, *Computational complexity in lattice theory*, Research Note 128A, Carnegie Mellon University, Pittsburgh, PA, December, 1986, research article in preparation.

[7] Peter Konig, *Composition of functions*, Proceedings of the Conference on Universal Algebra (Kingston, 1969).

[8] Peter Konig, *Composition of functions*, Proceedings of the Conference on Universal Algebra (G. H. Birnbaum, ed.), vol. 7, Canadian Mathematical Society, Queen's Univ., Kingston, ON, available from the Montreal office, pp. 1–106 (English).

[9] William A. Landau, *Representations of complete lattices*, Abstract: Notices Amer. Math. Soc., **18**, 937.

[10] William A. Landau, *Representations of complete lattices*, Abstract: Notices Amer. Math. Soc. **18**, 937, December, 1975.

[11] George A. Menuhin, *Universal algebra*, D. van Nostrand, Princeton, 1968.

[12] George A. Menuhin, *Universal algebra*, second ed., University Series in Higher Mathematics, vol. 58, D. van Nostrand, Princeton, March, 1968 (English), no Russian translation.

[13] Ernest T. Moynahan, *On a problem of M. Stone*, Acta Math. Acad. Sci. Hungar. **8** (1957), 455–460.

[14] Ernest T. Moynahan, *On a problem of M. Stone*, Acta Math. Acad. Sci. Hungar. **8** (1957), 455–460 (English), Russian translation available.

Figure 6.4: The most important bibliographic entry types.

```
\bibitem{pK69a}
   Peter Konig,
   \emph{Composition of functions},
   Proceedings of the Conference on Universal Algebra
   (G.~H. Birnbaum, ed.),
   vol.~7, Canadian Mathematical Society,
   Queen's Univ., Kingston, ON,
   available from the Montreal office, pp.~1--106 (English).
\bibitem{wL75}
   William~A. Landau,
   \emph{Representations of complete lattices},
   Abstract: Notices Amer. Math. Soc., \textbf{18}, 937.
\bibitem{wL75a}
   William~A. Landau,
   \emph{Representations of complete lattices},
   Abstract: Notices Amer. Math. Soc. \textbf{18}, 937,
   December, 1975.
\bibitem{gM68}
   George~A. Menuhin,
   \emph{Universal algebra},
   D.~van Nostrand, Princeton, 1968.
\bibitem{gM68a}
   George~A. Menuhin,
   \emph{Universal algebra}, second ed.,
   University Series in Higher Mathematics, vol.~58,
   D.~van Nostrand, Princeton,
   March, 1968 (English), no Russian translation.
\bibitem{eM57}
   Ernest~T. Moynahan,
   \emph{On a problem of M. Stone},
   Acta Math. Acad. Sci. Hungar. \textbf{8}~(1957), 455--460.
\bibitem{eM57a}
   Ernest~T. Moynahan,
   \emph{On a problem of M. Stone},
   Acta Math. Acad. Sci. Hungar. \textbf{8}~(1957), 455--460
   (English), Russian translation available.
\end{thebibliography}
```

I use the convention that the label for a `\bibitem` consists of the initials of the author and the year of publication. The first cited publication by Andrew B. Reich in 1987 would have the label `aR87`; the second, `aR87a`. Of course, you can use any label you choose, but such conventions make the items much easier to reuse.

The `thebibliography` environment takes an argument; in the previous example, this argument is 99, telling LaTeX that the widest reference number it must generate is two digits wide; for fewer than 10 items, use 9; for 100 or more items, use 999.

If the argument of `\begin{thebibliography}` is missing, you will get the error message

```
! LaTeX Error: Something's wrong--perhaps a missing \item.

l.5 \bibitem
            {hA70}
```

Each bibliographic item is introduced with `\bibitem`, which is just like the `\label` command. In your text, use `\cite`, which is similar to `\ref`. So if the thirteenth bibliographic item is introduced with

```
\bibitem{eM57}
```

then

```
\cite{eM57}
```

refers to that item and typesets as [13]. A bibliography is automatically numbered by LaTeX.

Tip Do not leave spaces in a `\cite` command; for example, `\cite{eM57␣}` will produce [?] indicating an unknown reference.

You can use `\cite` to cite two (or more) items in the form

```
\cite{hA70,eM57}
```

which typesets as [1, 13]. There is also an optional argument for `\cite` to specify additional information. For example,

```
\cite[pages~2--15]{eM57}
```

typesets as [13, pages 2–15].

If you wish to use labels rather than numbers to identify bibliographic items, then you can specify those labels with an optional argument of the `\bibitem` command:

[EM57] Ernest T. Moynahan, *On a problem of M. Stone*, Acta Math. Acad. Sci. Hungar. **8** (1957), 455–460.

typed as

```
\bibitem[EM57]{eM57}
  Ernest~T. Moynahan, \emph{On a problem of M. Stone},
   Acta Math. Acad. Sci. Hungar. \textbf{8} (1957), 455--460.
```

If this optional argument of `\bibitem` is used, the `\cite` command will produce [EM57]. The argument of `\begin{thebibliography}` must be set wide enough to allow for such labels; in this case, it should be `EM99`.

Rule ■ Label for a bibliographic item
A label cannot contain a comma or a space.

Ⓐ The examples I have used follow the formatting rules set by the AMS. Only titles are emphasized, and only volume numbers of journals are set in boldface. You also have to watch the order in which the items are given, the punctuation, and the capitalization.

If an author appears repeatedly, use the `\bysame` command, which replaces the author's name with a long dash followed by a thin space. For example,

```
\bibitem{gF86}
   Grant~H. Foster,
   \emph{Computational complexity in lattice theory},
   tech. report, Carnegie Mellon University, 1986.
\bibitem{gF86a}
   \bysame,
   \emph{Computational complexity in lattice theory},
   Research Note 128A, Carnegie Mellon University,
   Pittsburgh PA, December 1986, research article in preparation.
```

See `sampart.tex` on page 297 for a typeset example.

Ⓐ Because the standard LaTeX document classes do not provide the `\bysame` command (the AMS document classes do), it is included in the `lattice.sty` command file (see Section 9.3). In case you want to include it in your document, I present it here:

```
\providecommand{\bysame}{\makebox[3em]{\hrulefill}\thinspace}
```

See Section 9.1.5 for an explanation of the `\providecommand` command.

Tip If you want a different title for your bibliography, say Bibliography, place the command

```
\renewcommand{\bibname}{Bibliography}
```

anywhere before the `thebibliography` environment (see Section 9.1.6).

Tip You may have more than one `thebibliography` environment in a document. Because each bibliography would number the entries from 1, you should provide labels (as optional parameters of the `\bibitem` commands) for cross-referencing.

6.5.2 *Simple indexes*

Using the `\label` and `\pageref` commands (see Section 6.4.2), it is quite simple to produce a small index in a `theindex` environment. At each point in the text that you want to reference in the index, place a `\label` command. The corresponding entry in the index will typeset the page number with the `\pageref` command.

The `\item`, `\subitem`, and `\subsubitem` commands create an entry, subentry, and subsubentry, respectively. If you need additional vertical spacing when the first letter changes (for instance, between the "h" entries and the "i" entries), you can use the `\indexspace` command.

Here are some examples of index entries:

```
\begin{theindex}
\item Lakser, H., \pageref{Lakser}
\item Lattice, 14,  \textbf{\pageref{Lattice}}
   \subitem distributive, \pageref{Lattice_distributive}
   \subitem modular, \pageref{Lattice_distributive},
       \textbf{\pageref{Lattice_distributive2}}
\item Linear subspace, \pageref{Linear_subspace}
\end{theindex}
```

the typeset index

Index

Lakser, H., 2
Lattice, 14, **25**
    distributive, 18
    modular, 19, **37**
Linear subspace, 38

For a larger index, you should use the *MakeIndex* application (see Chapter 11).

6.6 *Visual design*

In this chapter, we have discussed the logical design of a LaTeX document; visual design is largely left to the document class. But there is one small aspect of the visual design we have to discuss: the page style.

To get a visual representation of the page style of your document, use Kent McPherson's layout package (see Section 7.3.1). Load the package with

```
\usepackage{layout}
```

and place the `\layout` command somewhere in the body of your article. LaTeX will produce a graphical representation of the page layout. Figure 6.5 shows the page layout for the `article` document class with no options. Two-sided typesetting produces two pictures (one for the odd and one for the even pages).

A typeset page has three parts: the *running head* (or header), the *body*, and the *footer*. As a rule, the document class will take care of the contents and formatting of all three parts.

For the running head and footer, however, you can override the page design of the document class with the command

```
\pagestyle{style}
```

where the argument *`style`* is one of the following:

`plain` The running head is empty and the footer contains only the page number

`empty` Both the running head and the footer are blank

`headings` The running head contains the information provided by the document class and the footer is empty

`myheadings` The running head contains the information provided by the commands `\markboth` and `\markright`; the footer is empty

The `\markright` command takes only one argument; the last `\markright` on a page provides the running head information for that page. The `\markboth` command has two arguments: the first provides the running head information for the left-hand page; the second provides the running head information for the right-hand page.

The `\thispagestyle` command is the same as `\pagestyle` except that it only affects the current page.

For instance, if the current page is a full-page graphic, you might want to issue the command

```
\thispagestyle{empty}
```

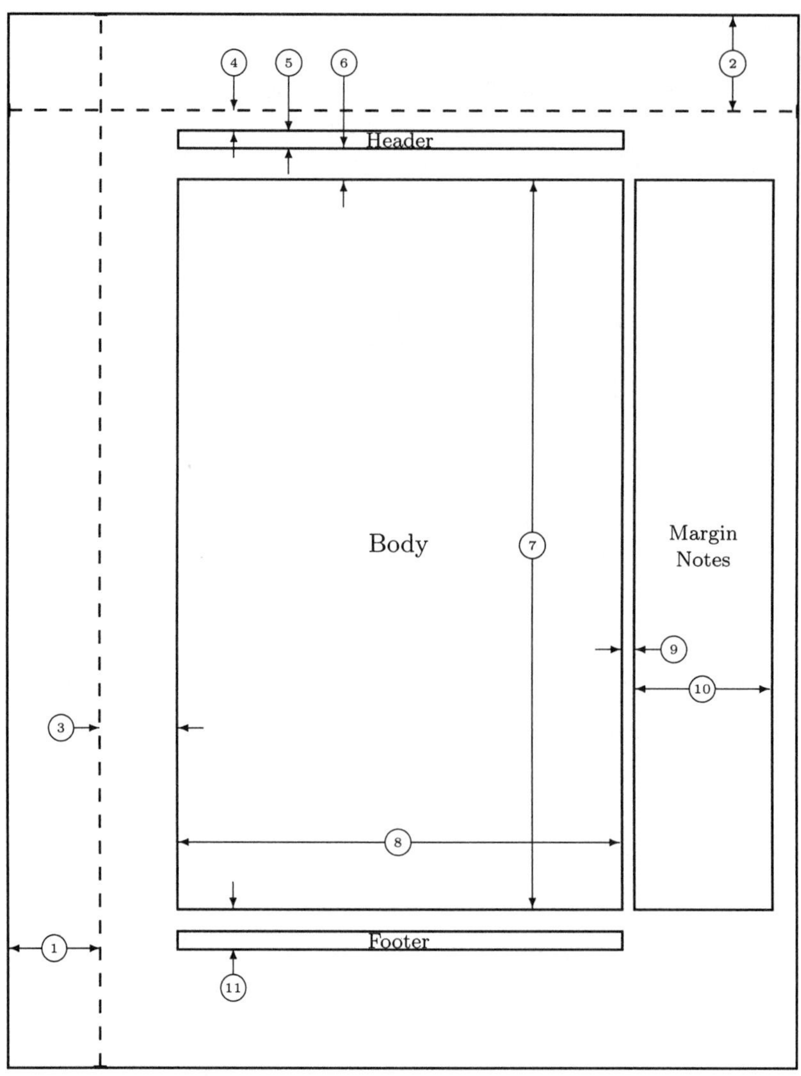

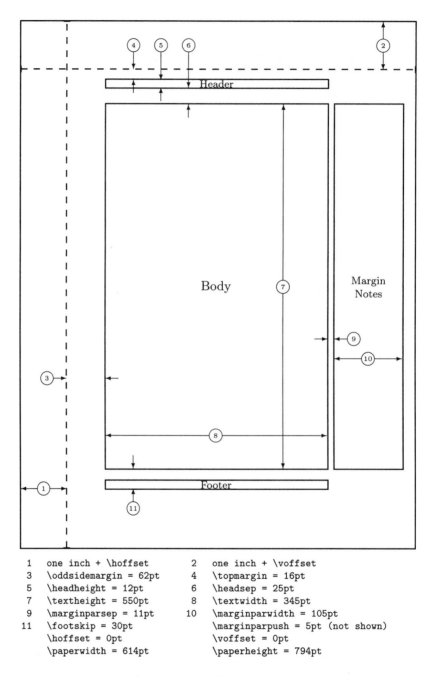

1	`one inch + \hoffset`	2	`one inch + \voffset`
3	`\oddsidemargin = 62pt`	4	`\topmargin = 16pt`
5	`\headheight = 12pt`	6	`\headsep = 25pt`
7	`\textheight = 550pt`	8	`\textwidth = 345pt`
9	`\marginparsep = 11pt`	10	`\marginparwidth = 105pt`
11	`\footskip = 30pt`		`\marginparpush = 5pt (not shown)`
	`\hoffset = 0pt`		`\voffset = 0pt`
	`\paperwidth = 614pt`		`\paperheight = 794pt`

Figure 6.5: Page layout for the `article` document class.

The `\maketitle` command automatically issues a

```
\thispagestyle{plain}
```

command, so if you want to suppress the page number on the first page of a document, you have to put

```
\thispagestyle{empty}
```

immediately after the `\maketitle` command.

The commands listed in Figure 6.5 are length commands, discussed in Section 9.5.2; they can be changed with the commands introduced in that section. As a rule, you do not have to worry about these settings; they are made by the document class for you. Sometimes, however, you will have a job that requires such changes: I once had to submit a research plan on a form with a 7.5 inch by 5 inch box. To be able to cut and paste the typeset report, I had to produce the text with a `\textwidth` of 7 inches. If I simply set

```
\setlength{\textwidth}{7in}
```

the text would overflow the printed page and the last few characters of each line would be missing. So I had to change the margins by starting the document with

```
\documentclass[12pt]{report}
\setlength{\textwidth}{7in}
\setlength{\oddsidemargin}{0pt}
```

All of Chapter 4 of *The LaTeX Companion* [17] deals with the page layout. Piet van Oostrum's excellent package, fancyhdr, allows you to create your own page style (see also my article, *Advances in TeX. IV. Header and footer control in LaTeX* [25] describing the package as of 1994). Chapter 13 of this book should assist you in getting this package from CTAN, where it can be found in the directory

```
/tex-archive/macros/latex/contrib/supported/fancyhdr/
```

CHAPTER

7

Standard LaTeX documents

As you know, LaTeX is a markup language. The markup (commands and environments) you add to the document combines with the rules defined by LaTeX, the document class you choose, the packages you load, and the user-defined commands and environments you introduce to produce a typeset document.

In this chapter, we will discuss all of the standard LaTeX document classes except for the `book` class, which we will take up in Chapter 12. Your choice of document class strongly affects the appearance of your typeset copy; compare an article typeset with the `article` document class (on pages 44–45) with a similar article typeset with the `amsart` document class (on pages 286–288); they are dramatically different.

We conclude this chapter with a description of the components of the standard LaTeX distribution.

7.1 *Articles and reports*

Most shorter LaTeX documents are written with one of the two standard LaTeX document classes: `article` or `report` (or variants thereof). In Sections 1.7 to 1.9, we discussed how to write an article using the `article` document class. To see how the `report` and `article` document classes differ, typeset the article `intrart.tex` with the `report` document class; that is, change the

```
\documentclass{article}
```

command to

```
\documentclass{report}
```

and then typeset. There is one substantive difference to remember: The `report` document class has two additional sectioning commands, `\chapter` and `\part`. We will discuss these commands in Section 12.1.1.

The markup rules for the two document classes are more or less the same, but the appearance of the same document typeset with each of the two document classes is quite different. For instance, the `report` document class provides a separate page for the abstract by default, but the `article` document class does not.

7.1.1 Options

A document's appearance is primarily determined by the document class; however, the behavior of the document class can be substantially influenced by its options. The two document classes discussed in this section have eight standard options affecting many attributes. Combining the two document classes with the various options allows you to produce very different versions of the same document.

Each attribute has a *default value* that is used if another value is not specified.

Font size

Options: `10pt`
`11pt`
`12pt`

Default: `10pt`

Each option declares the specified size to be the default font size. You may want to use the `12pt` option for proofreading,

```
\documentclass[12pt]{article}
```

However, you should recognize that changing the font size changes the line breaks (the `line too wide` problem; see Section 1.1.3), so changing the `12pt` option back to `10pt` may require some additional editing.

Paper size

Options:	`letterpaper`	(8.5 inches by 11 inches)
	`legalpaper`	(8.5 inches by 14 inches)
	`executivepaper`	(7.25 inches by 10.5 inches)
	`a4paper`	(210 mm by 297 mm)
	`a5paper`	(148 mm by 210 mm)
	`b5paper`	(176 mm by 250 mm)
Default:	`letterpaper`	

Draft

Options: `draft`
`final`

Default: `final`

The `draft` option places a slug in the margin next to each line that is too wide (see Section 1.1.3). The `final` option does not.

Landscape printing

Option: `landscape`

The `landscape` option prints the document in landscape format (swapping the width and height of the paper).

Two-sided printing

Options: `twoside`
`oneside`

Default: `oneside`

The `twoside` option formats the output for printing on both sides of the paper (duplexing).

Two-column printing

Options: `twocolumn`
`onecolumn`

Default: `onecolumn`

The `twocolumn` option prints the document in two-column format.

Title page

Options: `titlepage`
`notitlepage`

Default: depends on the document class

The `titlepage` option creates a separate title page and places the abstract on a separate page. The `notitlepage` option places the title and the abstract together on the first page. For the `article` document class the default is `notitlepage`; the `report` document class defaults to `titlepage`.

Equations and equation numbers

Options: `leqno`
`reqno`

Default: `reqno`

The `leqno` option places any equation number in the document on the left side; `reqno` places them on the right. In this book, I have used the `leqno` option, which is the default used by the AMS document classes (see Section 8.5). 

Option: `fleqn`

The `fleqn` option sets displayed formulas flush left; this option is typically used in conjunction with the `reqno` option.

Bibliography

Option: `openbib`

The `openbib` option typesets the bibliography in an "open" format; see Figure 7.1, and compare it with the bibliography on page 253.

Combinations

Of course, these options can be combined with each other and are used by most document classes. For instance,

```
\documentclass[12pt,a4paper,twoside,twocolumn]{report}
```

will produce a double-columned, two-sided (duplexed) report on A4 paper (the European standard) at the 12-point font size.

7.2 Letters

The `letter` document class was developed for writing letters. One document can contain any number of letters, each in its own `letter` environment. In the following example (`letter.tex` in the `samples` directory) there is only a single letter:

[1] Soo-Key Foo.
Lattice Constructions.
PhD thesis, University of Winnebago, Winnebago, MN, December 1990.

[2] George A. Menuhin.
Universal Algebra.
D. van Nostrand, Princeton, 1968.

[3] Ernest T. Moynahan.
Ideals and congruence relations in lattices. II.
Magyar Tud. Akad. Mat. Fiz. Oszt. Közl., 7:417–434, 1957.

[4] Ernest T. Moynahan.
On a problem of M. Stone.
Acta Math. Acad. Sci. Hungar., 8:455–460, 1957.

[5] Ferenc R. Richardson.
General Lattice Theory.
Mir, Moscow, expanded and revised edition, 1982.

Figure 7.1: The `openbib` option.

```
% Sample file: letter.tex
% Typeset with LaTeX format
\documentclass{letter}

\begin{document}

\address{George Gr\"{a}tzer\\
         Department of Mathematics\\
         University of Manitoba\\
         Winnipeg, MB, R3T 2N2\\
         Canada}
\signature{George Gr\"{a}tzer}
\date{}

\begin{letter}{Prof.~John Hurtig\\
               Computer Science Department\\
               University of Winnebago\\
               Winnebago, Minnesota 23714}
\opening{Dear John,}
Enclosed you will find the first draft of the five-year plan.
\closing{Friendly greetings,}
\cc{Carla May\\
    Barry Bold}
\encl{Five-year plan}
```

```
\ps{P.S. Remember our lunch meeting tomorrow! G.}
\end{letter}

\end{document}
```

The argument of the `letter` environment is the name and address of the recipient. It is a required argument; if omitted you will get an error message such as

```
! Incomplete \iffalse; all text was ignored after line 21.
<inserted text>
                \fi
l.21 \end{letter}
```

As with all multiline arguments, the lines are separated by `\\`.

The arguments of some commands may apply to all the letter environments in the document. Such commands should be placed before the first `letter` environment. In the example, `\signature` and `\address` are so placed.

If the `\date` command is absent, today's date will be typeset. If you want no date, use an empty argument `\date{}`, as in the example. If you want all the letters in the same document to have the same date, the `\date` command should precede the first `letter` environment. Many of the options listed in Section 7.1.1 can also be invoked for the `letter` document class.

7.3 The LaTeX distribution

The LaTeX distribution contains a huge number of document classes and packages, most of which you probably received with your TeX software. If you find that you are missing some files, see Chapter 13 on how to get them from CTAN.

The files of the distribution on CTAN are grouped into four subdirectories:

`base` contains all the files necessary to install the system. `install.txt` explains how to unpack the files and create the `LaTeX` format. You will also find the documentation as LaTeX files here.

`doc` contains all the documentation files in PostScript, DVI, and HTML formats.

`required` contains the directories

`amslatex`, `babel`, `cyrillic`, `graphics`, `psnfss`, `tools`.

`unpacked` contains the unpacked LaTeX distribution.

There are nine document classes. Of the five not discussed in this book, two may be of interest to the general user: the `slides` document class, for preparing lecture slides, and the proc document class, for typesetting conference proceedings.

There are a number of packages included in the base directory; the following should be especially interesting for readers of this book:

latexsym Some symbol definitions (see the tables in Appendix A).

alltt The alltt environment, which is like the verbatim environment except that \, and {, } retain their usual meanings.

exscale Scaled versions of the math extension font.

makeidx Commands for producing indexes (see Chapter 11).

showidx A package to allow you to typeset the index entries in the margin of your typeset document (see Chapter 11).

The nfssfont.tex file (in the base directory) allows you to generate font tables for use with the \symbol command (see Section 2.4.4).

In the required directory, there are also some major software distributions related to LaTeX:

Ⓐ AMS-LaTeX Discussed in detail in this book; the math packages and document classes are in this directory, while the font-related files are in the directory

```
/tex-archive/fonts/amsfonts/latex/
```

babel For typesetting languages other than American English.

cyrillic For typesetting with the Cyrillic alphabet.

graphics For the inclusion and transformation of graphics and for typesetting in color (discussed in Section 6.4.3); these packages require you to have a suitable printer and DVI printer driver.

psnfss For typesetting with a wide range of PostScript fonts (see Appendix D).

tools Discussed in Section 7.3.1.

Each of these distributions come with its own documentation. They are also described in *The LaTeX Companion* [17] (as of 1994).

7.3.1 Tools

Some of these packages are so important that they could well have been incorporated into LaTeX proper. Here is a brief listing:

afterpage Implements the \afterpage command (the commands specified in its argument are expanded after the current page is output).

array Contains extended versions of the `array` and `tabular` environments with many extra features.

bm Gives access to bold math symbols.

calc Allows algebraic manipulation of lengths and counter values when specifying lengths and counters.

dcolumn Provides alignment on decimal points in tabular entries; requires the array package.

delarray Adds "large delimiters" around arrays; requires array.

enumerate Customizes the `enumerate` environment (see Sections 3.1.4 and 9.2.1).

fontsmpl Produces a test file for displaying "font samples."

ftnright Places all footnotes in the right-hand column of documents typeset with the `twocolumn` document class option.

hhline Provides control over horizontal lines in tables.

indentfirst Indents the first paragraph of each section.

layout Shows the page layout defined by a document class; see Section 6.6.

longtable Helps to create multipage tables; it does not require array, but it will use array's extended features if both packages are loaded.

multicol Provides multicolumn typesetting with some advanced features.

rawfonts Preloads fonts using the old font names of LaTeX 2.09.

showkeys Selectively prints the labels used by `\label`, `\ref`, `\cite`, and so forth, in the margin (see Section 6.4.2).

somedefs Allows the elective handling of package options; used by the rawfonts package.

tabularx Defines a variant of the `tabular` environment where all the columns are the same width. It requires the array package.

theorem Allows the definition of proclamations in flexible formats; an AMS variant, the amsthm package, is discussed in Section 3.4.2. 

varioref Provides smart (as well as multilingual) handling of page references.

verbatim Extends the `verbatim` environment and provides the `comment` environment (see Section 2.5).

xr Creates cross-references among documents.

xspace Provides a "smart space" command that helps you avoid the common mistake of missing space after commands; it is mainly used in commands that expand to some text (see Section 9.1.1).

All of these packages include documentation; for instance, to get the documentation for the showkeys package, you

1. Typeset the `tools.ins` file with `LaTeX` format; this produces the `showkeys.sty` file (among others).
2. Typeset the `showkeys.dtx` file with the `LaTeX` format.

All of these packages (as they were in 1994) are discussed in *The LaTeX Companion* [17].

CHAPTER

8

AMS documents and packages

In this chapter, we discuss the AMS document classes and the AMS packages.[1] Since the whole chapter deals with AMS topics, the marginal warnings will be omitted for the remainder of the chapter.

The AMS document class for journal articles, `amsart`, is introduced in Section 8.1 (the AMS book document class will be discussed in Chapter 12). Section 8.2 introduces the rules governing the top matter in the `amsart` document class. Section 8.3 presents the AMS sample article, source and typeset. By following the steps in Section 8.4, you will create an article template for the `amsart` document class that will serve your needs. A document class is shaped by its options; in Section 8.5 we discuss the options of the `amsart` document class. Section 8.6 briefly describes the various packages in the AMS distribution and their interdependencies.

[1]The AMS refers to the AMS document classes and packages together as $\mathcal{A}_{\mathcal{M}}\mathcal{S}$-LaTeX; this is slightly confusing because $\mathcal{A}_{\mathcal{M}}\mathcal{S}$-LaTeX 1.0 and 1.1 were LaTeX variants (incompatible with the LaTeX of the day, LaTeX 2.09), not document classes and packages of the standard LaTeX.

8.1 *Two AMS document classes for articles*

For general information on the AMS journals, go to

```
http://www.ams.org/jourhtml/authors.html
```

You will find the links to the AMS journals at

```
http://www.ams.org/journals/
```

So if you want to submit an article to the *Proceedings*, you link to

```
http://www.ams.org/proc/procauthorpac.html
```

where option 6 provides you with the document class file, `proc-l.cls`. All the AMS journal document classes are based on `amsart`, so it is sufficient to discuss only the `amsart` document class in this book. The more specific document classes deal with issues such as logos that should not concern you.

The AMS also has a document class for articles in proceedings of meetings that appear in book form. The differences in the rules for the `amsart` and `amsproc` document classes are so minor that you can safely ignore them.

The `amsart` document class produces typeset articles that look very different from articles typeset with the `article` document class. Compare the `amsart` sample article on pages 286–288 to the `article` sample article on pages 44–45.

You should note one small, but important, difference between the structure of AMS and LaTeX article document classes: The AMS document classes require you to place your abstract *before* the

```
\maketitle
```

command; if your abstract is after the `\maketitle` command, LaTeX will generate a warning, such as

```
Class amsart Warning: Abstract should precede \maketitle
in AMS documentclasses; reported on input line 73.
```

8.1.1 *Font-size commands*

In the AMS document classes, there are five font-size commands below the size provided by the `\normalsize` command (LaTeX has four, see Section 2.6.7); see Table 8.1. Two commands allow the user to increase or decrease font size: `\larger` moves up one size and `\smaller` moves down one. Both commands take an optional argument; for example, `\larger[2]` moves up 2 sizes.

Command	LaTeX sample text	AMS sample text(A)
`\Tiny`	[not available]	sample text
`\tiny`	sample text	sample text
`\SMALL` or `\scriptsize`	sample text	sample text
`\Small` or `\footnotesize`	sample text	sample text
`\small`	sample text	sample text
`\normalsize`	sample text	sample text
`\large`	sample text	sample text
`\Large`	sample text	sample text
`\LARGE`	sample text	sample text
`\huge`	sample text	sample text
`\Huge`	sample text	sample text

Table 8.1: LaTeX and AMS font size commands.

8.2 *The top matter*

For a fairly representative example, see the typeset top matter of the `sampart.tex` sample article on page 286. Title-page information is provided as arguments of several commands. For your convenience, I will divide them into three groups.

There is only one general rule:

Rule ■ Top-matter commands

All top-matter commands are *short*.

This means that there can be no blank lines (or `\par` commands) in the argument of any of these commands (see Section 2.3.3).

8.2.1 *Article information*

Rule ■ Titles

- Command: `\title`
- Separate lines with `\\`
- Optional argument: Short title for running head
- Do not put a period at the end of a title

Many titles are too long to be typeset on a single line in the type used by the amsart document class for titles. If the way LaTeX breaks the title is not satisfactory, you can indicate where the title should be broken with \\ commands.

The *running head* (see Section 6.6) is the title on odd-numbered pages, set in capital letters. If the title is more than a few words long, use an optional argument to specify a short title for the running head. Do not use \\ in the short title.

Example of a title:

```
\title{A construction of distributive lattices}
```

A title with a short title:

```
\title[Complete-simple distributive lattices]%
{A construction of complete-simple\\
distributive lattices}
```

Rule ■ Translators

- Command: \translator
- Do not put a period at the end of the argument

Example:

```
\translator{Harry~M. Goldstein}
```

Rule ■ Dedications

- Command: \dedicatory
- Separate lines with \\

Example:

```
\dedicatory{To the memory of my esteemed
   friend and teacher,\\ Harry~M. Goldstein}
```

Rule ■ Dates

- Command: \date

Examples:

```
\date{January 22, 2000}
```

You can use the `\today` command to get today's date:

```
\date{\today}
```

To suppress the date, use `\date{}` or omit the `\date` command entirely.

Note that this command behaves differently in an AMS article than in a LaTeX article—LaTeX typesets todays's date if the `\date` command is omitted.

8.2.2 *Author information*

Rule ■ Authors

- Command: `\author`
- Optional argument: Short form of the name for the running head

Examples:
An author:

```
\author{George~A. Menuhin}
```

An author with a short form of the name for the running head:

```
\author[G.A. Menuhin]{George~A. Menuhin}
```

Section 8.2.4 explains how to specify multiple authors.

Rule ■ Addresses

- Command: `\address`
- Separate lines with `\\`
- Optional argument: Name of author

Example:

DEPARTMENT OF APPLIED MATHEMATICS, UNIVERSITY OF WINNEBAGO, WINNEBAGO, MN 53714

which is typed as

```
\address{Department of Applied Mathematics\\
         University of Winnebago\\
         Winnebago, MN 53714}
```

Notice that with the AMS document class, LaTeX replaces the \\ line separators with commas.

If there are several authors, you can use an optional argument of \address (the author's name) to avoid ambiguity. See Example 4 in Section 8.2.5 (page 283) for a complete example.

Rule ■ Current addresses

- Command: \curraddr
- Separate lines with \\
- Optional argument: name of author

Example:

Current address: Department of Mathematics, University of York, Heslington, York, England

typed as

```
\curraddr{Department of Mathematics\\
          University of York\\
          Heslington, York, England}
```

If there are several authors, you can use an optional argument (the author's name) of \curraddr to avoid ambiguity; for some examples, see Section 8.2.5.

Rule ■ E-mail addresses

- Command: \email
- Optional argument: Name of author

Example:

```
\email{gmen@ccw.uwinnebago.edu}
```

Tip Some e-mail addresses contain the percent symbol (%); recall that you have to type \% to get % (see Section 2.4.4).

Example:

```
\email{h1175moy\%ella@relay.eu.net}
```

Tip Some e-mail addresses contain the special underscore character (_). Recall (Section 2.4.4) that you have to type _ to get _.

Example:

```
\email{George\_Gratzer@umanitoba.ca}
```

Rule ■ Web (home) page (URL)

- Command: `\urladdr`
- Optional argument: Name of author

Example:

```
\urladdr{http://www.maths.umanitoba.ca/homepages/gratzer/}
```

Rule ■ Research support or other acknowledgments

- Command: `\thanks`
- Do not specify linebreaks
- Terminate the sentence with a period

Example:

```
\thanks{Research was supported in part by NSF grant PAL-90-2466.}
```

A `\thanks{}` command will be ignored in typesetting.

8.2.3 *AMS information*

The following are collected at the bottom of the first page as unmarked footnotes along with the arguments of the `\thanks` and `\date` commands:

Rule ■ AMS subject classifications

- Command: `\subjclass`
- Optional argument: 2000; the default is 1991
- The AMS document class supplies the phrase 1991 *Mathematics Subject Classification* and a period at the end of the subject classification; with the optional argument 2000, the phrase is 2000 *Mathematics Subject Classification*
- The argument should be either a five-digit code or the phrase `Primary:`, followed by a five-digit code, a semicolon, the phrase `Secondary:`, and one or more additional five-digit codes

---

Examples:

```
\subjclass[2000]{06B10}
\subjclass[2000]{Primary: 06B10; Secondary: 06D05}
```

The current subject classification scheme is available from the AMS electronically (see Chapter 13 on how to access it) at the address

`http://www.ams.org/msc/`

Rule ■ Keywords

- Command: `\keywords`
- Do not indicate line breaks
- The AMS document class supplies the phrase *Key words and phrases.* and a period at the end of the list of keywords

---

Example:

```
\keywords{Complete lattice, distributive lattice, complete
   congruence, congruence lattice}
```

Further footnotes An additional `\thanks` command creates an additional footnote.
Examples:

```
\thanks{This is a preliminary version of this article,
        prepared for the Second Annual Meeting of the
        Statistical Association of Winnebago.}
\thanks{This article is in final form, and no version of it
        will be submitted elsewhere.}
```

The second example may be used in conference proceedings to indicate that your article is reviewed.

8.2.4 *Multiple authors*

If an article has several authors, repeat the author information commands for each one. Take care that the e-mail address follows the address.

If two authors share the same address, omit the `\address` command for the second author (who can still have a different e-mail address and Web homepage). An additional `\thanks` command for the first author should precede any `\thanks` commands for the second author. Since the footnotes are not marked, the argument of the `\thanks` command for research support should contain a reference to the author:

```
\thanks{The research of the first author was supported in part by
        NSF grant PAL-90-2466.}
\thanks{The research of the second author was supported by
        the Hungarian National Foundation for Scientific Research,
        under Grant No.~9901.}
```

Finally, if an article has more than two authors, supply the author information for each author as usual, but explicitly specify the running heads with the `\markboth` command (see Section 6.6):

```
\markboth{first author ET AL.}{short title}
```

If there are multiple authors, sometimes it may not be clear whose address, current address, e-mail address, or Web home page is being given. In such cases you can give the name of the author as an optional argument of the command. For example,

Email address, Ernest T. Moynahan: `emoy@ccw.uwinnebago.edu`.

is typed as

```
\email[Ernest~T. Moynahan]{emoy@ccw.uwinnebago.edu}
```

See also Example 4 in Section 8.2.5.

8.2.5 *Examples*

The following examples show typical top-matter commands; they can be found in the `topmat.tpl` file in the `samples` directory (see page 4).

Example 1 One author.

```
% Article information
\title[Complete-simple distributive lattices]
      {A construction of complete-simple\\
       distributive lattices}
\date{\today}

% Author information
\author{George~A. Menuhin}
\address{Computer Science Department\\
         University of Winnebago\\
         Winnebago, MN 53714}
\email{gmen@ccw.uwinnebago.edu}
\urladdr{http://math.uwinnebago.edu/homepages/menuhin/}
\thanks{This research was supported by
        the NSF under grant number 23466.}

% AMS information
\keywords{Complete lattice, distributive lattice,
          complete congruence, congruence lattice}
\subjclass[2000]{Primary: 06B10; Secondary: 06D05}
```

In the `\title` command, supplying the optional argument for the running head is the rule, not the exception. All the items shown are required except for the `\email` and `\urladdr` commands.

Example 2 Two authors; only the first has a Web page. I have only shown the author information section here; the other commands would be the same as in Example 1.

```
% Author information
\author{George~A. Menuhin}
\address{Computer Science Department\\
         University of Winnebago\\
         Winnebago, MN 53714}
\email{gmen@ccw.uwinnebago.edu}
\urladdr{http://math.uwinnebago.edu/homepages/menuhin/}
\thanks{The research of the first author was
        supported by the NSF under grant number 23466.}
\author{Ernest~T. Moynahan}
\address{Mathematical Research Institute
         of the Hungarian Academy of Sciences\\
         Budapest, P.O.B. 127, H-1364\\
         Hungary}
```

```
\email{h1175moy\%ella@relay.eu.net}
\thanks{The research of the second author
        was supported by the Hungarian
        National Foundation for Scientific Research,
        under Grant No. 9901.}
```

Example 3 Two authors, same department. I have only shown the author information section here; the other commands would be identical to those in Example 1.

```
%  Author information
\author{George~A. Menuhin}
\address{Computer Science Department\\
         University of Winnebago\\
         Winnebago, MN 53714}
\email[George~A. Menuhin]{gmen@ccw.uwinnebago.edu}
\urladdr[George~A. Menuhin]%
        {http://math.uwinnebago.edu/homepages/menuhin/}
\thanks{The research of the first author was
        supported by the NSF under grant number~23466.}
\author{Ernest~T. Moynahan}
\email[Ernest~T. Moynahan]{emoy@ccw.uwinnebago.edu}
\thanks{The research of the second author was supported by
        the Hungarian National Foundation for Scientific
        Research, under Grant No. 9901.}
```

Note that the second author has no `\address`.

Example 4 Three authors, the first two from the same department, the second and third with e-mail addresses and research support. I have only shown the author information section; the other commands would be unchanged. There are various ways of handling this situation; this example is only one possible solution.

```
%  Author information
\author{George~A. Menuhin}
\address[George~A. Menuhin and Ernest~T. Moynahan]
   {Computer Science Department\\
    University of Winnebago\\
    Winnebago, MN 53714}
\email[George~A. Menuhin]{gmen@ccw.uwinnebago.edu}
\urladdr[George~A. Menuhin]%
        {http://math.uwinnebago.edu/homepages/menuhin/}
\thanks{The research of the first author was
        supported by the NSF under grant number 23466.}
```

```
\author{Ernest~T. Moynahan}
\email[Ernest~T. Moynahan]{emoy@ccw.uwinnebago.edu}
\thanks{The research of the second author was supported by
        the Hungarian National Foundation for Scientific
        Research, under Grant No. 9901.}
\author{Ferenc~R. Richardson}
\address[Ferenc~R. Richardson]
   {Department of Mathematics\\
    California United Colleges\\
    Frasco, CA 23714}
\email[Ferenc~R. Richardson]{frich@ccu.frasco.edu}
\thanks{The research of the third author was
        supported by the NSF under grant number 23466.}
```

Tip The most common mistake in the top matter is the misspelling of a command name; for instance, \adress. The error message LaTeX provides,

```
! Undefined control sequence.
l.37 \adress
            {Computer Science Department\\
```

tells you exactly what you mistyped. Similarly, if you drop a closing brace, as in

```
\email{menuhin@ccw.uwinnebago.edu
```

you will be told clearly what went wrong. Because the top-matter commands are short (see Section 2.3.3), LaTeX gives the error message

```
Runaway argument?
{menuhin@ccw.uwinnebago.edu \thanks {The research of th\ETC.
! Paragraph ended before \email was complete.
<to be read again>
                   \par
l.52
```

If you drop an opening brace,

```
\author George~A. Menuhin}
```

you will get the error message

```
! Too many }'s.
l.43 \author George~A. Menuhin}
```

If you enclose an optional argument in braces instead of brackets,

```
\title{Complete-simple distributive lattices}%
      {A construction of complete-simple\\
       distributive lattices}
```

the amsart document class will use the short title as the title (the real title will be typeset before the title lines).

8.2.6 Abstract

As we discussed in Section 6.3.1, you type your abstract in an abstract environment, which you would normally place as the last item before the \maketitle command. The abstract should be self-contained; in particular, do not cite from the bibliography.

8.3 The AMS sample article

sampart.tex is the source file for our sample article using the AMS article document class, amsart. (It is also in the samples directory; see page 4). A simpler article using the LaTeX article document class, intrart.tex, was presented in Part I (see Section 1.7).

The typeset sampart.tex is shown on the following three pages.

A CONSTRUCTION OF COMPLETE-SIMPLE DISTRIBUTIVE LATTICES

GEORGE A. MENUHIN

ABSTRACT. In this note we prove that there exist *complete-simple distributive lattices,* that is, complete distributive lattices in which there are only two complete congruences.

1. INTRODUCTION

In this note we prove the following result:

Main Theorem. *There exists an infinite complete distributive lattice K with only the two trivial complete congruence relations.*

2. THE $D^{\langle 2 \rangle}$ CONSTRUCTION

For the basic notation in lattice theory and universal algebra, see Ferenc R. Richardson [5] and George A. Menuhin [2]. We start with some definitions:

Definition 1. Let V be a complete lattice, and let $\mathfrak{p} = [u, v]$ be an interval of V. Then $\mathfrak{p}$ is called *complete-prime* if the following three conditions are satisfied:

(1) u is meet-irreducible but u is *not* completely meet-irreducible;
(2) v is join-irreducible but v is *not* completely join-irreducible;
(3) $[u, v]$ is a complete-simple lattice.

Now we prove the following result:

Lemma 1. *Let D be a complete distributive lattice satisfying conditions* (1) *and* (2). *Then $D^{\langle 2 \rangle}$ is a sublattice of D^2; hence $D^{\langle 2 \rangle}$ is a lattice, and $D^{\langle 2 \rangle}$ is a complete distributive lattice satisfying conditions* (1) *and* (2).

Proof. By conditions (1) and (2), $D^{\langle 2 \rangle}$ is a sublattice of D^2. Hence, $D^{\langle 2 \rangle}$ is a lattice.

Since $D^{\langle 2 \rangle}$ is a sublattice of a distributive lattice, $D^{\langle 2 \rangle}$ is a distributive lattice. Using the characterization of standard ideals in Ernest T. Moynahan [3], $D^{\langle 2 \rangle}$ has a zero and a unit element, namely, $\langle 0, 0 \rangle$ and $\langle 1, 1 \rangle$. To show that $D^{\langle 2 \rangle}$ is complete, let $\varnothing \neq A \subseteq D^{\langle 2 \rangle}$, and let $a = \bigvee A$ in D^2. If $a \in D^{\langle 2 \rangle}$, then $a = \bigvee A$ in $D^{\langle 2 \rangle}$; otherwise, a is of the form $\langle b, 1 \rangle$ for some $b \in D$ with $b < 1$. Now $\bigvee A = \langle 1, 1 \rangle$ in D^2 and the dual argument shows that $\bigwedge A$ also exists in D^2. Hence D is complete. Conditions (1) and (2) are obvious for $D^{\langle 2 \rangle}$. □

Corollary 1. *If D is complete-prime, then so is $D^{\langle 2 \rangle}$.*

The motivation for the following result comes from Soo-Key Foo [1].

Date: March 15, 2000.

2000 *Mathematics Subject Classification.* Primary: 06B10; Secondary: 06D05.

Key words and phrases. Complete lattice, distributive lattice, complete congruence, congruence lattice.

Research supported by the NSF under grant number 23466.

The motivation for the following result comes from Soo-Key Foo [1].

Lemma 2. *Let* Θ *be a complete congruence relation of* $D^{\langle 2 \rangle}$ *such that*

$$\langle 1, d \rangle \equiv \langle 1, 1 \rangle \pmod{\Theta}, \tag{2.1}$$

for some $d \in D$ *with* $d < 1$. *Then* $\Theta = \iota$.

Proof. Let Θ be a complete congruence relation of $D^{\langle 2 \rangle}$ satisfying (2.1). Then $\Theta = \iota$. □

3. The Π^* construction

The following construction is crucial to our proof of the Main Theorem:

Definition 2. Let D_i, for $i \in I$, be complete distributive lattices satisfying condition (2). Their Π^* product is defined as follows:

$$\Pi^*(D_i \mid i \in I) = \Pi(D_i^- \mid i \in I) + 1;$$

that is, $\Pi^*(D_i \mid i \in I)$ is $\Pi(D_i^- \mid i \in I)$ with a new unit element.

Notation. If $i \in I$ and $d \in D_i^-$, then

$$\langle \dots, 0, \dots, \overset{i}{d}, \dots, 0, \dots \rangle$$

is the element of $\Pi^*(D_i \mid i \in I)$ whose i-th component is d and all the other components are 0.

See also Ernest T. Moynahan [4]. Next we verify:

Theorem 1. *Let* D_i, *for* $i \in I$, *be complete distributive lattices satisfying condition* (2). *Let* Θ *be a complete congruence relation on* $\Pi^*(D_i \mid i \in I)$. *If there exist* $i \in I$ *and* $d \in D_i$ *with* $d < 1_i$ *such that for all* $d \leq c < 1_i$,

$$\langle \dots, 0, \dots, \overset{i}{d}, \dots, 0, \dots \rangle \equiv \langle \dots, 0, \dots, \overset{i}{c}, \dots, 0, \dots \rangle \pmod{\Theta}, \tag{3.1}$$

then $\Theta = \iota$.

Proof. Since

$$\langle \dots, 0, \dots, \overset{i}{d}, \dots, 0, \dots \rangle \equiv \langle \dots, 0, \dots, \overset{i}{c}, \dots, 0, \dots \rangle \pmod{\Theta}, \tag{3.2}$$

and Θ is a complete congruence relation, it follows from condition (3) that

$$\begin{aligned} &\langle \dots, \overset{i}{d}, \dots, 0, \dots \rangle \\ &\equiv \bigvee (\langle \dots, 0, \dots, \overset{i}{c}, \dots, 0, \dots \rangle \mid d \leq c < 1) \equiv 1 \pmod{\Theta}. \end{aligned} \tag{3.3}$$

Let $j \in I$ for $j \neq i$, and let $a \in D_j^-$. Meeting both sides of the congruence (3.2) with $\langle \dots, 0, \dots, \overset{j}{a}, \dots, 0, \dots \rangle$, we obtain

$$\begin{aligned} 0 &= \langle \dots, 0, \dots, \overset{i}{d}, \dots, 0, \dots \rangle \wedge \langle \dots, 0, \dots, \overset{j}{a}, \dots, 0, \dots \rangle \\ &\equiv \langle \dots, 0, \dots, \overset{j}{a}, \dots, 0, \dots \rangle \pmod{\Theta}. \end{aligned} \tag{3.4}$$

Using the completeness of Θ and (3.4), we get:

$$0 \equiv \bigvee (\langle \dots, 0, \dots, \overset{j}{a}, \dots, 0, \dots \rangle \mid a \in D_j^-) = 1 \pmod{\Theta},$$

hence $\Theta = \iota$. □

Theorem 2. *Let D_i, for $i \in I$, be complete distributive lattices satisfying conditions (2) and (3). Then $\Pi^*(D_i \mid i \in I)$ also satisfies conditions (2) and (3).*

Proof. Let Θ be a complete congruence on $\Pi^*(D_i \mid i \in I)$. Let $i \in I$. Define

$$\widehat{D}_i = \{\langle \dots, 0, \dots, \overset{i}{d}, \dots, 0, \dots \rangle \mid d \in D_i^- \} \cup \{1\}.$$

Then $\widehat{D}_i$ is a complete sublattice of $\Pi^*(D_i \mid i \in I)$, and $\widehat{D}_i$ is isomorphic to D_i. Let Θ_i be the restriction of Θ to $\widehat{D}_i$.

Since D_i is complete-simple, so is $\widehat{D}_i$, and hence Θ_i is ω or ι. If $\Theta_i = \rho$ for all $i \in I$, then $\Theta = \omega$. If there is an $i \in I$, such that $\Theta_i = \iota$, then $0 \equiv 1 \pmod{\Theta}$, hence $\Theta = \iota$. □

The Main Theorem follows easily from Theorems 1 and 2.

References

[1] Soo-Key Foo, *Lattice Constructions*, Ph.D. thesis, University of Winnebago, Winnebago, MN, December, 1990.

[2] George A. Menuhin, *Universal Algebra*, D. van Nostrand, Princeton, 1968.

[3] Ernest T. Moynahan, *On a problem of M. Stone*, Acta Math. Acad. Sci. Hungar. **8** (1957), 455–460.

[4] ———, *Ideals and congruence relations in lattices*. II, Magyar Tud. Akad. Mat. Fiz. Oszt. Közl. **9** (1957), 417–434 (Hungarian).

[5] Ferenc R. Richardson, *General Lattice Theory*, Mir, Moscow, expanded and revised ed., 1982 (Russian).

Computer Science Department, University of Winnebago, Winnebago, Minnesota 53714

E-mail address: `menuhin@ccw.uwinnebago.edu`

URL: `http://math.uwinnebago.edu/homepages/menuhin/`

On the next eight pages, the source file and the typeset version are shown juxtaposed, so that you can see how the marked-up source file becomes the typeset article.

```
% Sample file: sampart.tex
% The sample article for the amsart document class
% Typeset with LaTeX format

\documentclass{amsart}
\usepackage{amssymb,latexsym}

\theoremstyle{plain}
\newtheorem{theorem}{Theorem}
\newtheorem{corollary}{Corollary}
\newtheorem*{main}{Main~Theorem}
\newtheorem{lemma}{Lemma}
\newtheorem{proposition}{Proposition}

\theoremstyle{definition}
\newtheorem{definition}{Definition}

\theoremstyle{remark}
\newtheorem*{notation}{Notation}

\numberwithin{equation}{section}

\begin{document}
\title[Complete-simple distributive lattices]
      {A construction of complete-simple\\
       distributive lattices}
\author{George~A. Menuhin}
\address{Computer Science Department\\
         University of Winnebago\\
         Winnebago, MN 53714}
\email{menuhin@ccw.uwinnebago.edu}
\urladdr{http://math.uwinnebago.edu/homepages/menuhin/}
\thanks{Research supported by the NSF under grant number
23466.}
\keywords{Complete lattice, distributive lattice,
   complete congruence, congruence lattice}
\subjclass[2000]{Primary: 06B10; Secondary: 06D05}
\date{March 15, 2000}
\begin{abstract}
   In this note we prove that there exist \emph{complete-simple distributive
   lattices,} that is, complete distributive lattices in which there are
   only two complete congruences.
\end{abstract}

\maketitle

\section{Introduction}\label{S:intro}
In this note we prove the following result:

\begin{main}
   There exists an infinite complete distributive lattice~$K$ with only
   the two trivial complete congruence relations.
\end{main}

\section{The $D^{\langle 2 \rangle}$ construction}\label{S:Ds}
For the basic notation in lattice theory and universal algebra, see Ferenc~R.
Richardson~\cite{fR82} and George~A. Menuhin~\cite{gM68}.  We start with some
definitions:
```

A CONSTRUCTION OF COMPLETE-SIMPLE DISTRIBUTIVE LATTICES

GEORGE A. MENUHIN

ABSTRACT. In this note we prove that there exist *complete-simple distributive lattices,* that is, complete distributive lattices in which there are only two complete congruences.

1. INTRODUCTION

In this note we prove the following result:

Main Theorem. *There exists an infinite complete distributive lattice K with only the two trivial complete congruence relations.*

2. THE $D^{\langle 2 \rangle}$ CONSTRUCTION

For the basic notation in lattice theory and universal algebra, see Ferenc R. Richardson [5] and George A. Menuhin [2]. We start with some definitions:

Date: March 15, 2000.

2000 *Mathematics Subject Classification.* Primary: 06B10; Secondary: 06D05.

Key words and phrases. Complete lattice, distributive lattice, complete congruence, congruence lattice.

Research supported by the NSF under grant number 23466.

Definition 1. Let V be a complete lattice, and let $\mathfrak{p} = [u, v]$ be an interval of V. Then $\mathfrak{p}$ is called *complete-prime* if the following three conditions are satisfied:

(1) u is meet-irreducible but u is *not* completely meet-irreducible;
(2) v is join-irreducible but v is *not* completely join-irreducible;
(3) $[u, v]$ is a complete-simple lattice.

Now we prove the following result:

Lemma 1. *Let D be a complete distributive lattice satisfying conditions* (1) *and* (2). *Then $D^{\langle 2 \rangle}$ is a sublattice of D^{2}; hence $D^{\langle 2 \rangle}$ is a lattice, and $D^{\langle 2 \rangle}$ is a complete distributive lattice satisfying conditions* (1) *and* (2).

Proof. By conditions (1) and (2), $D^{\langle 2 \rangle}$ is a sublattice of D^{2}. Hence, $D^{\langle 2 \rangle}$ is a lattice.

```
\begin{definition}\label{D:prime}
   Let $V$ be a complete lattice, and let $\mathfrak{p} = [u, v]$ be
   an interval of $V$.  Then $\mathfrak{p}$ is called
   \emph{complete-prime} if the following three conditions are satisfied:
   \begin{enumerate}
      \item $u$ is meet-irreducible but $u$ is \emph{not}
         completely meet-irreducible;\label{m-i}
      \item $v$ is join-irreducible but $v$ is \emph{not}
         completely join-irreducible;\label{j-i}
      \item $[u, v]$ is a complete-simple lattice.\label{c-s}
   \end{enumerate}
\end{definition}

Now we prove the following result:

\begin{lemma}\label{L:ds}
   Let $D$ be a complete distributive lattice satisfying
   conditions \eqref{m-i} and~\eqref{j-i}.  Then
   $D^{\langle 2 \rangle}$ is a sublattice of $D^{2}$;
   hence $D^{\langle 2 \rangle}$ is a lattice, and
   $D^{\langle 2 \rangle}$ is a complete distributive
   lattice satisfying conditions \eqref{m-i} and~\eqref{j-i}.
\end{lemma}

\begin{proof}
   By conditions~\eqref{m-i} and \eqref{j-i},
   $D^{\langle 2 \rangle}$ is a sublattice
   of $D^{2}$.  Hence, $D^{\langle 2 \rangle}$ is a lattice.
```

Since $D^{\langle 2 \rangle}$ is a sublattice of a distributive lattice, $D^{\langle 2 \rangle}$ is a distributive lattice. Using the characterization of standard ideals in Ernest T. Moynahan [3], $D^{\langle 2 \rangle}$ has a zero and a unit element, namely, $\langle 0, 0 \rangle$ and $\langle 1, 1 \rangle$. To show that $D^{\langle 2 \rangle}$ is complete, let $\varnothing \ne A \subseteq D^{\langle 2 \rangle}$, and let $a = \bigvee A$ in D^{2}. If $a \in D^{\langle 2 \rangle}$, then $a = \bigvee A$ in $D^{\langle 2 \rangle}$; otherwise, a is of the form $\langle b, 1 \rangle$ for some $b \in D$ with $b < 1$. Now $\bigvee A = \langle 1, 1\rangle$ in D^{2} and the dual argument shows that $\bigwedge A$ also exists in D^{2}. Hence D is complete. Conditions (1) and (2) are obvious for $D^{\langle 2 \rangle}$. ☐

Corollary 1. *If D is complete-prime, then so is $D^{\langle 2 \rangle}$.*

The motivation for the following result comes from Soo-Key Foo [1].

Lemma 2. *Let Θ be a complete congruence relation of $D^{\langle 2 \rangle}$ such that*

$$\langle 1, d \rangle \equiv \langle 1, 1 \rangle \pmod{\Theta}, \tag{2.1}$$

for some $d \in D$ with $d < 1$. Then $\Theta = \iota$.

```
   Since $D^{\langle 2 \rangle}$ is a sublattice of a distributive
   lattice, $D^{\langle 2 \rangle}$ is a distributive lattice.  Using
   the characterization of standard ideals in Ernest~T. Moynahan~\cite{eM57},
   $D^{\langle 2 \rangle}$ has a zero and a unit element,
   namely, $\langle 0, 0 \rangle$ and $\langle 1, 1 \rangle$.
   To show that $D^{\langle 2 \rangle}$ is complete, let
   $\varnothing \ne A \subseteq D^{\langle 2 \rangle}$, and let
   $a = \bigvee A$ in $D^{2}$.  If
   $a \in D^{\langle 2 \rangle}$, then
   $a = \bigvee A$ in $D^{\langle 2 \rangle}$; otherwise, $a$
   is of the form $\langle b, 1 \rangle$ for some
   $b \in D$ with $b < 1$.  Now $\bigvee A = \langle 1, 1\rangle$
   in $D^{2}$ and the dual argument shows that $\bigwedge A$ also
   exists in $D^{2}$.  Hence $D$ is complete. Conditions \eqref{m-i}
   and~\eqref{j-i} are obvious for $D^{\langle 2 \rangle}$.
\end{proof}

\begin{corollary}\label{C:prime}
   If $D$ is complete-prime, then so is $D^{\langle 2 \rangle}$.
\end{corollary}

The motivation for the following result comes from Soo-Key Foo~\cite{sF90}.

\begin{lemma}\label{L:ccr}
   Let $\Theta$ be a complete congruence relation of
   $D^{\langle 2 \rangle}$ such that
   \begin{equation}\label{E:rigid}
      \langle 1, d \rangle \equiv \langle 1, 1 \rangle \pmod{\Theta},
   \end{equation}
   for some $d \in D$ with $d < 1$. Then $\Theta = \iota$.
\end{lemma}
```

Proof. Let Θ be a complete congruence relation of $D^{\langle 2 \rangle}$ satisfying (2.1). Then $\Theta = \iota$. □

3. The Π^* construction

The following construction is crucial to our proof of the Main Theorem:

Definition 2. Let D_i, for $i \in I$, be complete distributive lattices satisfying condition (2). Their Π^* product is defined as follows:

$$\Pi^*(D_i \mid i \in I) = \Pi(D_i^- \mid i \in I) + 1;$$

that is, $\Pi^*(D_i \mid i \in I)$ is $\Pi(D_i^- \mid i \in I)$ with a new unit element.

Notation. If $i \in I$ and $d \in D_i^-$, then

$$\langle \dots, 0, \dots, \overset{i}{d}, \dots, 0, \dots \rangle$$

is the element of $\Pi^*(D_i \mid i \in I)$ whose i-th component is d and all the other components are 0.

```
\begin{proof}
   Let $\Theta$ be a complete congruence relation of
   $D^{\langle 2 \rangle}$ satisfying \eqref{E:rigid}. Then $\Theta =
\iota$.
\end{proof}

\section{The $\Pi^{*}$ construction}\label{S:P*}
The following construction is crucial to our proof of the Main Theorem:

\begin{definition}\label{D:P*}
   Let $D_{i}$, for $i \in I$, be complete distributive lattices
   satisfying condition~\eqref{j-i}.  Their $\Pi^{*}$ product is defined
   as follows:
   \[
      \Pi^{*} ( D_{i} \mid i \in I ) = \Pi ( D_{i}^{-} \mid i \in I ) + 1;
   \]
   that is, $\Pi^{*} ( D_{i} \mid i \in I )$ is $\Pi ( D_{i}^{-} \mid
   i \in I )$ with a new unit element.
\end{definition}

\begin{notation}
   If $i \in I$ and $d \in D_{i}^{-}$, then
   \[
      \langle \dots, 0, \dots, \overset{i}{d}, \dots, 0, \dots \rangle
   \]
   is the element of $\Pi^{*} ( D_{i} \mid i \in I )$ whose $i$-th
   component is $d$ and all the other components are $0$.
\end{notation}
```

See also Ernest T. Moynahan [4]. Next we verify:

Theorem 1. *Let D_i, for $i \in I$, be complete distributive lattices satisfying condition* (2). *Let Θ be a complete congruence relation on $\Pi^*(D_i \mid i \in I)$. If there exist $i \in I$ and $d \in D_i$ with $d < 1_i$ such that for all $d \leq c < 1_i$,*

$$\langle \dots, 0, \dots, \overset{i}{d}, \dots, 0, \dots \rangle \equiv \langle \dots, 0, \dots, \overset{i}{c}, \dots, 0, \dots \rangle \pmod{\Theta}, \tag{3.1}$$

then $\Theta = \iota$.

Proof. Since

$$\langle \dots, 0, \dots, \overset{i}{d}, \dots, 0, \dots \rangle \equiv \langle \dots, 0, \dots, \overset{i}{c}, \dots, 0, \dots \rangle \pmod{\Theta}, \tag{3.2}$$

and Θ is a complete congruence relation, it follows from condition (3) that

$$\begin{split} &\langle \dots, \overset{i}{d}, \dots, 0, \dots \rangle \\ &\equiv \bigvee (\langle \dots, 0, \dots, \overset{i}{c}, \dots, 0, \dots \rangle \mid d \leq c < 1) \equiv 1 \pmod{\Theta}. \end{split} \tag{3.3}$$

Let $j \in I$ for $j \neq i$, and let $a \in D_j^-$. Meeting both sides of the congruence (3.2) with $\langle \dots, 0, \dots, \overset{j}{a}, \dots, 0, \dots \rangle$, we obtain

```
See also Ernest~T. Moynahan \cite{eM57a}.  Next we verify:

\begin{theorem}\label{T:P*}
   Let $D_{i}$, for $i \in I$, be complete distributive lattices
   satisfying condition~\eqref{j-i}.  Let $\Theta$ be a complete
congruence
   relation on $\Pi^{*} ( D_{i} \mid i \in I )$.  If there exist
   $i \in I$ and $d \in D_{i}$ with $d < 1_{i}$ such that for
   all $d \leq c < 1_{i}$,
   \begin{equation}\label{E:cong1}
      \langle \dots, 0, \dots,\overset{i}{d},
      \dots, 0, \dots \rangle \equiv \langle \dots, 0, \dots,
      \overset{i}{c}, \dots, 0, \dots \rangle \pmod{\Theta},
   \end{equation}
   then $\Theta = \iota$.
\end{theorem}

\begin{proof}
   Since
   \begin{equation}\label{E:cong2}
      \langle \dots, 0, \dots, \overset{i}{d}, \dots, 0,
         \dots \rangle \equiv \langle \dots, 0, \dots,
         \overset{i}{c}, \dots, 0, \dots \rangle \pmod{\Theta},
   \end{equation}
   and $\Theta$ is a complete congruence relation, it follows from
   condition~\eqref{c-s} that
   \begin{equation}\label{E:cong}
   \begin{split}
       &\langle \dots, \overset{i}{d}, \dots, 0,
          \dots \rangle\\
       &\equiv \bigvee ( \langle \dots, 0, \dots,
         \overset{i}{c}, \dots, 0, \dots \rangle \mid d \leq c < 1 )
         \equiv 1 \pmod{\Theta}.
   \end{split}
   \end{equation}

   Let $j \in I$ for $j \neq i$, and let $a \in D_{j}^{-}$.
   Meeting both sides of the congruence \eqref{E:cong2} with
   $\langle \dots, 0, \dots, \overset{j}{a}, \dots, 0, \dots \rangle$,
   we obtain
```

$$
\begin{split}
0 &= \langle \dots, 0, \dots, \overset{i}{d}, \dots, 0, \dots \rangle \wedge \langle \dots, 0, \dots, \overset{j}{a}, \dots, 0, \dots \rangle\\
&\equiv \langle \dots, 0, \dots, \overset{j}{a}, \dots, 0, \dots \rangle \pmod{\Theta}.
\end{split} \tag{3.4}
$$

Using the completeness of Θ and (3.4), we get:

$$
0 \equiv \bigvee (\langle \dots, 0, \dots, \overset{j}{a}, \dots, 0, \dots \rangle \mid a \in D_{j}^{-}) = 1 \pmod{\Theta},
$$

hence $\Theta = \iota$. □

Theorem 2. *Let D_{i}, for $i \in I$, be complete distributive lattices satisfying conditions* (2) *and* (3). *Then $\Pi^{*}(D_{i} \mid i \in I)$ also satisfies conditions* (2) *and* (3).

Proof. Let Θ be a complete congruence on $\Pi^{*}(D_{i} \mid i \in I)$. Let $i \in I$. Define

$$
\widehat{D}_{i} = \{ \langle \dots, 0, \dots, \overset{i}{d}, \dots, 0, \dots \rangle \mid d \in D_{i}^{-} \} \cup \{ 1 \}.
$$

Then $\widehat{D}_{i}$ is a complete sublattice of $\Pi^{*}(D_{i} \mid i \in I)$, and $\widehat{D}_{i}$ is isomorphic to D_{i}. Let Θ_{i} be the restriction of Θ to $\widehat{D}_{i}$.

```
 \begin{equation}\label{E:comp}
   \begin{split}
     0 &= \langle \dots, 0, \dots, \overset{i}{d}, \dots, 0, \dots
       \rangle \wedge \langle \dots, 0, \dots, \overset{j}{a}, \dots, 0,
       \dots \rangle\\
        &\equiv \langle \dots, 0, \dots, \overset{j}{a}, \dots, 0, \dots
       \rangle \pmod{\Theta}.
   \end{split}
  \end{equation}
   Using the completeness of $\Theta$ and \eqref{E:comp}, we get:
   \[
     0 \equiv \bigvee ( \langle \dots, 0, \dots, \overset{j}{a},
     \dots, 0, \dots \rangle \mid a \in D_{j}^{-} ) = 1 \pmod{\Theta},
   \]
   hence $\Theta = \iota$.
\end{proof}

\begin{theorem}\label{T:P*a}
   Let $D_{i}$ for $i \in I$ be complete distributive lattices
   satisfying conditions \eqref{j-i} and~\eqref{c-s}.  Then
   $\Pi^{*} ( D_{i} \mid i \in I )$ also satisfies
   conditions~\eqref{j-i} and \eqref{c-s}.
\end{theorem}

\begin{proof}
   Let $\Theta$ be a complete congruence on
   $\Pi^{*} ( D_{i} \mid i \in I )$. Let $i \in I$.  Define
   \[
     \widehat{D}_{i} = \{ \langle \dots, 0, \dots, \overset{i}{d},
     \dots, 0, \dots \rangle \mid d \in D_{i}^{-} \} \cup \{ 1 \}.
   \]
   Then $\widehat{D}_{i}$ is a complete sublattice of
   $\Pi^{*} ( D_{i} \mid i \in I )$, and $\widehat{D}_{i}$ is
   isomorphic to $D_{i}$.  Let $\Theta_{i}$ be the restriction of
   $\Theta$ to $\widehat{D}_{i}$.
```

Since D_i is complete-simple, so is $\widehat{D}_i$, and hence Θ_i is ω or ι. If $\Theta_i = \rho$ for all $i \in I$, then $\Theta = \omega$. If there is an $i \in I$, such that $\Theta_i = \iota$, then $0 \equiv 1 \pmod{\Theta}$, hence $\Theta = \iota$. □

The Main Theorem follows easily from Theorems 1 and 2.

References

[1] Soo-Key Foo, *Lattice Constructions*, Ph.D. thesis, University of Winnebago, Winnebago, MN, December, 1990.

[2] George A. Menuhin, *Universal algebra*, D. van Nostrand, Princeton, 1968.

[3] Ernest T. Moynahan, *On a problem of M. Stone*, Acta Math. Acad. Sci. Hungar. **8** (1957), 455–460.

[4] ———, *Ideals and congruence relations in lattices*. II, Magyar Tud. Akad. Mat. Fiz. Oszt. Közl. **9** (1957), 417–434 (Hungarian).

[5] Ferenc R. Richardson, *General lattice theory*, Mir, Moscow, expanded and revised ed., 1982 (Russian).

Computer Science Department, University of Winnebago, Winnebago, MN 53714

E-mail address: menuhin@ccw.uwinnebago.edu

URL: http://math.uwinnebago.edu/homepages/menuhin/

```
   Since $D_{i}\) is complete-simple, so is $\widehat{D}_{i}$, and
   hence $\Theta_{i}$ is $\omega$ or $\iota$.  If
   $\Theta_{i} = \rho$ for all $i \in I$, then
   $\Theta = \omega$.  If there is an $i \in I$, such that
   $\Theta_{i} = \iota$, then $0 \equiv 1 \pmod{\Theta}$, hence
   $\Theta = \iota$.
\end{proof}

The Main Theorem follows easily from Theorems \ref{T:P*} and~\ref{T:P*a}.

\begin{thebibliography}{9}

   \bibitem{sF90}
      Soo-Key Foo, \emph{Lattice Constructions}, Ph.D. thesis, University
      of Winnebago, Winnebago, MN, December, 1990.

   \bibitem{gM68}
      George~A. Menuhin, \emph{Universal algebra}, D.~van Nostrand,
      Princeton, 1968.

   \bibitem{eM57}
      Ernest~T. Moynahan, \emph{On a problem of M. Stone}, Acta Math.
        Acad. Sci. Hungar. \textbf{8} (1957), 455--460.

   \bibitem{eM57a}
      \bysame, \emph{Ideals and congruence relations in lattices}. II,
     Magyar Tud. Akad. Mat. Fiz. Oszt. K\"{o}zl. \textbf{9} (1957),
     417--434  (Hungarian).

   \bibitem{fR82}
      Ferenc~R. Richardson, \emph{General lattice theory}, Mir, Moscow,
      expanded and revised ed., 1982 (Russian).

\end{thebibliography}
\end{document}
```

8.4 AMS article templates

In this section, we will create a template you can use for your AMS articles, using the `amsart` document class. A template is a read-only file; you open it with a text editor and save it under a different name. You can then start to write your new article using the new file, without having to remember the details governing the preamble and the top matter.

Create the template, which will contain a customized preamble, preformatted top matter, and sample bibliographic items, in several steps:

Step 1 Open the `amsart.tpl` document from the `samples` directory (see page 4, or type in the lines as shown in this section) in your text editor, and save it in your `work` subdirectory as `myams.tpl`.

The first few lines of the file are

```
% Sample file: amsart.tpl
% Typeset with LaTeX format

% Preamble
\documentclass{amsart}
\usepackage{amssymb,latexsym}
```

Notice the use of commented-out lines (lines that start with `%`) for including comments about the file.

Edit line 1 to read

```
% Sample file: myams.tpl
```

The lines

```
\documentclass{amsart}
\usepackage{amssymb,latexsym}
```

specify the `amsart` document class and the use of the amssymb and latexsym packages to gain access to all the symbols listed in Appendix A by name.

Step 2 After the \usepackage command, there are sets of proclamation definitions corresponding to the examples in Section 3.4.2.

Choose Option 5 for `myams.tpl` by deleting all the lines related to the other options. You will be left with the lines

```
% Theorems, corollaries, lemmas, and propositions, in the most
% emphatic (plain) style; all are numbered separately.
% There is a Main Theorem in the most emphatic (plain)
% style, unnumbered. There are definitions, in the less emphatic
% (definition) style. There are notations, in the least emphatic
% (remark) style, unnumbered.
```

```
\theoremstyle{plain}
\newtheorem{theorem}{Theorem}
\newtheorem{corollary}{Corollary}
\newtheorem*{main}{Main Theorem}
\newtheorem{lemma}{Lemma}
\newtheorem{proposition}{Proposition}

\theoremstyle{definition}
\newtheorem{definition}{Definition}

\theoremstyle{remark}
\newtheorem*{notation}{Notation}
```

Step 3 Two more choices are presented: one or two authors (for more complex situations; see Section 8.2.4). For the `myams.tpl` template, choose one author by deleting everything between

```
%  Two authors
```

and

```
%  End Two authors
```

inclusive. You will be left with

```
\begin{document}
% One author
\title[shorttitle]{titleline1\\
                   titleline2}
\author{name}
\address{line1\\
         line2\\
         line3}
\email{name@address}
\urladdr{http://webaddress}
\thanks{thanks}
% End one author

\keywords{keywords}
\subjclass[2000]{Primary: subject; Secondary: subject}
\date{date}

\begin{abstract}
   abstract
\end{abstract}
```

```
\maketitle

\begin{thebibliography}{99}

\end{thebibliography}
\end{document}
```

In the top matter, you should fill in your own personal information. For instance, I edited

```
\author{name}
```

to read

```
\author{George~Gr\"{a}tzer}
```

I also edited \address, \email, \urladdr, and \thanks; after editing, I had the following:

```
% top matter
\title[shorttitle]{titleline1\\
                  titleline2}
\author{George~Gr\"{a}tzer}
\address{University of Manitoba\\
         Department of Mathematics\\
         Winnipeg, MB R3T 2N2\\
         Canada}
\email{gratzer@cc.umanitoba.ca}
\urladdr{http://server.maths.umanitoba.ca/homepages/gratzer/}
\thanks{Research supported by the NSERC of Canada.}

\keywords{keywords}
\subjclass[2000]{Primary: subject; Secondary: subject}
\date{date}

\begin{abstract}
   abstract
\end{abstract}
\maketitle

\begin{thebibliography}{99}

\end{thebibliography}
\end{document}
```

Since this template is meant to be used for all my future articles, I do not edit the lines that change from article to article (`\title`, `\keywords`, and so on).

Remember that the short title is for running heads, the title shown at the top of every odd-numbered page other than the title page. If the title of your article is only one line long, delete the separation mark `\\` and the second line (except for the closing brace). If the full title of your article is short, delete `[shorttitle]`.

Now save `myams.tpl`. (I saved my template under the name `ggamsart.tpl`. You can find it the `samples` directory; see page 4.) You can also make an additional template with two authors to be used as a template for joint articles. Note that at the end of the template, just before the line `\end{document}`, there are two lines:

```
\begin{thebibliography}{99}

\end{thebibliography}
```

The argument of `\begin{thebibliography}` should be `9` if there are fewer than 10 references; `99` with 10–99 references; and so forth. We discussed how to format bibliographic items in Sections 1.9.4 and 6.5.1; the `amsart` document class follows the same rules. The templates for bibliographic items are listed after the `\end{document}` line.

To make sure that you do not overwrite your template, I recommend that you make it read-only; how you do so, depends on your computer system.

8.5 *Options*

The AMS document classes support a number of options, affecting many attributes.

For each attribute there is a *default value* that is used if a value is not specified.

Some of these options are similar to the LaTeX options we discussed in Section 7.1.1; some have a wider range of values (e.g., font size), some have a narrower range of values (e.g., paper size), some have the same values but a different default (e.g., the placement of equation numbers).

Font size

Options: `8pt`
`9pt`
`10pt`
`11pt`
`12pt`

Default: `10pt`

These options declare the default font size. You may want to use the `12pt` option for proofreading:

```
\documentclass[12pt]{amsart}
```

Remember, however, that changing the font size changes the line breaks, so changing the `12pt` option back to `10pt` may require some adjustments; see Section 1.1.3.

Paper size

Options:	`letterpaper`	(8.5 inches by 11 inches)
	`legalpaper`	(8.5 inches by 14 inches)
	`a4paper`	(210 mm by 297 mm)
Default:	`letterpaper`	

Draft

Options: `draft`
`final`

Default: `final`

The `draft` option prints a slug in the margin next to each line that is too wide. The `final` option does not.

Equations and equation numbers

A number of options deal with the placement of equations and equation numbers.

Options: `leqno`
`reqno`

Default: `leqno`

By default, equation numbers are placed on the left (the `leqno` option). The `reqno` option places the equation numbers on the right. Note that this setting is the reverse of the LaTeX default (Section 7.1.1).

Option: `fleqn`

This option positions equations a fixed distance from the left margin rather than centering them; the `fleqn` option is typically used used in conjunction with the `reqno` option. Here is how an equation looks with the `fleqn` and `reqno` options:

$$\int_0^\pi \sin x \, dx = 2 \tag{1}$$

Options: `tbtags`
`centertags`

Default: `centertags`

The `tbtags` option uses *top-or-bottom tags* for a `split` environment; that is, it places the equation number level with the last line if numbers are on the right, or level with the first line if the numbers are on the left:

$$
\begin{aligned}
(1) \qquad f &= (x_1x_2x_3x_4x_5x_6)^2\\
&= (x_1x_2x_3x_4x_5 + x_1x_3x_4x_5x_6 + x_1x_2x_4x_5x_6 + x_1x_2x_3x_5x_6)^2\\
&= (x_1x_2x_3x_4 + x_1x_2x_3x_5 + x_1x_2x_4x_5 + x_1x_3x_4x_5)^2
\end{aligned}
$$

The `centertags` option (the default) vertically centers the equation number in a `split` subsidiary math environment.

Two-sided printing

Options: `twoside`
`oneside`

Default: `twoside`

The `twoside` option formats the output for printing on both sides of the paper; the opposite is the `oneside` option. This option influences running heads, the placement of page numbers, and so on.

Two-column printing

Options: `twocolumn`
`onecolumn`

Default: `onecolumn`

The `twocolumn` option typesets the document in two columns.

Titlepage

Options: `titlepage`
`notitlepage`

Default: `notitlepage`

The `titlepage` option creates a separate title page and also places the abstract on a separate page. The `notitlepage` option places both on the first page of the document.

Fonts

Option: `noamsfonts`

With this option, the document class does not load the packages necessary for the use of the AMSFonts font set.

Option: `psamsfonts`

The `psamsfonts` option tells LaTeX that you use the PostScript version of the AMSFonts set; see Section D.1.

No math

Option: `nomath`

By default, the AMS document classes load the amsmath package (which, in turn, loads three more math packages). If you want to use the title page and related features without the math features, you can use the `nomath` option.

If both options, `noamsfonts` and `nomath` are used, the AMS document class loads a single package: amsgen.

8.5.1 Math options

The amsmath package has many options of its own.

The `fleqn`, `reqno`, `leqno`, `tbtags`, and `centertags` document-class options (see Section 8.5) are passed on to the amsmath package. They can also be given directly to the package; for example,

```
\documentclass{article}
\usepackage[leqno]{amsmath}
```

Limits

Options: `intlimits`
`nointlimits`

Default: `nointlimits`

The `intlimits` option places the subscripts and superscripts of integral symbols above and below the integral symbol rather than on the side; `nointlimits` positions them on the side.

Options: `sumlimits`
`nosumlimits`

Default: `sumlimits`

The `sumlimits` option places the subscripts and superscripts of large operators (e.g., $\prod$, $\coprod$, $\bigotimes$, $\bigoplus$) above and below the large operator. `nosumlimits` positions them on the side (see Table 4.5 and Section A.7.3).

Options: `namelimits`
`nonamelimits`

Default: `namelimits`

The `namelimits` option places the subscripts and superscripts of operators such as det, inf, lim, max, min, and so on, above and below the operator. `nonamelimits` positions them on the side. (See Tables 4.2, 4.3, and Section A.7.)

PostScript AMSFonts

Option: `cmex10`

The amsmath package has to be told if the PostScript AMSFonts set is used (see Section D.1); this is normally done with the `psamsfonts` option of the document class, which is then passed on to amsmath. If the amsmath package is loaded directly, you must use the `cmex10` option; for instance,

```
\documentclass{article}
\usepackage[cmex10]{amsmath}
```

In addition, if you want to use the `12pt` document class option, then you must also load the exscale package (see Section 7.3):

```
\usepackage{exscale}
```

8.6 The AMS packages

The AMS distribution contains many packages that can be loaded together or by themselves.

If you follow the recommendation on page xxxvi and begin each article with

```
\documentclass{amsart}
\usepackage{amssymb,latexsym}
\begin{document}
```

then you can safely ignore most of the information in this section.

Math enhancements

amsmath The primary math enhancement package; automatically loads the packages: amsgen, amsbsy, amsopn, and amstext.

amsbsy Provides two commands for the use of bold math symbols: `\boldsymbol` and `\pmb` (see Section 4.13.3).

amscd Provides commands for creating simple commutative diagrams (see Section 5.8).

amsgen An auxiliary package that is never invoked directly; automatically loaded by all the AMS math packages (except for upref).

amsopn Provides operator names and the `\DeclareMathOperator` command for defining new ones (see Section 4.7).

amstext Defines the `\text` command and redefines commands such as `\textrm` and `\textbf` to behave like the `\text` command (see Section 4.5).

amsxtra Provides the "sp" math accents (see Sections 4.9 and A.8.1); automatically loads the amsmath package.

upref Ensures that the `\ref` command always produces upright numbers.

AMSFonts

amsfonts Contains the basic commands needed to utilize the AMSFonts; it also defines the `\mathfrak` command which makes the Euler Fraktur math alphabet (see Section 4.13.2) available. If you use the PostScript AMSFonts font set (see Section D.1), you should load this package with the option

```
\usepackage[psamsfonts]{amsfonts}
```

In addition, if you want to use the `12pt` document class option, then you must also load the exscale package (see Section 7.3):

```
\usepackage{exscale}
```

amssymb Defines the symbol table; automatically loads amsfonts.

eucal Replaces the calligraphic math alphabet with the Euler Script math alphabet (see Section 4.13.2); if you load it with the option `mathscr`, as in

```
\usepackage[mathscr]{eucal}
```

then both the `\mathscr` and the `\mathcal` commands will be available, so you can have both $\mathcal{C}\mathcal{E}$ and $\mathscr{C}\mathscr{E}$, typed as
`$\mathcal{C} \mathcal{E}$ and $\mathscr{C} \mathscr{E}$`.

eufrak Defines the Euler Fraktur math alphabet (see Section 4.13.2).

Document classes

The AMS document classes contain code to provide more flexible formatting of proclamations and the `proof` environment (see Sections 3.4.2 and 3.5). By loading the amsthm package you can add this functionality to a non-AMS document class; amsthm automatically loads the amsgen package.

The AMS document classes automatically load the amsmath, amsbsy, amstext, amsopn, and amsgen packages from the math enhancements group, and the amsfonts package from the AMSFonts group. So for normal work, it is sufficient to invoke an AMS document class with

```
\documentclass{amsart}
\usepackage{amssymb,latexsym}
```

A typical article using the LaTeX `article` document class and the AMS enhancements would normally have

```
\documentclass{article}
\usepackage{amsmath}% math enhancements
\usepackage{amssymb,latexsym}% AMSFonts and AMS and LaTeX symbols
```

and perhaps one or both of the following:

```
\usepackage{amsthm}% proclamations with style
\usepackage{eucal}% Euler Script
```

Note that it is not critical for you to remember which packages load others automatically. No harm is done if you type

```
\usepackage{amsmath}
\usepackage{amsbsy}
```

The amsbsy package will be automatically loaded by the amsmath package, and the

```
\usepackage{amsbsy}
```

line will be ignored by LaTeX.

Documentation

The documentation provided by the AMS is available electronically on CTAN (see Section 13.1):

- amsmath package: `amsldoc.tex`

  `/tex-archive/macros/latex/required/amslatex/math/`

- AMS document classes: `instr-l.tex` and `amsthdoc.tex`

  `/tex-archive/macros/latex/required/amslatex/classes/`

- AMSFonts: `amsfndoc.tex`

  `/tex-archive/fonts/amsfonts/doc/`

To obtain the AMS packages with ready-to-use installation, go to the AMS Web site:

`http://www.ams.org/tex/amslatex.html`

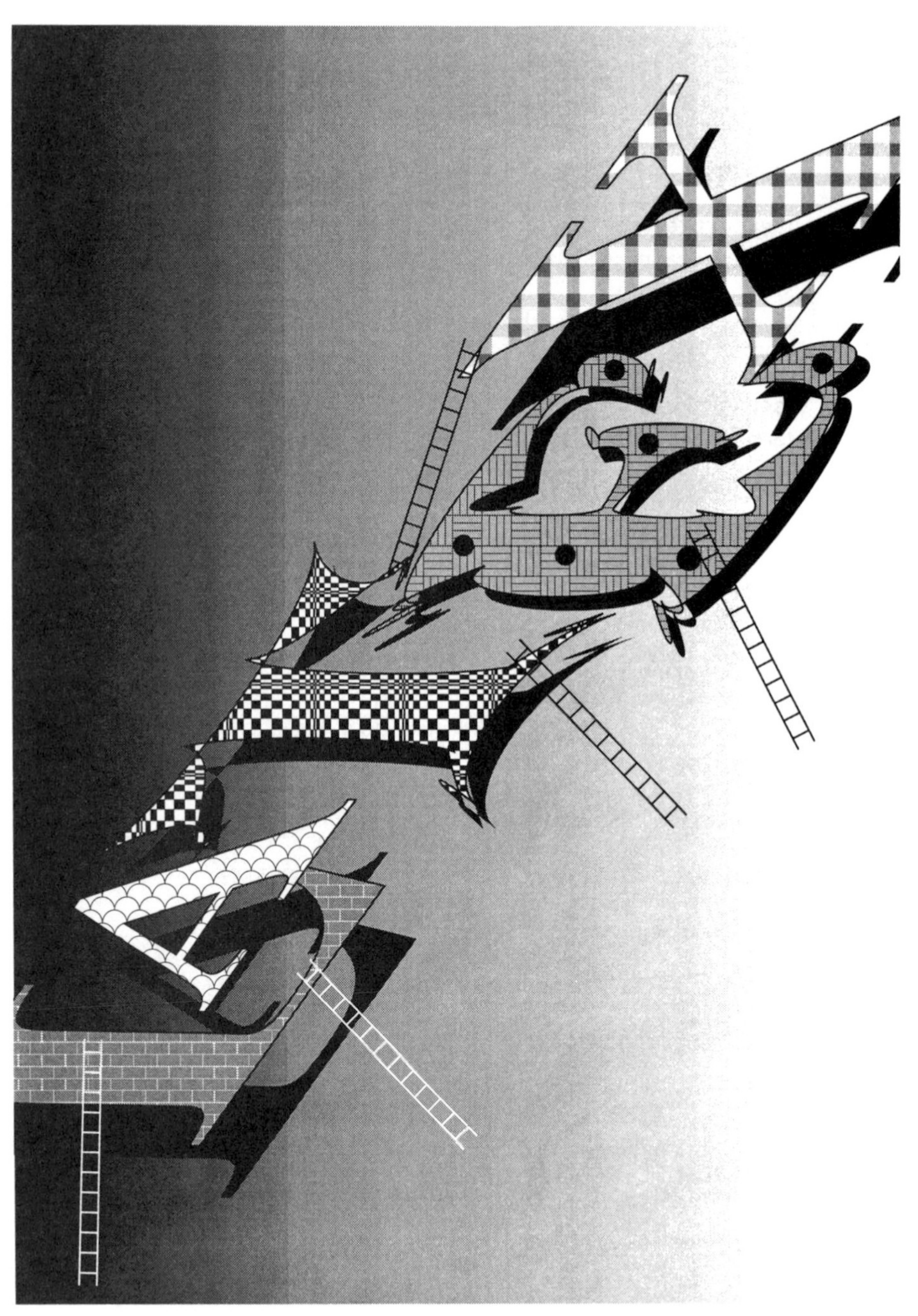

PART IV

Customization

CHAPTER

9

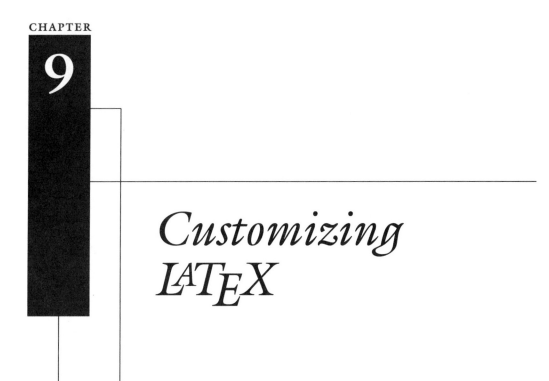

Customizing LaTeX

There are many techniques you can use to speed up the typing and typesetting of your document. In this chapter, I will cover some of the basics.

You can

- Introduce user-defined commands and environments in order to enhance LaTeX to meet your particular needs; see Sections 9.1 and 9.2
- Utilize delimited commands to write LaTeX documents in a more readable fashion; see Section 9.1.8
- Collect your frequently used user-defined commands in a command file; an example is presented in Section 9.3
- Manipulate *counters* (integers such as equation numbers and section numbers) and *length commands* (distance measurements such as the `\voffset` command); see Section 9.5
- Create customized list environments with the `list` environment; see Section 9.6
- Make custom formats that speed up typesetting; see Section 9.7

9.1 User-defined commands

LaTeX provides hundreds of commands. Chances are good, however, that you will still have specific needs that are not directly addressed by these commands. By judiciously adding your own *user-defined commands* (or *macros*) you can satisfy your particular needs.

9.1.1 Examples and rules

Commands as shorthand

Let us start with a few examples of user-defined commands as shorthand for longer command(s) or text.

1. If you use the `\leftarrow` command a lot, you could define

   ```
   \newcommand{\la}{\leftarrow}
   ```

   Then you would only have to type `\la` to obtain a left arrow.
2. Instead of

   ```
   \widetilde{a}
   ```

   you could simply type `\wa` after defining

   ```
   \newcommand{\wa}{\widetilde{a}}
   ```

   I will show you how to define a generalized version of such a command in Section 9.1.2.
3. If you want to suppress the ligature in iff (see Section 2.4.6), you would normally have to type

   ```
   if\textcompwordmark f
   ```

   By defining a command ("tight iff"),

   ```
   \newcommand{\tiff}{if\textcompwordmark f}
   ```

   you can type `\tiff` to get iff.
4. If you use the construct $D^{[2]} \times D^{[3]}$ often, you could introduce the `\DD` command,

   ```
   \newcommand{\DD}{D^{[2]}\times D^{[3]}}
   ```

   and then type `\DD` instead of `D^{[2]} \times D^{[3]}` throughout your document.
5. As you have learned in Section 2.4.4, to get a backslash in typewriter type you normally have to type

```
\texttt{\symbol{92}}
```

Introduce the \bsl command,

```
\newcommand{\bsl}{\texttt{\symbol{92}}}
```

and \bsl will typeset as \.

6. You can also use commands as a shorthand for text. For instance, if you use the phrase subdirectly irreducible many times in your document, you could define

   ```
   \newcommand{\si}{subdirectly irreducible}
   ```

   \si is now shorthand for subdirectly irreducible.

7. If you define

   ```
   \newcommand{\beq}{\begin{equation}}
   \newcommand{\eeq}{\end{equation}}
   ```

   then you can type an equation as

   ```
   \beq
      a = b + c^2
   \eeq
   ```

   Ⓐ Note that you cannot create such a shortcut for the AMS multiline math environments.

Rule ■ User-defined commands

1. Issue the \newcommand command.
2. In braces, type the name of your new command, including the backslash (\).
3. In a second pair of braces, define the new command.
4. Use your commands as \si\␣ \si{} before a space, as \si{} before an alphabetical character, and \si otherwise.

Example for Rule 4: The shorthand for the phrase subdirectly irreducible lattice is `\si{} lattice` or `\si\ lattice` and not `\si lattice`. Indeed, typesetting `\si lattice` will result in subdirectly irreduciblelattice. Curiously, by the first spacing rule (see Section 2.2.1), `\si  lattice` is not any better.

Using commands

It is good practice to place user-defined commands in the preamble of your document or in a command (style) file you load with a \usepackage command (see

Section 9.3); then you will always know where to look for the definition of such a command. An exception is the definition of a user-defined command that works only within a segment of the document: Delimit the segment with braces and define the user-defined command within those braces; see Section 2.3.2.

Tip If errors occur, reintroduce new user-defined commands one at a time, so you can isolate the one that causes the problem. LaTeX only checks whether the braces match when the command is defined. Other mistakes will not be found until your command is first used.

Be careful not to define a user-defined command with a name that is already in use. If you do, you will get an error message such as

```
! LaTeX Error: Command \la already defined.
```

To correct the error, replace the command name with a new one. On the other hand, if you need to replace an existing command, you will have to *redefine* it; see Section 9.1.5 for how to do so.

Tip Use spaces to make your source file more readable, but avoid them in definitions.

For example, type

```
$D^{ \langle 2 \rangle } + 2 = x^{ \mathbf{a} }$
```

This may help you see how the braces match, easily identify relations and operations, and so on. *Do not add these spaces in command definitions, however!* Doing so wastes memory and may result in unwanted spaces in your typeset document. You may start a new line to increase the readability of a command definition, provided that you terminate the line with `%`, as shown in the example on page 319.

Tip In the definition of a new command, command declarations need an extra pair of braces (see Section 2.3.3).

Suppose you want to define a command that typesets the warning: *Do not redefine this variable!* It is very easy to make the following mistake:

```
\newcommand{\Warn}{\em Do not redefine this variable!}
```

`\Warn` will typeset the warning emphasized, but everything that follows the warning will also be emphasized (more precisely, until the end of the `\Warn` command's scope). Indeed, `\Warn` is replaced by

```
\em Do not redefine this variable!
```

so the effect of `\em` goes beyond the sentence (to the closing brace of the scope of this `\Warn` command).

The correct definition is:

```
\newcommand{\Warn}{{\em Do not redefine this variable!}}
```

Optionally, you could use a command with an argument:

```
\newcommand{\Warn}{\emph{Do not redefine this variable!}}
```

Tip Commands that change font characteristics are good candidates for user-defined commands as shorthand (see Section 9.3).

However, try not to yield to the temptation to rename them to the old two-letter commands (see Section 2.6.9), for instance, `\textbf` to `\bf`. There are several reasons for not doing so:

- Some older packages or document classes may use the two-letter commands internally.
- Other people reading the source document may misunderstand what they do.
- The old `\bf` was a command declaration, whereas `\textbf` is a command with an argument; your redefined `\bf` command will not work the same way the old `\bf` command did.

The xspace *package*

Rule 4 (on page 313) is the source of many annoying problems in LaTeX. David Carlisle's xspace package (see Section 7.3.1) helps eliminate such problems. In your preamble, load the package with

```
\usepackage{xspace}
```

Whenever you define a command that may have such problems, add the `\xspace` command to the definition; for instance, define `\si` as

```
\newcommand{\si}{subdirectly irreducible\xspace}
```

All of the following will now typeset `subdirectly irreducible lattice` correctly:

```
\si\␣lattice
\si{}␣lattice
\si␣lattice
```

Note that `\xspace` does not add space if followed by a punctuation mark; so to get the lattice is subdirectly irreducible., type `the lattice is \si.`

Tip Be careful not to use \xspace twice in a definition.

For instance, if you define

```
\newcommand{\tex}{\TeX\xspace}
\newcommand{\bibtex}{\textsc{Bib}\kern-.1em\tex\xspace}% Bad!!!
```

then

```
\bibtex, followed by a comma
```

will be typeset as

BIBTEX , followed by a comma

The correct definitions are

```
\newcommand{\tex}{\TeX\xspace}
\newcommand{\bibtex}{\textsc{Bib}\kern-.1em\TeX\xspace}% Correct!
```

Ensuring math

The \ensuremath command is useful for defining commands that work both in text and math mode. Suppose you want to define a shorthand for $D^{\langle 2\rangle}$. If you define it as

```
\newcommand{\Ds}{D^{\langle2\rangle}}
```

then you can use the command in math mode, but not in text mode. If you define it as

```
\newcommand{\Ds}{$D^{\langle2\rangle}$}
```

then it works in text mode, but not in math mode. Instead, define this command as

```
\newcommand{\Ds}{\ensuremath{D^{\langle2\rangle}}}
```

so that \Ds will work correctly in both contexts.

This example also shows the editorial advantages of user-defined commands. Suppose a referee suggests that you change the notation to $D^{[2]}$. To carry out the change you only have to change one line:

```
\newcommand{\Ds}{\ensuremath{D^{[2]}}}
```

Directory structure

In Section 12.3.2 we discuss the `\graphicspath` command, which lists a series of subdirectories in which you can place your graphics files; this command tells the `\includegraphics` command where to look for files. For this book, I use

```
\graphicspath{%
{:chapters:pi:}{:chapters:sc:}{:chapters:mm:}%
{:chapters:ld:}{:chapters:amsp:}{:chapters:cust:}%
{:chapters:long:}{:chapters:web:}%
{:chapters:apt:}{:chapters:apo:}}%
```

which means that—on my Macintosh computer—the graphics files are in the `pi`, `sc`, `mm`, `ld`, `amsp`, `cust`, `long`, `web`, `apt`, and `apo` subdirectories of the `chapters` directory. The problem is that my editor works on a UNIX computer and, of course, the : reference to directories is Macintosh specific. So I introduced the user-defined command

```
\newcommand{\dirsep}{:} %Mac
\newcommand{\dirpref}{:} %Mac
```

and rewrote the `\graphicspath` command as

```
\graphicspath{{\dirpref chapters\dirsep pi\dirsep}%
{\dirpref chapters\dirsep sc\dirsep}%
                 ...
{\dirpref chapters\dirsep apt\dirsep}%
{\dirpref chapters\dirsep apo\dirsep}}
```

Now to work with my manuscript, my editor only has to change the definition of these two commands to

```
\newcommand{\dirsep}{/} %UNIX
\newcommand{\dirpref}{} %UNIX
```

On a PC, one would have to change it to

```
\newcommand{\dirsep}{\} %PC
\newcommand{\dirpref}{} %PC
```

My manuscript is now almost platform independent.

More examples of user-defined commands can be found in Section 9.3.

9.1.2 Arguments

Define

```
\newcommand{\fsq}{(f^2)^{[[\frac{A^2}{B-1}]]}}
```

Then `\fsq` typesets as $(f^2)^{[[\frac{A^2}{B-1}]]}$ in a math formula. If you want to use `\fsq` in math and also by itself in text, you can define it with `\ensuremath`, as

```
\newcommand{\fsq}{\ensuremath{(f^2)^{[[\frac{A^2}{B-1}]]}}}
```

However, if you use this construct for many functions, then you may need a generalized command, such as

```
\newcommand{\sq}[1]{\ensuremath{(#1^2)^{[[\frac{A^2}{B-1}]]}}}
```

Now `\sq{g}` typesets $(g^2)^{[[\frac{A^2}{B-1}]]}$. The form of this `\newcommand` is the same as before, except that after the name of the command (`{\sq}`) we specify the number of arguments in brackets (in this example we use `[1]`). We can now use `#1` in the definition of the command. When the command is invoked, the argument you provide replaces `#1` in the definition: Typing `$\sq{q}$` results in the formula $(q^2)^{[[\frac{A^2}{B-1}]]}$; while `$\sq{r}$` gives $(r^2)^{[[\frac{A^2}{B-1}]]}$. (Notice that these examples disrupt the normal spacing between lines—a practice to avoid!)

A user-defined command may have up to nine arguments.

Following are some simple examples of user-defined commands with arguments.

1. In the preamble of the source file for this book, I have defined

   ```
   \newcommand{\env}[1]{\textup{\texttt{#1}}}
   ```

   The `\env` command is used to typeset environment names. So the environment name `center` is typed as

   ```
   \env{center}
   ```

   Again the editorial advantage is obvious: If your editor wants the environment names to be emphasized, only one line in the book has to be changed to alter every occurrence of a typeset environment name:

   ```
   \newcommand{\env}[1]{\emph{#1}}
   ```

2. An argument (e.g., `#1`) may occur more than once in a definition. A natural example is provided by the `\index` command (see Section 11.1). Typically, if you wanted to include a phrase, say subdirectly irreducible lattice, in your index, you would have to type

```
this proves that $L$ is a subdirectly irreducible
lattice\index{subdirectly irreducible lattice}
```

You could instead define an "index entry" command such as

```
\newcommand{\ie}[1]{#1\index{#1}}
```

The argument of this command is a phrase to be both typeset and included in the index. Using this command, you can simply write

```
this proves that $L$ is a \ie{subdirectly irreducible lattice}
```

to do both.

If you wanted all such index entries to be typeset in italics, the definition of `\ie` becomes

```
\newcommand{\ie}[1]{#1\index{#1@\textit{#1}}}
```

in which `#1` occurs three times. (See Chapter 11 for more information about index commands.)

3. Let us define a command with three arguments for congruences:

```
\newcommand{\con}[3]{#1\equiv#2\pod{#3}}
```

Now you could type `$\con{a}{b}{\theta}$` to typeset the congruence $a \equiv b \pod{\theta}$. In Section 9.1.8, I present another command for typesetting congruences.

Ⓐ 4. In the `sampartu.tex` sample article (see Section 8.3), there are a lot of vectors with only one nonzero entry:

$$\langle \dots, 0, \dots, \overset{i}{d}, \dots, 0, \dots \rangle$$

the i above the d indicates that it is the ith component of the vector. Using the
Ⓐ amsmath package, a command producing this symbol can be defined as

```
\newcommand{\vct}[2]{\langle\dots,0,\dots,%
\overset{#1}{#2},\dots,0,\dots\rangle}
```

`\vct{i}{d}` in a math formula will now produce $\langle \dots, 0, \dots, \overset{i}{d}, \dots, 0, \dots \rangle$.

5. In the formula gallery (Section 1.5), Formula 20,

$$\mathbf{A} = \begin{pmatrix} \dfrac{\varphi \cdot X_{n,1}}{\varphi_1 \times \varepsilon_1} & (x + \varepsilon_2)^2 & \cdots & (x + \varepsilon_{n-1})^{n-1} & (x + \varepsilon_n)^n \\ \dfrac{\varphi \cdot X_{n,1}}{\varphi_2 \times \varepsilon_1} & \dfrac{\varphi \cdot X_{n,2}}{\varphi_2 \times \varepsilon_2} & \cdots & (x + \varepsilon_{n-1})^{n-1} & (x + \varepsilon_n)^n \\ \hdotsfor{5} \\ \dfrac{\varphi \cdot X_{n,1}}{\varphi_n \times \varepsilon_1} & \dfrac{\varphi \cdot X_{n,2}}{\varphi_n \times \varepsilon_2} & \cdots & \dfrac{\varphi \cdot X_{n,n-1}}{\varphi_n \times \varepsilon_{n-1}} & \dfrac{\varphi \cdot X_{n,n}}{\varphi_n \times \varepsilon_n} \end{pmatrix} + \mathbf{I}_n$$

is a good candidate for user-defined commands. By defining

```
\newcommand{\quot}[2]{%
   \dfrac{\varphi \cdot X_{n, #1}}%
   {\varphi_{#2}\times \varepsilon_{#1}}}
\newcommand{\exn}[1]{(x+\varepsilon_{#1})^{#1}}
```

the two new commands,

```
\[
   \quot{2}{3} \qquad \exn{n}
\]
```

are typeset as

$$\frac{\varphi \cdot X_{n,2}}{\varphi_3 \times \varepsilon_2} \qquad (x+\varepsilon_n)^n$$

With these user-defined commands, you can rewrite Formula 20 as follows:

```
\[
   \mathbf{A} =
   \begin{pmatrix}
      \quot{1}{1} & \exn{2} & \cdots & \exn{n - 1}
         & \exn{n}\\[10pt]
      \quot{1}{2} & \quot{2}{2} & \cdots & \exn{n - 1}
         &\exn{n}\\
      \hdotsfor{5}\\
      \quot{1}{n} & \quot{2}{n} & \cdots &
       \quot{n - 1}{n} & \quot{n}{n}
   \end{pmatrix}
    + \mathbf{I}_{n}
\]
```

Observe how much shorter this form is than the version shown on page 32 and how much easier it is to read.

9.1.3 Short arguments

We have discussed three ways of defining new commands:

`\newcommand \renewcommand \providecommand`

They define commands that can take any number of paragraphs as arguments. The $*$-ed versions of these commands define *short* commands (see Section 2.3.3) that take only one paragraph as an argument. For instance,

```
\newcommand{\LB}[1]{{\large\bfseries#1}}
```

makes its argument large and bold. So

```
\LB{First paragraph.

Second paragraph.}
```

prints

First paragraph.
Second paragraph.

as expected. On the other hand, if you define

```
\newcommand*{\LB}[1]{{\large\bfseries#1}}
```

and then attempt to typeset the previous example, you will get the error message

```
! Paragraph ended before \LB was complete.
<to be read again>
                   \par
```

Short commands are often preferable because of their improved error checking.

9.1.4 Optional arguments

You can define a command whose first argument is *optional*, and provide a *default value* for this optional argument. To illustrate, let us define the command

```
\newcommand{\Sum}{a_{1}+a_{2}+\cdots+a_{n}}
```

`$\Sum$` will now produce $a_1 + a_2 + \cdots + a_n$. Now we will change this command so that we can sum from 1 to m if necessary, with n as the default:

```
\newcommand{\NewSum}[1][n]{a_{1}+a_{2}+\cdots+a_{#1}}
```

`$\NewSum$` still produces $a_1 + a_2 + \cdots + a_n$, but `$\NewSum[m]$` typesets as $a_1 + a_2 + \cdots + a_m$.

A `\newcommand` may have up to nine arguments; *only the first* may be optional. The following command has two arguments, one optional:

```
\newcommand{\NNsum}[2][n]{#2_{1}+#2_{2}+\cdots+#2_{#1}}
```

With `\NNsum`,

`$\NNsum{x}$`	typesets as	$x_1 + x_2 + \cdots + x_n$
`$\NNsum{a}$`	typesets as	$a_1 + a_2 + \cdots + a_n$
`$\NNsum[i]{a}$`	typesets as	$a_1 + a_2 + \cdots + a_i$

9.1.5 Redefining commands

As you have seen on page 314, LaTeX makes sure that you do not inadvertently define a new command with the same name as an existing command. Assuming that you have already defined the \la command as in Section 9.1.1 (to typeset $\leftarrow$), to *redefine* \la, use \renewcommand:

```
\renewcommand{\la}{\Longleftarrow}
```

and now \la typesets as $\Longleftarrow$.

Tip Use the \renewcommand command sparingly and make sure that you understand the consequences of redefining an existing command. Redefining LaTeX (or Plain TeX) commands may cause LaTeX to behave in unexpected ways, or even crash.

Blind redefinition is the route to madness.

You can also use \renewcommand to redefine the way that commands defined by LaTeX or any package work. For instance, the AMS document classes (and the amsmath package) define an end of proof symbol: \qedsymbol. To change this symbol to the solid black square that some people prefer (defined in the amssymb package), issue the command Ⓐ

```
\renewcommand{\qedsymbol}{$\blacksquare$}
```

Even better, define

```
\renewcommand{\qedsymbol}{\ensuremath{\blacksquare}}
```

so that you can use \qedsymbol in both text and math mode. More on redefining names will be found in Section 9.1.6.

The \renewcommand command has a companion, the \providecommand command. If the command it defines has already been defined, the original command is left unchanged. Otherwise, the \providecommand command acts exactly like \newcommand. For instance, the \bysame command (see Section 6.5.1, page 257), is defined in some document classes as

```
\newcommand{\bysame}{\makebox[3em]{\hrulefill}\thinspace}
```

If you want to use the \bysame command in your bibliography and include this definition in your document, LaTeX will generate an error message when you typeset your document using a document class that already defines \bysame. If you define \bysame in your document using \providecommand,

```
\providecommand{\bysame}{\makebox[3em]{\hrulefill}\thinspace}
```

the \bysame command will typeset correctly whether or not the document class defines it.

9.1.6 Redefining names

A number of phrases, such as Table, List of Tables, Abstract, and so on, are inserted into your typeset document by LaTeX. You can easily change these phrases.

For instance, if you are preparing your manuscript for the proceedings of a meeting, and Abstract has to be changed to Summary, you can do so with

```
\renewcommand{\abstractname}{Summary}
```

In this book there are two indexes: the Quick Finder at the front of the book and the index proper at the end. At the beginning of the book, the command

```
\renewcommand{\indexname}{Quick Finder}
```

names the index Quick Finder, and before the main index, the command

```
\renewcommand{\indexname}{Index}
```

renames it to Index.

Ⓐ Table 9.1 lists the commands that define such names in various LaTeX and AMS document classes, along with their default definitions and the major document classes using the commands. It is easy to check whether your document class defines such a command: Open the appropriate cls file and search for the command.

If your document has photographs rather than figures, you could redefine

```
\renewcommand{\figurename}{Photograph}
\renewcommand{\listfigurename}{List of Photographs}
```

9.1.7 Showing the definitions of commands

If you are defining a new command with \newcommand and an error message informs you that the command name is already in use, then it may be useful to find out the existing definition of the command. For instance, the \vct command is defined in sampartu.tex (in the samples directory and in Section 8.3). It would have been natural to call this new command \vec, but if you did, you would get the error message

```
! LaTeX Error: Command \vec already defined.
```

You can find out the definition of the \vec command by getting into interactive mode (see Section 1.13.2) and typing

```
*\show \vec
```

LaTeX responds with

```
> \vec=macro:
->\mathaccent "017E .
<*> \show \vec
```

informing you that \vec is a command, and, specifically, a math accent (see Sections 4.9 and A.8.1). Now try \hangafter (see Section 2.7.2):

```
*\show \hangafter

> \hangafter=\hangafter.
<*> \show \hangafter
```

Command	Default Value	Defined by Document Class
\abstractname	Abstract	aa, ab, ap, a, p, r
\appendixname	Appendix	aa, ab, ap, a, b, r
\bibname	Bibliography	aa, ab, ap, b, r
\ccname	Cc	l
\chaptername	Chapter	ab, b, r
\contentsname	Contents	aa, ab, ap, a, b, r
\datename	Date	aa, ab, ap
\enclname	Enclosure	l
\figurename	Figure	aa, ab, ap, a, b, r
\headtoname	To	l
\indexname	Index	aa, ab, ap, a, b, r
\keywordsname	Key words and phrases	aa, ab, ap
\listfigurename	List of Figures	aa, ab, ap, a, b, r
\listtablename	List of Tables	aa, ab, ap, a, b, r
\pagename	Page	l, p
\partname	Part	aa, ab, ap, a, b, r
\proofname	Proof	aa, ab, ap
\refname	References	aa, ab, ap, a
\seename	see also.	aa, ab, ap
\subjclassname	1991 Mathematics Subject Classification	aa, ab, ap
\tablename	Table	aa, ab, ap, a, b, r

Document class codes: aa amsart, ab amsbook, ap amsproc, a article, b book, l letter, p proc, and r report

Table 9.1: Redefinable name commands in LaTeX.

The response indicates that \hangafter is a *primitive*, defined by TEX itself. Redefining a primitive is not a good idea.

Try one more command, \medskip (see Section 2.8.2), to find out how large it is:

```
*\show \medskip
> \medskip=macro:
->\vspace \medskipamount .
```

The third line indicates that the length is stored in \medskipamount. If we use \show to ask what \medskipamount is defined to be:

```
*\show \medskipamount
> \medskipamount=\skip14.
```

we do not get a very useful answer. \medskipamount is unlike most of the commands you have seen so far: It is a *length command* (see 9.5.2), containing the value of \medskip. You can ask for the value of a length command (or parameter) with the \showthe command:

```
*\showthe \medskipamount

> 6.0pt plus 2.0pt minus 2.0pt.
```

So \medskip is a vertical space of 6 points that can stretch or shrink by up to 2 points.

LATEX has many registers that contain numbers: counters containing integers (such as 3), dimensions (such as 10.2pt; we have already seen \textwidth as an example), and lengths (written in the form 6.0pt plus 2.0pt minus 2.0pt), also called *glues* or *rubber lengths* (see Sections 9.5.2 and C.2.2). Use the \showthe command to display the value for any of these commands.

You can also type the \show and \showthe commands directly into your document rather than go into interactive mode. LATEX's response will appear on your monitor (and will also be written into the log file).

9.1.8 Delimited commands

You can define new commands in TEX using characters and symbols to delimit arguments. Such *delimited commands* provide a way to write more readable source documents.

First we have to learn how to define a command using TEX's \def command: Type \def, followed by the new command name (not in braces), then the definition in braces. For example, the first command defined in Section 9.1.1,

```
\newcommand{\la}{\leftarrow}
```

could be typed

```
\def\la{\leftarrow}
```

TeX's `\def` command does not check whether a new command name was already in use, so `\def` behaves differently from `\newcommand`, `\renewcommand`, and `\providecommand` (see Section 9.1.5); if the `\la` command was defined previously, the original definition is overwritten.

Tip The responsibility of ensuring that your command name is unique is *yours* when you define a command using `\def`; LaTeX will not provide any protection. Use the techniques introduced in Section 9.1.7 to check a name before you define a command with `\def`.

Now we can start discussing delimited commands with a simple example, defining a command for vectors:

```
\def\vv<#1>{\langle#1\rangle}
```

Note that `\vv` is a command with one argument, `#1`. When invoked, it will typeset $\langle$, the argument, and then $\rangle$.

In the definition of `\vv`, the argument `#1` is delimited by `<` and `>`. When the command is invoked, the argument must be delimited the same way. So to typeset the vector $\langle a, b\rangle$, we invoke `\vv` with

```
\vv<a,b>
```

which looks somewhat like a vector, with the name `\vv` serving as an additional reminder.

You have to be careful with delimited commands because the math spacing rules (see Section 4.2) do not hold in either the definition or the invocation. So if there is a space before `#1`, in the definition of `\vv`,

```
\def\vv<␣#1>{\langle#1\rangle}
```

then `$\vv<a,b>$` will result in the error message

```
! Use of \vv doesn't match its definition.
l.12 $\vv<a
           ,b>$
```

which is clear enough. If the space is on the other side of the `#1`, as in

```
\def\vv<#1 >{\langle#1\rangle}
```

the error message is slightly more confusing:

```
Runaway argument?
a,b>$
! Paragraph ended before \vv was complete.
<to be read again>
                   \par
```

The moral is that if you use delimited commands, you must be very careful that each invocation completely matches the definition.

In Example 3 of Section 9.1.2, we introduced (using the amsmath package) a command with three arguments for typing congruences:

```
\newcommand{\con}[3]{#1\equiv#2\pod{#3}}
```

`$\con{a}{b}{\theta}$` produces $a \equiv b \ \ (\theta)$. This command saves a little typing, but it does not make the source file much easier to read; for that, we use a delimited command.

Let us redo the congruence example (using the amsmath package) with a delimited command:

```
\def\con#1=#2(#3){#1\equiv#2\pod{#3}}
```

so that `$\con a=b(\theta)$` produces $a \equiv b \ \ (\theta)$. In the source document, the formula `\con a=b(\theta)` looks a bit like the typeset congruence and is easier to read; I included this definition in the `lattice.sty` command file—see Section 9.3.

There is only one catch. Suppose you want to typeset the formula

$$x = a \equiv b \quad (\theta)$$

If you type `$\con x=a=b(\theta)$`, LaTeX will typeset it as $x \equiv a = b \ \ (\theta)$. Indeed, `x` is delimited on the right by the first `=`; hence, LaTeX believes that the first argument is `x`. The second argument is delimited by the first `=` and the left parenthesis; hence, the second argument is `a=b`. In such cases, you can help LaTeX find the correct first argument by enclosing it in braces:

```
$\con{x=a}=b(\theta)$
```

For our final example, recall that in Section 2.3.1 we discussed the problem of typing a command such as `\TeX` (the example there was `\today`) in the form `\TeX\␣` so that it will be typeset as a separate word. The problem is that if you type `\TeX` without the trailing `\␣`, TeX is merged with the next word, and no error message will warn you. One solution is to use a delimited command:

```
\def\tex/{\TeX}
```

Now to get TeX, type `\tex/`; if a space is needed after it, then type `\tex/␣`. If you forget the closing `/`, you will get an error message.

A better solution to this problem is the use of the xspace package (see Section 9.1.1); however, many documents use the delimited construct (including the AMS documentation), so you should be familiar with it.

9.2 User-defined environments

Most user-defined commands are new commands. *User-defined environments*, as a rule, modify existing environments. We will start with such user-defined environments (Section 9.2.1) and then proceed to investigate

- Arguments (Section 9.2.2)
- Optional arguments (Section 9.2.3)
- Short arguments (Section 9.2.4)

Finally, we will discuss defining brand-new environments (Section 9.2.5).

9.2.1 Modifying existing environments

If you do not like the name of the `proof` environment (defined in the AMS document classes and in the amsthm package) and would prefer to use the name `demo`, define Ⓐ

```
\newenvironment{demo}
   {\begin{proof}}
   {\end{proof}}
```

Note that this does not change the `proof` environment, only the way it is invoked.

To modify an existing environment, type

```
\newenvironment{name}
   {begin_text}
   {end_text}
```

where *begin_text* contains the command `\begin{`*oldname*`}` and *end_text* contains the command `\end{`*oldname*`}`, where *oldname* is the name of the modified environment.

Tip Do not give a new environment the name of an existing command or environment.

For instance, if you define

```
\newenvironment{parbox}
   {...}
   {...}
```

you will get the error message

```
! LaTeX Error: Command \parbox already defined.
```

If there is an error in such a user-defined environment, the message generated refers to the environment that was modified, not to your environment. For instance, if you misspell `proof` as `prof` when you define

```
\newenvironment{demo}
   {\begin{prof}}
   {\end{proof}}
```

then at the first use of the demo environment you will get the message

```
! LaTeX Error: Environment prof undefined.

l.13 \begin{demo}
```

If you define

```
\newenvironment{demo}
   {\begin{proof}\em}
   {\end{prof}}
```

at the first use of demo you will get the message

```
! LaTeX Error: \begin{proof} on input line 5 ended by \end{prof}.

l.14 \end{demo}
```

Here are three more examples of modified environments:

1. The command

   ```
   \newenvironment{demo}
      {\begin{proof}\em}
      {\end{proof}}
   ```

   defines a demo environment that typesets a proof emphasized. Note that the scope of \em is the demo environment.

Ⓐ

2. The following example uses the amsthm package to define an environment that takes an argument to be typeset as the name of a theorem:

   ```
   \newtheorem*{namedtheorem}{\theoremname}
   \newcommand{\theoremname}{testing}
   \newenvironment{named}[1]{\renewcommand{\theoremname}{#1}
      \begin{namedtheorem}}
      {\end{namedtheorem}}
   ```

   For example,

   ```
   \begin{named}{Name of the theorem}
    Body of theorem.
   \end{named}
   ```

produces

Name of the theorem. *Body of theorem.*

in the style appropriate for the \newtheorem* declaration. This type of environment is often used to produce an unnumbered **Main Theorem**—see Section 9.4 for this example—or when typesetting an article or book in which the theorem numbering is already fixed (for instance, when publishing a book in LaTeX that was originally typeset by another typesetting system).

3. In Sections 3.1.4 and 7.3.1, we came across the enumerate package, which allows you to customize the enumerate environment. If the enumerate package is loaded, you can invoke the enumerate environment with an optional argument specifying how the counter should be typeset. For instance, with the option [\upshape (i)],

```
\begin{enumerate}[\upshape (i)]
   \item First item\label{First}
\end{enumerate}
```

items will be numbered (i), (ii), and so on. You can use the AMS \eqref command (see Section 4.3) so that a reference to the item \eqref{First} will be typeset as (i); note that with \eqref references will be typeset upright even in emphasized text. Ⓐ

So now we define

```
\newenvironment{enumeratei}{\begin{enumerate}[\upshape (i)]}%
                                  {\end{enumerate}}
```

and we can invoke the new environment with (see Sections 9.3 and 9.4)

```
\begin{enumeratei}
   \item \label{ }
\end{enumerate}
```

4. You want to define an environment for displaying text that is numbered as an equation.[1] You might try

```
\newenvironment{texteqn}
   {\begin{equation} \begin{minipage}{0.9\linewidth}}
   {\end{minipage} \end{equation}}
```

But there is a problem: If you use this environment in the middle of a paragraph, an interword space will appear at the beginning of the first line after the environment. To remove this unwanted space, use the \ignorespacesafterend command, as in

```
\newenvironment{texteqn}
   {\begin{equation} \begin{minipage}{0.9\linewidth}}
   {\end{minipage} \end{equation} \ignorespacesafterend}
```

[1] This example is taken from *LaTeX News*, December, 1996.

Examples 2 and 3 are included in the `lattice.sty` command file; see Section 9.3. See the sample article, `sampartu.tex` in Section 9.4, for some instances of their use.

See Section 9.6.3 for custom lists as user-defined environments.

Redefine an existing environment with the `\renewenvironment` command, which is similar to the `\renewcommand` command (see Section 9.1.5).

9.2.2 *Arguments*

An environment defined by the `\newenvironment` command can take arguments, but they can only be used in the *begin_text* argument of the `\newenvironment` command. Here is a simple example: Define a `theorem` proclamation in the preamble (Section 3.4), and then define

```
\newenvironment{theoremRef}[1]
   {\begin{theorem}\label{T:#1}}
   {\end{theorem}}
```

(a theorem that can be Referenced), which is invoked with

```
\begin{theoremRef}{label}
```

The `theoremRef` environment is a modified environment: It is a `theorem` that can be referenced (with the `\ref` command, of course); it invokes the `theorem` environment and defines `T:`*label* to be the label for cross-referencing.

9.2.3 *Optional arguments with default values*

The first argument of an environment created with the `\newenvironment` command may be an *optional argument with a default value.* For example,

```
\newenvironment{narrow}[1][3in]
   {\noindent\begin{minipage}{#1}}
   {\end{minipage}}
```

creates a `narrow` environment; by default, it sets the body of the environment in a 3-inch wide box, with no indentation.

```
\begin{narrow}
   This text was typeset in a \texttt{narrow} environment,
   in a 3-inch wide box, with no indentation.
\end{narrow}
```

typesets as

This text was typeset in a `narrow` environment, in
a 3-inch wide box, with no indentation.

You can also give an optional argument to specify the width; for example,

```
\begin{narrow}[3.5in]
   This text was typeset in a \texttt{narrow} environment,
   in a 3 inch wide box, with no indentation.
\end{narrow}
```

which produces the following (false) statement:

This text was typeset in a `narrow` environment, in a 3 inch wide box, with no indentation.

9.2.4 *Short arguments*

We have discussed two commands that define new environments,

`\newenvironment` and `\renewenvironment`

These commands allow you to define environments whose arguments (*begin_text* and *end_text*; see page 328) can include any number of paragraphs. The *-ed versions of these commands define *short* environments whose arguments can only be one paragraph long. The body of the new environment, of course, can contain any number of paragraphs.

9.2.5 *Brand-new environments*

Some user-defined environments are not modifications of existing environments. I present two examples:

1. You remember that a newly defined command remains effective only within its scope (see Section 2.3.2). Now suppose that you want to make a change, say redefining a counter, for only a few paragraphs. You could simply place braces around these paragraphs (which are hard to keep track of) or you could define

   ```
   \newenvironment{exception}
      {\relax}
      {\relax}
   ```

   and then

   ```
   \begin{exception}
       new commands
       body
   \end{exception}
   ```

The environment stands out better than a pair of braces reminding you later about the special circumstances. The `\relax` command does nothing; it is customary to include a `\relax` command in such a definition to make it more readable.

2. Now we define a new environment that centers its body vertically on a new page:

```
\newenvironment{vcenterpage}
               {\newpage\vspace*{\fill}}
               {\vspace*{\fill}\par\pagebreak}
```

9.3 *A custom command file*

User-defined commands, of course, are a matter of individual need and taste. I have collected some commands for writing papers in lattice theory in the `lattice.sty` file (which you can find in the `samples` directory—see page 4). I hope that this model will help you to develop a command file of your own. Please remember that everything we will discuss in this section is a reflection of *my* work habits. Many experts disagree with one or another aspect of the things done in this section; take whatever suits your needs.

This file was named `lattice.sty` so that it can be loaded with `\usepackage` instead of `\input`. This mechanism has a number of advantages, as you will see.

Your command names should be mnemonic; if you cannot easily remember a command's name, rename it. The implication here is that your command file should not be very large unless you have an unusual ability to recall abbreviations.

Here are the first few lines of the `lattice.sty` command file:

```
% lattice.sty
% Command file for lattice papers
\NeedsTeXFormat{LaTeX2e}[1999/06/01]
\ProvidesPackage{lattice}[1999/10/19 Commands for lattices]
\RequirePackage{amsmath}
\RequirePackage{amssymb}
\RequirePackage{latexsym}
\RequirePackage{eucal}
\RequirePackage{verbatim}
\RequirePackage{enumerate}
\RequirePackage{xspace}
```

The line `\NeedsTeXFormat{LaTeX2e}[1999/06/01]` will give an error message if a document loading the lattice package is typeset with LaTeX 2.09 or with an older version of the standard LaTeX. The next line provides information that will be written in your log file.

The next seven lines declare what packages are required. If the packages have already been loaded, these lines will be ignored; otherwise, the missing packages will be loaded. A package loaded with `\RequirePackage` will not be reloaded.

Being able to specify the packages we need is one of the great advantages of command files. Whether I write a document using the `article` or `amsart` document class, the packages my command file loads, if necessary, will be there when I need them. 

You may want some justification for the inclusion of two of these packages in this list. The verbatim package is on the list so that I can use the `comment` environment to comment out large blocks of text (see Section 2.5), which is useful for finding errors and typesetting only parts of a longer document. The enumerate package is on the list because the `enumeratei` and `enumeratea` environments (defined in `lattice.sty`) require it.

If you start your article with

```
\documentclass{article}
\usepackage{lattice}
```

then the `\listfiles` command (see Section 1.13.3) will produce the following list when your document is typeset:

```
 *File List*
 article.cls    1999/01/07 v1.4a Standard LaTeX document class
  size10.clo    1999/01/07 v1.4a Standard LaTeX file
 lattice.sty    1999/10/19 Commands for lattices
 amsmath.sty    2000/01/06 v2.04 AMS math features
 amstext.sty    1999/11/15 v2.0
  amsgen.sty    1999/11/30 v2.0
  amsbsy.sty    1999/11/29 v1.2d
  amsopn.sty    1999/12/14 v2.01 operator names
 amssymb.sty    1996/11/03 v2.2b
amsfonts.sty    1997/09/17 v2.2e
latexsym.sty    1998/08/17 v2.2e Standard LaTeX package
   eucal.sty    1995/01/06 v2.2 Euler Script fonts
verbatim.sty    1997/04/30 v1.5k LaTeX2e package for verbatim
enumerate.sty   1999/03/05 v3.00 enumerate extensions
  xspace.sty    1997/10/13 v1.06 Space after command names
 ***********
```

After the introductory section dealing with LaTeX and the packages, we define some commands for writing about lattices and sets:

```
% Lattice operations
\newcommand{\jj}{\vee}% join
\newcommand{\mm}{\wedge}% meet
```

```
\newcommand{\JJ}{\bigvee}% big join
\newcommand{\MM}{\bigwedge}% big meet
\newcommand{\JJm}[2]{\JJ(\,#1\mid#2\,)}% big join with a middle
\newcommand{\MMm}[2]{\MM(\,#1\mid#2\,)}% big meet with a middle

% Set operations
\newcommand{\uu}{\cup}% union
\newcommand{\ii}{\cap}% intersection
\newcommand{\UU}{\bigcup}% big union
\newcommand{\II}{\bigcap}% big intersection
\newcommand{\UUm}[2]{\UU(\,#1\mid#2\,)}% big union with a middle
\newcommand{\IIm}[2]{\II(\,#1\mid#2\,)}
   % big intersection with a middle

% Sets
\newcommand{\ci}{\subseteq}% contained in with equality
\newcommand{\nc}{\nsubseteq}% not \ci
\newcommand{\sci}{\subset}% strictly contained in
\newcommand{\nci}{\nc}% not \ci
\newcommand{\ce}{\supseteq}% containing with equality
\newcommand{\nce}{\nsupseteq}% not \ce
\newcommand{\nin}{\notin}% not \in
\newcommand{\es}{\varnothing}% the empty set
\newcommand{\set}[1]{\{#1\}}% set
\newcommand{\setm}[2]{\{\,#1\mid#2\,\}}% set with a middle
\def\vv<#1>{\langle#1\rangle}% vector

% Partial ordering
\newcommand{\nle}{\nleq}% not \leq
```

So `$a \jj b$` produces $a \vee b$ and `$A \ci B$` produces $A \subseteq B$, and so on. Note that the original commands are not redefined; if a coauthor prefers `$a \vee b$` to `$a \jj b$`, the `\vee` command is still available.

The commands with a "middle" are exemplified by `\setm`:

```
$\setm{x \in R}{x^2 \leq 2}$
```

typesets as $\{\, x \in R \mid x^2 \leq 2 \,\}$.

Using the `\set` command, we can type the set $\{a, b\}$ as `$\set{a,b}$`, which is easier to read than `$\{a,b\}$`. Similarly, we type the vector $\langle a, b\rangle$ as `$\vv<a,b>$` (instead of `$\langle a,b\rangle$`), so it looks like a vector.

Next I map the Greek letters to shorter commands; for some, I prefer to use the variants, a matter of individual taste. (It is also a matter of taste whether or not to change the commands for the Greek letters at all, and how far one should go in abbreviating commonly used commands.)

```
% Greek letters
\newcommand{\ga}{\alpha}
\newcommand{\gb}{\beta}
\newcommand{\gc}{\chi}
\newcommand{\gd}{\delta}
\renewcommand{\ge}{\varepsilon}% use \geq for >=
\newcommand{\gf}{\varphi}
\renewcommand{\gg}{\gamma}% old use >>
\newcommand{\gh}{\eta}
\newcommand{\gi}{\iota}
\newcommand{\gk}{\kappa}
\newcommand{\gl}{\lambda}
\newcommand{\gm}{\mu}
\newcommand{\gn}{\nu}
\newcommand{\go}{\omega}
\newcommand{\gp}{\pi}
\newcommand{\gq}{\theta}
\newcommand{\gr}{\varrho}
\newcommand{\gs}{\sigma}
\newcommand{\gt}{\tau}
\newcommand{\gu}{\upsilon}
\newcommand{\gv}{\vartheta}
\newcommand{\gx}{\xi}
\newcommand{\gy}{\psi}
\newcommand{\gz}{\zeta}

\newcommand{\gG}{\Gamma}
\newcommand{\gD}{\Delta}
\newcommand{\gF}{\Phi}
\newcommand{\gL}{\Lambda}
\newcommand{\gO}{\Omega}
\newcommand{\gP}{\Pi}
\newcommand{\gQ}{\Theta}
\newcommand{\gS}{\Sigma}
\newcommand{\gU}{\Upsilon}
\newcommand{\gX}{\Xi}
\newcommand{\gY}{\Psi}
```

I also introduce some shorter names for text font commands by abbreviating `text` to `t` (so that `\textbf` becomes `\tbf`) and for math font commands by abbreviating `math` to `m` (so that `\mathbf` becomes `\mbf`).

```
% Font commands
\newcommand{\tbf}{\textbf}% text bold
\newcommand{\tit}{\textit}% text italic
\newcommand{\tsl}{\textsl}% text slanted
\newcommand{\tsc}{\textsc}% text small cap
\newcommand{\ttt}{\texttt}% text typewriter
\newcommand{\trm}{\textrm}% text roman
\newcommand{\tsf}{\textsf}% text sans serif
\newcommand{\tup}{\textup}% text upright

\newcommand{\mbf}{\mathbf}% math bold
\providecommand{\mit}{\mathit}% math italic
\newcommand{\msf}{\mathsf}% math sans serif
\newcommand{\mrm}{\mathrm}% math roman
\newcommand{\mtt}{\mathtt}% math typewriter
```

The math alphabets are invoked as commands with arguments: `\B` for bold, `\C` for calligraphic, `\D` for blackboard bold (double), and `\F` for fraktur (German Gothic) (see Section 4.13.2). Since I load the eucal package with no options, Euler Script substitutes for calligraphic (see Section 4.13.1). Notice that I can use both `\C` (calligraphic) and `\E` (Euler Script) for the Euler Script alphabet.

```
\newcommand{\B}{\boldsymbol}
   % Bold math symbol, use as \B{a}
\newcommand{\C}[1]{\mathcal{#1}}
   % Euler Script - only caps, use as \C{A}
\newcommand{\D}[1]{\mathbb{#1}}
   % Doubled - blackboard bold - only caps, use as \D{A}
\newcommand{\E}[1]{\mathcal{#1}}% same as \C
   % Euler Script - only caps, use as \E{A}
\newcommand{\F}[1]{\mathfrak{#1}}% Fraktur, use as \F{a}
```

Here are a few more commands and environments:

```
% Miscellaneous
\newcommand{\nl}{\newline}
\newcommand{\ol}[1]{\overline{#1}}
\newcommand{\ul}[1]{\underline{#1}}
\providecommand{\bysame}{\makebox[3em]{\hrulefill}\thinspace}
\newcommand{\q}{\quad}% spacing
\newcommand{\qq}{\qquad}% more spacing
\newcommand{\iso}{\cong}% isomorphic
\def\con#1=#2(#3){#1\equiv#2\pod{#3}}
   %congruence, use it as \con a=b(\theta)%
```

```
\newenvironment{enumeratei}{\begin{enumerate}[\upshape (i)]}%
                            {\end{enumerate}}
   %produces (i), (ii), etc. Cross-reference with \eqref.
\newenvironment{enumeratea}{\begin{enumerate}[\upshape (a)]}%
                            {\end{enumerate}}
   %produces (a), (b), etc. Cross-reference with \eqref.
\theoremstyle{plain}
\newtheorem*{namedtheorem}{\theoremname}
\newcommand{\theoremname}{testing}
\newenvironment{named}[1]{\renewcommand{\theoremname}{#1}
   \begin{namedtheorem}}
   {\end{namedtheorem}}
\endinput
```

The \con command was introduced in Section 9.1.8; the enumeratei environment was discussed in Section 9.2.1. The enumeratea environment is similar.

Finally, the named environment was introduced in Section 9.2.1.

This command file, like all command files, is terminated with the \endinput command. (In Section 12.3.1 we discuss the same rule for files that are \include-d and \input-ed.)

9.4 The sample article with user-defined commands

In this section, I present the sampartu.tex sample article (also in the samples directory), which is a rewrite of the sampart.tex sample article (see Section 8.3 and the samples directory) utilizing the user-defined commands collected in the command file lattice.sty (see Section 9.3 and the samples directory).

```
% Sample file: sampartu.tex
% The sample article for the amsart document class
% with user-defined commands and environments
% Typeset with LaTeX format

\documentclass{amsart}
\usepackage{amssymb,latexsym}
\usepackage{lattice}

\theoremstyle{plain}
\newtheorem{theorem}{Theorem}
\newtheorem{corollary}{Corollary}
\newtheorem{lemma}{Lemma}
\newtheorem{proposition}{Proposition}
```

```
\theoremstyle{definition}
\newtheorem{definition}{Definition}

\theoremstyle{remark}
\newtheorem*{notation}{Notation}

\numberwithin{equation}{section}

\newcommand{\Prodm}[2]{\gP(\,#1\mid#2\,)}
   % product with a middle
\newcommand{\Prodsm}[2]{\gP^{*}(\,#1\mid#2\,)}
   % product * with a middle
\newcommand{\vct}[2]{\vv<\dots,0,\dots,\overset{#1}{#2},%
\dots,0,\dots>}% special vector
\newcommand{\fp}{\F{p}}% Fraktur p
\newcommand{\Ds}{D^{\langle2\rangle}}

\begin{document}
\title[Complete-simple distributive lattices]
      {A construction of complete-simple\\
       distributive lattices}
\author{George~A. Menuhin}
\address{Computer Science Department\\
         University of Winnebago\\
         Winnebago, Minnesota 23714}
\email{menuhin@ccw.uwinnebago.edu}
\urladdr{http://math.uwinnebago.edu/homepages/menuhin/}
\thanks{Research supported by the NSF under grant number~23466.}
\keywords{Complete lattice, distributive lattice, complete
   congruence, congruence lattice}
\subjclass[2000]{Primary: 06B10; Secondary: 06D05}
\date{March 15, 2000}

\begin{abstract}
   In this note we prove that there exist \emph{complete-simple
   distributive lattices,} that is, complete distributive
   lattices in which there are only two complete congruences.
\end{abstract}
\maketitle

\section{Introduction}\label{S:intro}
In this note we prove the following result:
```

```
\begin{named}{Main Theorem}
   There exists an infinite complete distributive lattice
   $K$ with only the two trivial complete congruence relations.
\end{named}

\section{The $\Ds$ construction}\label{S:Ds}
For the basic notation in lattice theory and universal algebra,
see Ferenc~R. Richardson~\cite{fR82} and George~A.
Menuhin~\cite{gM68}. We start with some definitions:

\begin{definition}\label{D:prime}
   Let $V$ be a complete lattice, and let $\fp = [u, v]$ be
   an interval of $V$.  Then $\fp$ is called
   \emph{complete-prime} if the following three conditions
   are satisfied:
   \begin{enumeratei}
      \item $u$ is meet-irreducible but $u$ is \emph{not}
         completely meet-irreducible;\label{m-i}
      \item $v$ is join-irreducible but $v$ is \emph{not}
         completely join-irreducible;\label{j-i}
      \item $[u, v]$ is a complete-simple lattice.\label{c-s}
   \end{enumeratei}
\end{definition}

Now we prove the following result:

\begin{lemma}\label{L:ds}
   Let $D$ be a complete distributive lattice satisfying
   conditions \eqref{m-i} and~\eqref{j-i}.
   Then $\Ds$ is a sublattice of $D^{2}$; hence $\Ds$ is
   a lattice, and $\Ds$ is a complete distributive lattice
   satisfying conditions \eqref{m-i} and~\eqref{j-i}.
\end{lemma}

\begin{proof}
   By conditions~\eqref{m-i} and \eqref{j-i}, $\Ds$ is a
   sublattice of $D^{2}$.  Hence, $\Ds$ is a lattice.

   Since $\Ds$ is a sublattice of a distributive lattice,
   $\Ds$ is a distributive lattice.  Using the characterization
   of standard ideals in Ernest~T. Moynahan~\cite{eM57},
   $\Ds$ has a zero and a unit element, namely,
```

```
   $\vv<0, 0>$ and $\vv<1, 1>$.  To show that $\Ds$ is
   complete, let $\es \ne A \ci \Ds$, and let $a = \JJ A$
   in $D^{2}$.  If $a \in \Ds$, then
   $a = \JJ A$ in $\Ds$; otherwise, $a$ is of the form
   $\vv<b, 1>$ for some $b \in D$ with $b < 1$.  Now
   $\JJ A = \vv<1, 1>$ in $D^{2}$, and
   the dual argument shows that $\MM A$ also exists in
   $D^{2}$.  Hence $D$ is complete. Conditions \eqref{m-i}
   and~\eqref{j-i} are obvious for $\Ds$.
\end{proof}

\begin{corollary}\label{C:prime}
   If $D$ is complete-prime, then so is $\Ds$.
\end{corollary}

The motivation for the following result comes from Soo-Key
Foo~\cite{sF90}.

\begin{lemma}\label{L:ccr}
   Let $\gQ$ be a complete congruence relation of $\Ds$ such
   that
   \begin{equation}\label{E:rigid}
      \con \vv<1, d>=\vv<1, 1>(\gQ),
   \end{equation}
   for some $d \in D$ with $d < 1$. Then $\gQ = \gi$.
\end{lemma}

\begin{proof}
   Let $\gQ$ be a complete congruence relation of $\Ds$
   satisfying \eqref{E:rigid}. Then $\gQ = \gi$.
\end{proof}

\section{The $\gP^{*}$ construction}\label{S:P*}
The following construction is crucial to our proof of the
Main~Theorem:

\begin{definition}\label{D:P*}
   Let $D_{i}$, for $i \in I$, be complete distributive
   lattices satisfying condition~\eqref{j-i}.  Their $\gP^{*}$
   product is defined as follows:
```

```
  \[
    \Prodsm{ D_{i} }{i \in I} = \Prodm{ D_{i}^{-} }{i \in I}+1;
  \]
  that is, $\Prodsm{ D_{i} }{i \in I}$ is
  $\Prodm{ D_{i}^{-} }{i \in I}$ with a new unit element.
\end{definition}

\begin{notation}
  If $i \in I$ and $d \in D_{i}^{-}$, then
  \[
    \vct{i}{d}
  \]
  is the element of $\Prodsm{ D_{i} }{i \in I}$ whose
  $i$-th component is $d$ and all the other
  components are $0$.
\end{notation}

See also Ernest~T. Moynahan~\cite{eM57a}.  Next we verify:

\begin{theorem}\label{T:P*}
  Let $D_{i}$, for $i \in I$, be complete distributive
  lattices satisfying condition~\eqref{j-i}.  Let $\gQ$
  be a complete congruence relation on
  $\Prodsm{ D_{i} }{i \in I}$.  If there exist
  $i \in I$ and $d \in D_{i}$ with $d < 1_{i}$ such
  that for all $d \leq c < 1_{i}$,
  \begin{equation}\label{E:cong1}
    \con\vct{i}{d}=\vct{i}{c}(\gQ),
  \end{equation}
  then $\gQ = \gi$.
\end{theorem}

\begin{proof}
  Since
  \begin{equation}\label{E:cong2}
    \con\vct{i}{d}=\vct{i}{c}(\gQ),
  \end{equation}
  and $\gQ$ is a complete congruence relation, it follows
  from condition~\eqref{c-s} that
  \begin{equation}\label{E:cong}
  \begin{split}
     &\langle \dots, \overset{i}{d}, \dots, 0,
```

```
      \dots \rangle\\
     &\equiv \bigvee ( \langle \dots, 0, \dots,
      \overset{i}{c},\dots, 0,\dots \rangle \mid d \leq c < 1)
       \equiv 1 \pmod{\Theta}.
   \end{split}
   \end{equation}

   Let $j \in I$, for $j \neq i$, and let
   $a \in D_{j}^{-}$.  Meeting both sides of the congruence
   \eqref{E:cong} with $\vct{j}{a}$, we obtain
   \begin{equation}\label{E:comp}
      \begin{split}
         0 &= \vct{i}{d} \mm \vct{j}{a}\\
           &\equiv \vct{j}{a}\pod{\gQ}.
     \end{split}
   \end{equation}
  Using the completeness of $\gQ$ and \eqref{E:comp}, we get:
   \begin{equation}\label{E:cong3}
       \con{0=\JJm{ \vct{j}{a} }{ a \in D_{j}^{-} }}={1}(\gQ),
   \end{equation}
   hence $\gQ = \gi$.
\end{proof}

\begin{theorem}\label{T:P*a}
   Let $D_{i}$, for $i \in I$, be complete distributive
   lattices satisfying
   conditions \eqref{j-i} and~\eqref{c-s}.  Then
   $\Prodsm{ D_{i} }{i \in I}$ also satisfies
   conditions~\eqref{j-i} and \eqref{c-s}.
\end{theorem}

\begin{proof}
   Let $\gQ$ be a complete congruence on
   $\Prodsm{ D_{i} }{i \in I}$. Let $i \in I$.  Define
   \begin{equation}\label{E:dihat}
      \widehat{D}_{i} = \setm{ \vct{i}{d} }{ d \in D_{i}^{-} }
       \uu \set{1}.
   \end{equation}
   Then $\widehat{D}_{i}$ is a complete sublattice of
   $\Prodsm{ D_{i} }{i \in I}$, and $\widehat{D}_{i}$
   is isomorphic to $D_{i}$.  Let $\gQ_{i}$ be the
   restriction of $\gQ$ to $\widehat{D}_{i}$.  Since
```

```
   $D_{i}$ is complete-simple, so is $\widehat{D}_{i}$,
   hence $\gQ_{i}$ is $\go$ or $\gi$.  If $\gQ_{i} = \go$
   for all $i \in I$, then $\gQ = \go$.
   If there is an $i \in I$, such that $\gQ_{i} = \gi$,
   then $\con0=1(\gQ)$, and hence $\gQ = \gi$.
\end{proof}

The Main Theorem follows easily from Theorems~\ref{T:P*} and
\ref{T:P*a}.

\begin{thebibliography}{9}

   \bibitem{sF90}
      Soo-Key Foo, \emph{Lattice Constructions}, Ph.D. thesis,
      University of Winnebago, Winnebago, MN, December, 1990.

   \bibitem{gM68}
      George~A. Menuhin, \emph{Universal Algebra}, D.~van
      Nostrand, Princeton, 1968.

   \bibitem{eM57}
      Ernest~T. Moynahan, \emph{On a problem of M. Stone},
      Acta Math. Acad. Sci. Hungar. \tbf{8} (1957), 455--460.

   \bibitem{eM57a}
     \bysame, \emph{Ideals and congruence relations in
     lattices}.~II, Magyar Tud. Akad. Mat. Fiz. Oszt. K\"{o}zl.
     \tbf{9} (1957), 417--434  (Hungarian).

   \bibitem{fR82}
      Ferenc~R. Richardson, \emph{General Lattice Theory}, Mir,
      Moscow, expanded and revised ed., 1982 (Russian).

\end{thebibliography}
\end{document}
```

9.5 Numbering and measuring

LaTeX stores integers in *counters;* for example, the `section` counter contains the current section number. Distance measurements are saved in *length commands;* for instance, the `\textwidth` command contains the width of the text (for this book, `\textwidth` is set to 345.0 points).

equation	part	enumi
figure	chapter	enumii
footnote	section	enumiii
mpfootnote	subsection	enumiv
page	subsubsection	
table	paragraph	
	subparagraph	

Table 9.2: Standard LaTeX counters.

In this section, we will take a closer look at counters and length commands.

9.5.1 *Counters*

Counters may be defined by LaTeX, by document classes, by packages, or by the user.

Standard LaTeX counters

LaTeX automatically generates numbers for equations, sections, theorems, and so on. Each such number is stored in a *counter*. Table 9.2 shows the standard LaTeX counters; their names are (more or less) self-explanatory. In addition, for every proclamation *name*, there is a matching counter called `name` (see Section 3.4).

Setting counters

The command for setting a counter's value is `\setcounter`. When LaTeX generates a number, it first increments the appropriate counter; so if you want the next chapter to be numbered 3, you should set the `chapter` counter to 2 by typing

```
\setcounter{chapter}{2}
```

before the `\chapter` command. The only exception to this rule is the page number, which is first used to number the current page, and then incremented. If you wanted to set the current page number to 63, you would include the command

```
\setcounter{page}{63}
```

somewhere in the page.

LaTeX initializes and increments its standard counters automatically. Sometimes you may want to manipulate them yourself. For example, to typeset only `ch3.tex`, the third chapter of your book, start with

```
\setcounter{chapter}{2}
\include{ch3}
```

and when `ch3.tex` is typeset, the chapter (and any cross-references within it) will be properly numbered. You can also type

```
\setcounter{page}{63}
```

if the first page of this chapter is supposed to be 63. (Of course, the preferred way of typesetting parts of a larger document is with the `\includeonly` command; see Section 12.3.1.)

Tip If you need to manipulate counters, always look for solutions in which LaTeX will do the work for you.

Defining new counters

You can define your own counters. For example,

```
\newcounter{numb}
```

makes `numb` a new counter. In the definition, you can use an optional argument, the name of another counter:

```
\newcounter{numb}[hlnumb]
```

which will automatically reset `numb` to `0` whenever `hlnumb` changes value. This command has the same form as the command LaTeX uses internally for tasks such as numbering theorems and subsections within sections.

Rule ■ New counters

New counters should be defined in the preamble of the document; they cannot be defined in a file read in with an `\include` command (see Section 12.3.1).

Let us suppose that you define a new counter, `numb`, in `ch5.tex`, which is made part of your whole document with an `\include` command. When you typeset your document with an `\includeonly` command that does not include `ch5.tex`, you will get an error message, such as

```
! LaTeX Error: No counter 'numb' defined.
```

Counter styles

The value of the counter `numb` can be displayed in the typeset document with the command

Style	Command	Sample
Arabic	`\arabic{counter}`	1, 2, ...
Lowercase Roman	`\roman{counter}`	i, ii, ...
Uppercase Roman	`\Roman{counter}`	I, II, ...
Lowercase Letters	`\alph{counter}`	a, b, ..., z
Uppercase Letters	`\Alph{counter}`	A, B, ..., Z

Table 9.3: Counter styles.

```
\thenumb
```

If you want to change numb's appearance when typeset, issue the command

```
\renewcommand{\thenumb}{new_format}
```

where *new_format* specifies the new format.

A counter can be displayed in one of five styles, as shown in Table 9.3. The default style is arabic. Here is an example:

```
\renewcommand{\thechapter}{\arabic{chapter}}
\renewcommand{\thesection}{\thechapter-\arabic{section}}
\renewcommand{\thesubsection}%
    {\thechapter-\arabic{section}.\arabic{subsection}}
```

With these definitions, Subsection 2 of Section 1 of Chapter 3 would be numbered in the form 3-1.2.

The \pagenumbering command is a shorthand method for setting the page numbering in a given style. For instance, \pagenumbering{roman} numbers pages as i, ii, and so on.

Ⓐ The subequations environment (in the amsmath package; see Section 4.15) uses the counter parentequation. To change the format of the equation numbers from (2a), (2b), and so forth, to (2i), (2ii), and so on, type the following line inside the subequations environment

```
\renewcommand{\theequation}{\theparentequation\roman{equation}}
```

If you wanted the numbers to look like (2.i), (2.ii), and so on, you would type

```
\renewcommand{\theequation}{\theparentequation.\roman{equation}}
```

Counter arithmetic

The \stepcounter{hlnumb} command increments the counter hlnumb and sets all the counters that were defined with the optional argument hlnumb to 0. The variant `\refstepcounter{hlnumb}` does the same, and also sets the value for the next `\label` command; the previous example would cause the next `\label` to refer to the counter `hlnumb`.

You can do a little more arithmetic with the command

```
\addtocounter{counter}{n}
```

where *n* is an integer; for example,

```
\setcounter{numb}{5}
\addtocounter{numb}{2}
```

will set `numb` to 7.

The value stored in a counter can be accessed using the `\value` command, which is mostly used with the `\setcounter` or `\addtocounter` commands. For instance, you can set one counter, `numb`, equal to the value of another counter, `oldnumb`, by typing

```
\setcounter{numb}{\value{oldnumb}}
```

Here is a typical example of counter manipulation:

You might want a theorem (in a `theorem` environment) to be followed by several corollaries (each in a `corollary` environment) always starting with Corollary 1. In other words, Theorem 1 should be followed by Corollary 1, Corollary 2, and so forth. By default, LaTeX numbers the next corollary as Corollary 3, even if it follows a new theorem. To tell LaTeX to start numbering the corollaries from 1 again, you could put a

```
\setcounter{corollary}{0}
```

command after each theorem. But such a process is error-prone, and goes against the spirit behind LaTeX.

Instead, follow my advice on page 346, and get LaTeX do the work for you. In the preamble, type the proclamations

```
\newtheorem{theorem}{Theorem}
\newtheorem{corollary}{Corollary}[theorem]
```

We are almost there: Theorem 1 will now be followed by Corollary 1.1 and Corollary 1.2; Theorem 2 by Corollary 2.1. If we redefine `\thecorollary` (see Section 9.5.1),

```
\renewcommand{\thecorollary}{\arabic{corollary}}
```

Theorem 1 will be followed by Corollary 1 and Corollary 2, and Theorem 2 will also be followed by Corollary 1.

If you need to perform more complicated arithmetic with counters, use Kresten K. Thorup and Frank Jensen's calc package (see Section 7.3.1). This package is discussed in detail in Section A.4 of *The LaTeX Companion* [17].

Two special counters

The `secnumdepth` and `tocdepth` counters control which sectional units are numbered and which are listed in the table of contents, respectively. For example,

```
\setcounter{secnumdepth}{2}
```

sets `secnumdepth` to 2. As a result, chapters (if they are present in the document class), sections, and subsections are numbered, but subsubsections are not. This command must be placed in the preamble of the document.

9.5.2 *Length commands*

While a counter contains integers, a length command contains a *real number* and a *dimensional unit.*

LaTeX recognizes many different dimensional units; here we list five *absolute* units,

- `cm` centimeter
- `in` inch
- `pc` pica (`1 pc = 12 pt`)
- `pt` point (`1 in = 72.27 pt`)
- `mm` millimeter

and two *relative* units,

- `em`, approximately the width of the letter M in the current font
- `ex`, approximately the height of the letter x in the current font

LaTeX defines many length commands. For instance, Section 4.1 of *The LaTeX Companion* [17] lists 17 length commands for page layout alone (you can find some of them in Figure 6.5); a list environment sets about a dozen additional length commands (see Figure 9.2). Length commands are defined for almost every aspect of LaTeX's work, including displayed math environments—a complete list would probably contain a few hundred. Many are listed in Leslie Lamport's *LaTeX: A Document Preparation System* [39] and in *The LaTeX Companion* [17]; Ⓐ many more are hidden in packages such as amsmath.

The most common length commands are `\parindent` (the amount of indentation at the beginning of a paragraph), `\parskip` (the extra vertical space inserted between paragraphs—normally set to zero), and `\textwidth` (the width of the text on a page). A more esoteric example is `\marginparpush` (the minimal vertical space between two marginal notes). Luckily, you do not have to be familiar with many length commands because LaTeX and the document class set them for you.

Defining new length commands

You can define your own length commands. For example,

```
\newlength{\mylength}
```

makes `\mylength` a new length command with a value of 0 points. Note that while you have to type

```
\newcounter{numb}
```

to get a new counter, typing

```
\newlength{mylength}
```

(leaving out the \) results in an error message such as

```
! Missing control sequence inserted.
<inserted text>
                \inaccessible
l.3 \newlength{mylength}
```

Setting length

The `\setlength` command sets (or resets) the value of a length command. So

```
\setlength{\textwidth}{3in}
```

will create a very narrow page. The first argument of `\setlength` must be a length command, not simply the command name; that is,

```
\setlength{textwidth}{3in} % Bad
```

is incorrect. The second argument of `\setlength` must be a real number with a dimensional unit, for instance, `3in`, and *not simply a real number;* in other words,

```
\setlength{\textwidth}{3} % Bad
```

is also incorrect.

Tip A common mistake is to type a command such as

```
\setlength{\marginpar}{0}
```

Instead, type

```
\setlength{\marginpar}{0pt}
```

Always be sure to include a dimensional unit.

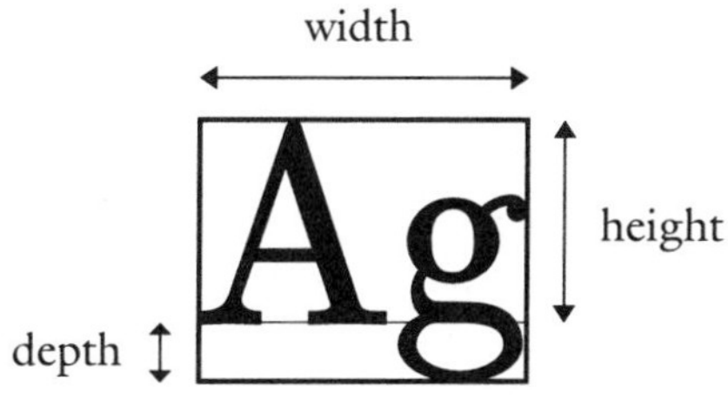

Figure 9.1: The measurements of a box.

The \addtolength command adds a quantity to the value of a length command. For instance,

```
\addtolength{\textwidth}{-10pt}
```

narrows the page width by 10 points.

If you define

```
\newlength{\shorterlength}
\setlength{\shorterlength}{\mylength}
\addtolength{\shorterlength}{-.5in}
```

then \parbox{\shorterlength}{...} will always typeset its second argument in a box 1/2 inch narrower than the parboxes set to be \mylength wide.

When LaTeX typesets some text (or math), it creates a box. Three measurements are used to describe the size of the box: the width, the height (from the baseline to the top), and the depth (from the baseline to the bottom), as illustrated in Figure 9.1. For instance, the box "aa" has a width of 10.00003 pt, a height of 4.30554 pt, and a depth of 0 pt. The box "ag" has the same width and height, but a depth of 1.94444 pt. The box "Ag" (see Figure 9.1) has a width of 12.50003 pt, a height of 6.83331 pt, and a depth of 1.94444 pt. The commands

```
\settowidth
\settoheight
\settodepth
```

each take two arguments: The first argument is a length command, the second is text (or math) to be measured by LaTeX. The corresponding measurement of the box in which the second argument is typeset is assigned to the length command in the first argument. For example, if \mylength is a length command, then

```
\settowidth{\mylength}{Ag}
```

assigns 12.50003 pt to \mylength. It should be clear from this example how the \phantom command (see Section 2.8.1) can be defined using \settowidth.

To perform more complicated arithmetic with length commands, use Kresten K. Thorup and Frank Jensen's calc package (see Section 7.3.1 in this book and Section A.4 in *The LaTeX Companion* [17]).

Rubber lengths

In addition to rigid lengths, such as `3in`, LaTeX can also set *rubber lengths*, that is, lengths that are allowed to stretch and shrink. Here is an example:

```
\setlength{\stretchspace}{3in plus 10pt minus 8pt}
```

Assuming that `\stretchspace` is a length command, this command assigns it a value of 3 inches that can stretch by 10 points or shrink by 8 points, if necessary. So a box of width `\stretchspace` will be 3 inches wide, plus up to 10 points, or minus up to 8 points.

Stretchable vertical spaces are often used before and after displayed text environments; LaTeX adjusts these spaces to make the page look balanced. An example can be found in Section 9.1.7: `\medskipamount` is defined as

```
6.0pt plus 2.0pt minus 2.0pt
```

See Section 9.6.3 for more examples.

9.6 *Custom lists*

Although there are three ready-made list environments provided by LaTeX (see Section 3.1), it is often necessary to create one of your own using LaTeX's `list` environment. In fact, LaTeX itself uses the `list` environment to define many of its standard environments, including

- The three list environments (Section 3.1)
- The `quote`, `quotation`, and `verse` environments (Section 3.3)
- Proclamations (Section 3.4)
- The style environments `center`, `flushleft`, and `flushright` (Section 3.8)
- The `thebibliography` environment (Section 6.5.1)
- The `theindex` environment (Section 6.5.2)

9.6.1 *Length commands for the* `list` *environment*

The general layout of a list is shown in Figure 9.2: It consists of six horizontal measurements and three vertical measurements that LaTeX calculates using six length commands for the horizontal measurements and four length commands for the vertical measurements. I will now list these length commands:

Vertical length commands

`\topsep` is most of the vertical space between the first item and the preceding text, and also between the last item and the following text. This space also

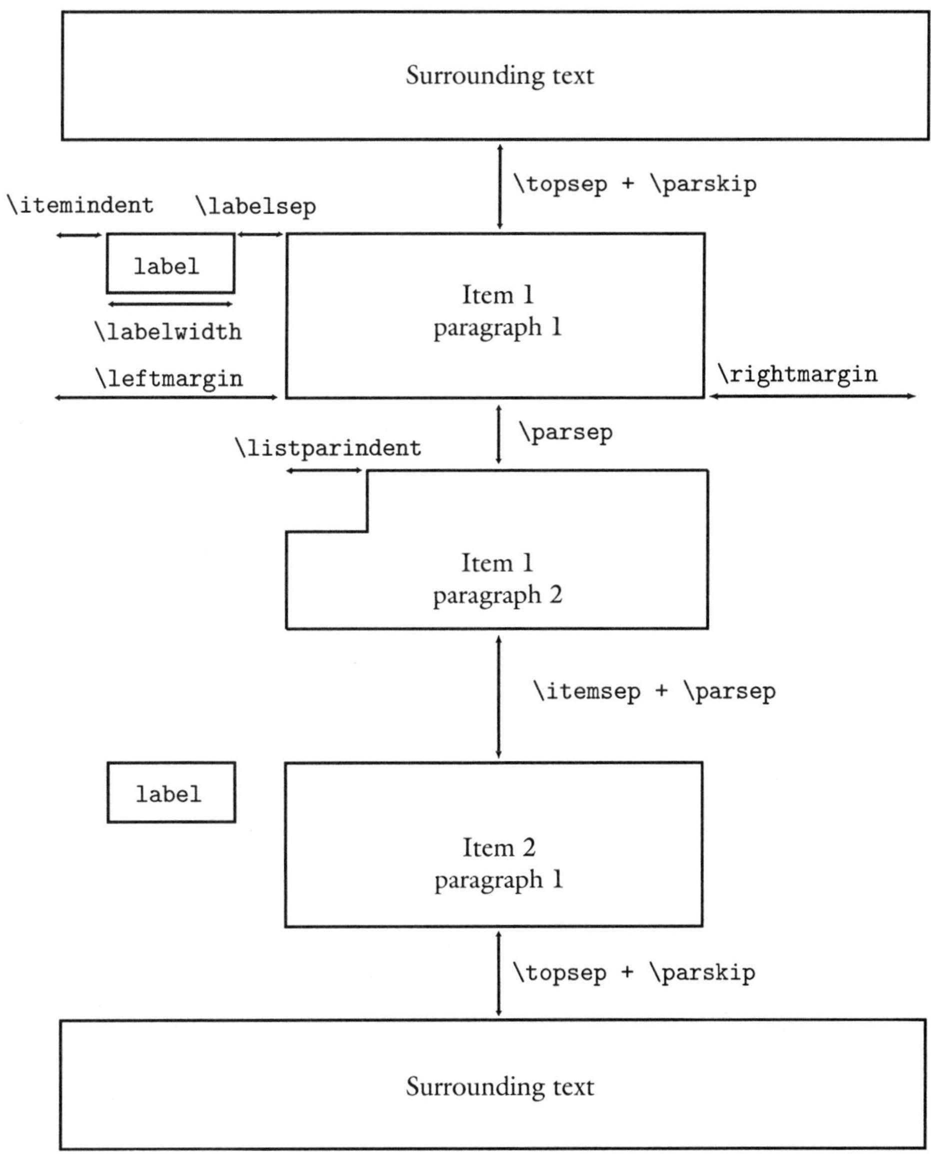

Figure 9.2: The layout of a custom list.

includes \parskip (the extra vertical space inserted between paragraphs—normally set to zero) and, optionally, \partopsep (provided that the list environment starts a new paragraph).

\parsep is the space between paragraphs of the same item.

\itemsep is the space between items. Like \topsep, the actual gap is the sum of \itemsep and \parsep.

All of these vertical length commands are rubber lengths (see Section 9.5.2).

Horizontal length commands

By default, the margins of a list environment are the same as the margins of the surrounding text. If the list is nested within a list, the margins are wider (the text is narrower).

The \leftmargin and \rightmargin length commands specify the distance between the edge of the item box and the left and right margins of the page.

The label is the text provided by the (optional) argument of an \item command or provided as a default in the definition of the list environment; it is typeset in a box of width \labelwidth, which is indented \itemindent units from the left margin, and separated by a space of \labelsep units from the text box. If the label is too wide to fit in the box, it will be typeset at its full natural width, and the first line in the text box will be indented.

The second and subsequent paragraphs of an item will be typeset with their first lines indented by \listparindent units.

9.6.2 *The* list *environment*

You create a custom list with the list environment, which is invoked using the following form:

```
\begin{list}{default_label}{declarations}
   \item item1
   \item item2
   ...
\end{list}
```

The arguments are

- *default_label*, the label for any items that do not specify their own (similar to the optional argument of the \item command)
- *declarations*, the vertical and horizontal length commands (and any other required parameters) for the list

Here is a very simple example:

Here are the most important LaTeX rules about spaces in text, sentences, and paragraphs:

- ♢ **Rule 1:** Two or more spaces in text are the same as one.
- ♢ **Rule 2:** A blank line (that is, two end-of-line characters separated only by blanks and tabs) indicates the end of a paragraph.

Rules 1 and 2 make typing and copying very convenient.

I have used the ♢ math symbol (`$\diamondsuit$`) as a default label, and I set the item box 0.5 inch from either margin. So this example is typed as follows:

```
\noindent Here are the most important \LaTeX\ rules about
spaces in text, sentences, and paragraphs:
\begin{list}{$\diamondsuit$}{\setlength{\leftmargin}{.5in}
                              \setlength{\rightmargin}{.5in}}
   \item \textbf{Rule 1:} Two or more spaces in text are
    the same as one.
   \item \textbf{Rule 2:} A blank line (that is, two end-of-line
    characters separated only by blanks and tabs) indicates
    the end of a paragraph.
\end{list}
Rules 1 and~2 make typing and copying very convenient.
```

Here is a second variant:

Here are the most important LaTeX rules about spaces in text, sentences, and paragraphs:

Rule 1: Two or more spaces in text are the same as one.

Rule 2: A blank line (that is, two end-of-line characters separated only by blanks and tabs) indicates the end of a paragraph.

Rules 1 and 2 make typing and copying very convenient.

In this example, I dropped the optional *default_label* and typed **Rule 1:** and **Rule 2:** as (optional) arguments of the `\item` commands:

```
\noindent Here are the most important \LaTeX\ rules about
spaces in text, sentences, and paragraphs:
\begin{list}{}{\setlength{\leftmargin}{.5in}
```

```
               \setlength{\rightmargin}{.5in}}
   \item[\textbf{Rule 1:}] Two or more spaces in text are
    the same as one.
   \item[\textbf{Rule 2:}] A blank line (that is, two
    end-of-line characters separated only by blanks and tabs)
    indicates the end of a paragraph.
\end{list}
Rules 1 and~2 make typing and copying very convenient.
```

For further simple examples, you can look at various document class files to see how standard environments such as verse, quote, and so on, are defined.

Using counters

It is not very LATEX-like to provide the numbers for the rules in the examples above; it would be more logical for LATEX to do the numbering. The following is a more LATEX-like coding of the second example:

```
\noindent Here are the most important \LaTeX\ rules about
spaces in text, sentences, and paragraphs:
\newcounter{spacerule}
\begin{list}{\textbf{Rule \arabic{spacerule}:}}
            {\setlength{\leftmargin}{.5in}
             \setlength{\rightmargin}{.5in}
             \usecounter{spacerule}}
   \item Two or more spaces in text are the same
    as one.\label{Li:Twoor}
   \item A blank line (that is, two end-of-line
    characters separated only by blanks and tabs) indicates
    the end of a paragraph.\label{Li:blankline}
\end{list}
Rules \ref{Li:Twoor} and~\ref{Li:blankline} make typing
and copying very convenient.
```

Note that

1. I declared the counter (before the list environment) with the line

   ```
   \newcounter{spacerule}
   ```

2. I defined the *default_label* as

   ```
   \textbf{Rule \arabic{spacerule}:}
   ```

3. In the *declarations*, I specified that the list should use the counter spacerule with the command

   ```
   \usecounter{spacerule}
   ```

9.6.3 Two complete examples

In the previous examples, I set the values of `\leftmargin` and `\rightmargin`; the other length commands were not redefined, so their values remained the values set by the document class. In the following examples, I will set the values of many more length commands.

Example 1 To get the following list,

Here are the most important LaTeX rules about spaces in text, sentences, and paragraphs:

Rule 1: *Two or more spaces in text are the same as one.*

Rule 2: *A blank line (that is, two end-of-line characters separated only by blanks and tabs) indicates the end of a paragraph.*

Rules 1 and 2 make typing and copying very convenient.

we type

```
\noindent Here are the most important \LaTeX\ rules about
spaces in text, sentences, and paragraphs:
\newcounter{spacerule}
\begin{list}{\upshape\bfseries Rule \arabic{spacerule}:}
            {\setlength{\leftmargin}{1.5in}
             \setlength{\rightmargin}{0.6in}
             \setlength{\labelwidth}{1.0in}
             \setlength{\labelsep}{0.2in}
             \setlength{\parsep}{0.5ex plus 0.2ex minus 0.1ex}
             \setlength{\itemsep}{0ex plus 0.2ex minus 0ex}
             \usecounter{spacerule}
             \itshape}
   \item Two or more spaces in text are the same
    as one.\label{Li:Twoor}
   \item A blank line (that is, two end-of-line
    characters separated only by blanks and tabs) indicates
    the end of a paragraph.\label{Li:blankline}
\end{list}
Rules \ref{Li:Twoor} and~\ref{Li:blankline} make typing
and copying very convenient.
```

Note that

1. I declared the counter as in the previous example.

2. The last item in *declarations* is \itshape, which typesets the entire list in italics.
3. The *default_label* is defined as

   ```
   \upshape\bfseries Rule \arabic{spacerule}:
   ```

   My first attempt was to define it as

   ```
   \bfseries Rule \arabic{spacerule}:
   ```

   which typesets Rule in bold italics; to force the label to be typeset upright, I start the *default_label* with the \upshape command.
4. The left margin is set to 1.5 inches and the right margin to 0.6 inches:

   ```
   \setlength{\leftmargin}{1.5in}
   \setlength{\rightmargin}{0.6in}
   ```

5. Next I set the width of the label to 1 inch, and the space between the label and the item to 0.2 inches:

   ```
   \setlength{\labelwidth}{1.0in}
   \setlength{\labelsep}{0.2in}
   ```

6. Finally, I set the paragraph separation to 0.5 ex (allowing stretching by 0.2 ex and shrinking by 0.1 ex) and the item separation to 0 ex (allowing stretching by 0.2 ex and no shrinking) by

   ```
   \setlength{\parsep}{0.5ex plus 0.2ex minus 0.1ex}
   \setlength{\itemsep}{0ex plus 0.2ex minus 0ex}
   ```

   The actual amount of item separation is calculated by adding the values specified for \parsep and \itemsep.

A complicated list such as this should be defined as a new environment. For example, you could define a myrules environment:

```
\newenvironment{myrules}
  {\begin{list}
    {\upshape \bfseries Rule \arabic{spacerule}:}
    {\setlength{\leftmargin}{1.5in}
    \setlength{\rightmargin}{0.6in}
    \setlength{\labelwidth}{1.0in}
    \setlength{\labelsep}{0.2in}
    \setlength{\parsep}{0.5ex plus 0.2ex minus 0.1ex}
    \setlength{\itemsep}{0ex plus 0.2ex minus 0ex}
    \usecounter{spacerule}
    \itshape} }
  {\end{list}}
```

and then use it anywhere, as in

```
\begin{myrules}
   \item Two or more spaces in text are the same
    as one.\label{Li:Twoor}
   \item A blank line (that is, two end-of-line
    characters separated only by blanks and tabs) indicates
    the end of a paragraph.\label{Li:blankline}
 \end{list}
Rules \ref{Li:Twoor} and~\ref{Li:blankline} make typing
and copying very convenient.
\end{myrules}
```

which typesets as the first example shown on page 357.

Example 2 In Section 2.7.2, we discussed the formatting of the following type of glossary:

sentence is a group of words terminated by a period, exclamation point, or question mark.

paragraph is a group of sentences terminated by a blank line or by the `\par` command.

Now we can create the glossary as a custom list:

```
\begin{list}{}
   {\setlength{\leftmargin}{30pt}
   \setlength{\rightmargin}{0pt}
   \setlength{\itemindent}{14pt}
   \setlength{\labelwidth}{40pt}
   \setlength{\labelsep}{5pt}
   \setlength{\parsep}{0.5ex plus 0.2ex minus 0.1ex}
   \setlength{\itemsep}{0ex plus 0.2ex minus 0ex}}
   \item[\textbf{sentence}\hfill] is a group of words terminated
    by a period, exclamation point, or question mark.
   \item[\textbf{paragraph}\hfill] is a group of sentences
    terminated by a blank line or by the \com{par} command.
\end{list}
```

There is nothing new in this example except the `\hfill` commands in the optional arguments to left adjust the labels; with the long words in the example this adjustment is not necessary, but it would be needed for shorter words.

The LaTeX Companion [17] has a great deal of material on lists; see Section 3.2.2 for more complicated custom lists and Section 3.2.1 on how to customize the three standard list environments.

9.6.4 The trivlist environment

LaTeX also provides a trivlist environment, meant more for programmers than users. The environment is invoked in the form

```
\begin{trivlist}
   body
\end{trivlist}
```

It is similar to the list environment except that there are no arguments, and all the length commands are trivially set (most to 0 points, except for \listparindent and \parsep, which are set equal to \parindent and \parskip, respectively). For instance, LaTeX defines the center environment as follows:

```
\begin{trivlist}
   \centering \item[]
\end{trivlist}
```

9.7 Custom formats

At some point, you will probably become annoyed by how long it takes LaTeX to process the lines

```
\documentclass{article}
\usepackage{amssymb,latexsym,amsmath}
```

You can speed up processing with custom formats.

First, create a new copy of latex.ltx and call it tmplatex.ltx. The last line of tmplatex.ltx before \endinput is \dump. Comment it out.

Now create a document called custart.tex (custom article) that contains all the lines of your document before the \begin{document} line, and add the line

```
\input tmplatex.ltx
```

to the beginning, and the line \dump to the end. For example, a very rudimentary custart.tex might read

```
\input tmplatex.ltx
\documentclass{article}
\usepackage{amssymb,latexsym,amsmath}
\dump
```

On the other hand, the `sampartu.tex` article is a little more complex:

```
\input tmplatex.ltx
\documentclass{amsart}
\usepackage{amssymb,latexsym}
\usepackage{lattice}

\theoremstyle{plain}
\newtheorem{theorem}{Theorem}
\newtheorem{corollary}{Corollary}
\newtheorem{lemma}{Lemma}
\newtheorem{proposition}{Proposition}

\theoremstyle{definition}
\newtheorem{definition}{Definition}

\theoremstyle{remark}
\newtheorem*{notation}{Notation}

\numberwithin{equation}{section}

\newcommand{\Prodm}[2]{\gP(\,#1\mid#2\,)}
   % product with a middle
\newcommand{\Prodsm}[2]{\gP^{*}(\,#1\mid#2\,)}
   % product * with a middle
\newcommand{\vct}[2]{\vv<\dots,0,\dots,\overset{#1}{#2},%
\dots,0,\dots>}% special vector
\newcommand{\fp}{\F{p}}% Fraktur p
\newcommand{\Ds}{D^{\langle2\rangle}}
\dump
```

Typeset `custart.tex` with `initex` and name the resulting format file `art.fmt`. In your document, comment out all the lines that have been included in the document `custart.tex`, and add the line

```
% Typeset with art format
```

The next time you typeset your document and specify your new format, you will be surprised by how fast LaTeX gets to the body of the document. Before you submit the document for publication, ***undo these changes***. Your editor will not have the `art` format.

Another approach is to use David Carlisle's mylatex.ltx, which can be found on CTAN (see Section 13.1) in the directory

```
/tex-archive/macros/latex/contrib/supported/carlisle/
```

Some UNIX users who typeset a LaTeX document called `article.tex` with the command

```
unix$ latex article
```

will have to learn a bit about UNIX to use a custom format.

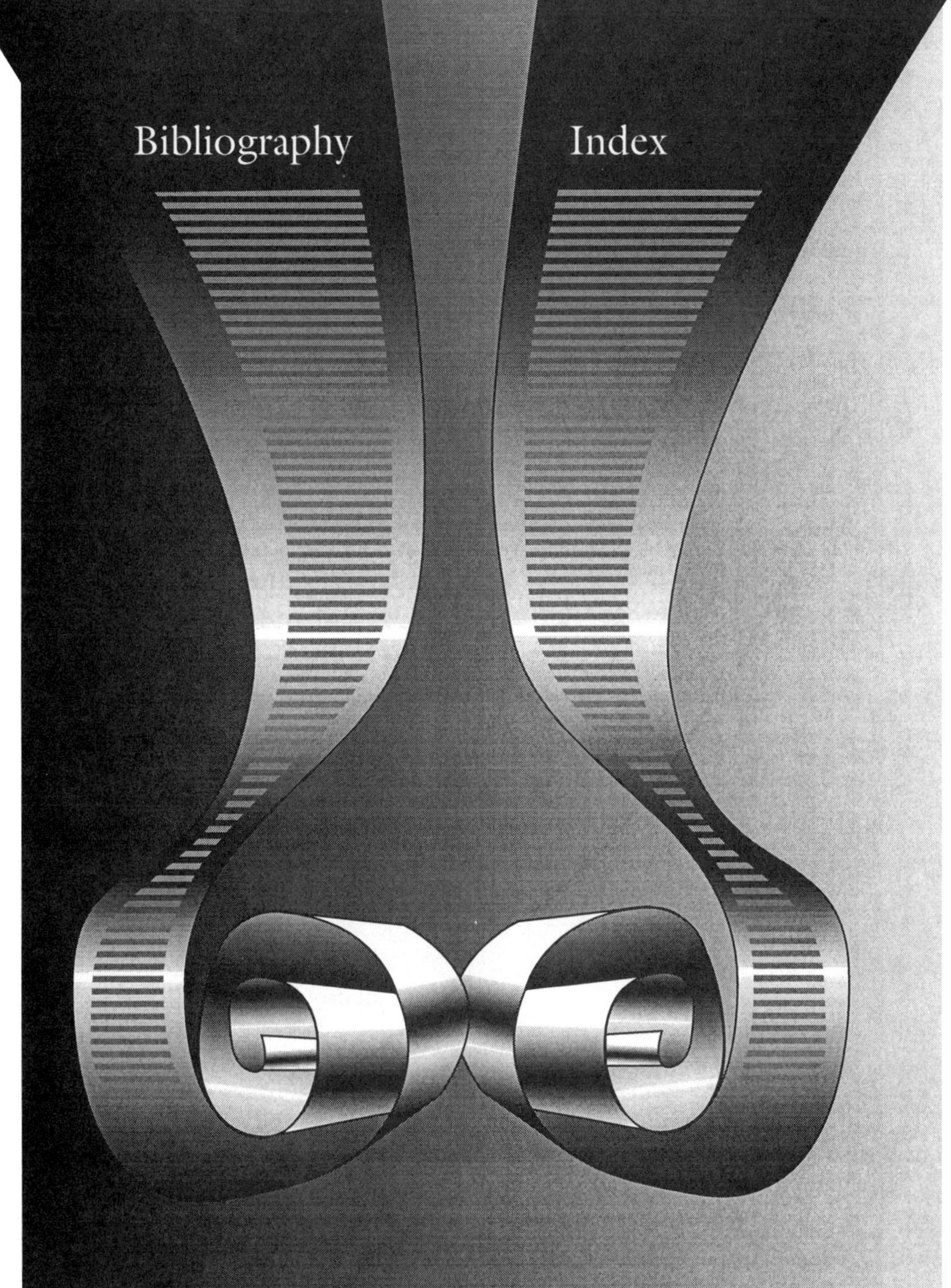
Bibliography
Index

PART V

Long documents

CHAPTER

10

BIBTEX

The BIBTEX application, written by Oren Patashnik, assists LATEX users in compiling bibliographies, especially long ones. Short bibliographies can easily be placed in the document directly (see Section 6.5.1).

It takes a little effort to learn BIBTEX. But in the long run, the advantages of building bibliographic databases that can be reused and shared outweighs the disadvantage of a somewhat steep learning curve.

The *bibliographic database files*—the bib files—contain the *bibliographic entries.* We will discuss the format of these entries in Section 10.1, and then describe how to use BIBTEX to create bibliographies in Section 10.2.

BIBTEX uses a style, called a *bibliographic style,* or bst file, to format entries. The next two pages show the bibliography of the sampartb.tex sample article typeset with eight different style files.

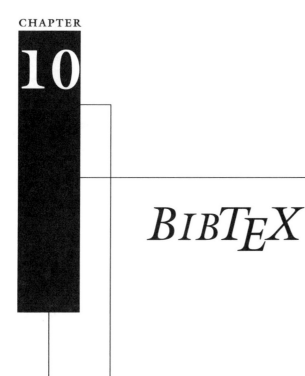

To simplify our discussions, in the rest of this chapter I will discuss only one style: the AMS plain style, amsplain.bst (version 1.2c—see the contents document in the sample files directory for a minor clarification). All of the examples shown are in this style, and several of the comments I make are true only for the AMS plain style. If you choose to use a different style, you should check its documentation for special rules.

[1] Soo-Key Foo. *Lattice Constructions.* PhD thesis, University of Winnebago, Winnebago, MN, December 1990.

[2] George A. Menuhin. *Universal Algebra.* D. van Nostrand, Princeton, 1968.

[3] Ernest T. Moynahan. Ideals and congruence relations in lattices. II. *Magyar Tud. Akad. Mat. Fiz. Oszt. Közl.*, 7:417–434, 1957.

[4] Ernest T. Moynahan. On a problem of M. Stone. *Acta Math. Acad. Sci. Hungar.*, 8:455–460, 1957.

[5] Ferenc R. Richardson. *General Lattice Theory.* Mir, Moscow, expanded and revised edition, 1982.

`plain.bst`

[Foo90] Soo-Key Foo. *Lattice Constructions.* PhD thesis, University of Winnebago, Winnebago, MN, December 1990.

[Men68] George A. Menuhin. *Universal Algebra.* D. van Nostrand, Princeton, 1968.

[Moy57a] Ernest T. Moynahan. Ideals and congruence relations in lattices. II. *Magyar Tud. Akad. Mat. Fiz. Oszt. Közl.*, 7:417–434, 1957.

[Moy57b] Ernest T. Moynahan. On a problem of M. Stone. *Acta Math. Acad. Sci. Hungar.*, 8:455–460, 1957.

[Ric82] Ferenc R. Richardson. *General Lattice Theory.* Mir, Moscow, expanded and revised edition, 1982.

`alpha.bst`

1. Soo-Key Foo, *Lattice constructions*, Ph.D. thesis, University of Winnebago, Winnebago, MN, December 1990.
2. George A. Menuhin, *Universal algebra*, D. van Nostrand, Princeton, 1968.
3. Ernest T. Moynahan, *Ideals and congruence relations in lattices.* II, Magyar Tud. Akad. Mat. Fiz. Oszt. Közl. **7** (1957), 417–434 (Hungarian).
4. ———, *On a problem of M. Stone*, Acta Math. Acad. Sci. Hungar. **8** (1957), 455–460.
5. Ferenc R. Richardson, *General lattice theory*, expanded and revised ed., Mir, Moscow, 1982 (Russian).

`amsplain.bst`

[Foo90] Soo-Key Foo, *Lattice constructions*, Ph.D. thesis, University of Winnebago, Winnebago, MN, December 1990.

[Men68] George A. Menuhin, *Universal algebra*, D. van Nostrand, Princeton, 1968.

[Moy57a] Ernest T. Moynahan, *Ideals and congruence relations in lattices.* II, Magyar Tud. Akad. Mat. Fiz. Oszt. Közl. **7** (1957), 417–434 (Hungarian).

[Moy57b] Ernest T. Moynahan, *On a problem of M. Stone*, Acta Math. Acad. Sci. Hungar. **8** (1957), 455–460.

[Ric82] Ferenc R. Richardson, *General lattice theory*, expanded and revised ed., Mir, Moscow, 1982 (Russian).

`amsalpha.bst`

[1] S.-K. Foo. *Lattice Constructions.* PhD thesis, University of Winnebago, Winnebago, MN, Dec. 1990.

[2] G. A. Menuhin. *Universal Algebra.* D. van Nostrand, Princeton, 1968.

[3] E. T. Moynahan. Ideals and congruence relations in lattices. II. *Magyar Tud. Akad. Mat. Fiz. Oszt. Közl.*, 7:417–434, 1957.

[4] E. T. Moynahan. On a problem of M. Stone. *Acta Math. Acad. Sci. Hungar.*, 8:455–460, 1957.

[5] F. R. Richardson. *General Lattice Theory.* Mir, Moscow, expanded and revised edition, 1982.

abbrv.bst

[1] S.-K. Foo, *Lattice Constructions*, PhD thesis, University of Winnebago, Winnebago, MN, Dec. 1990.

[2] G. A. Menuhin, *Universal Algebra*, D. van Nostrand, Princeton, 1968.

[3] E. T. Moynahan, *Ideals and congruence relations in lattices.* II, Magyar Tud. Akad. Mat. Fiz. Oszt. Közl., 7 (1957), pp. 417–434.

[4] ———, *On a problem of M. Stone*, Acta Math. Acad. Sci. Hungar., 8 (1957), pp. 455–460.

[5] F. R. Richardson, *General Lattice Theory*, Mir, Moscow, expanded and revised ed., 1982.

siam.bst

[1] F. R. Richardson, *General Lattice Theory.* Moscow: Mir, expanded and revised ed., 1982.

[2] G. A. Menuhin, *Universal Algebra.* Princeton: D. van Nostrand, 1968.

[3] E. T. Moynahan, "On a problem of M. Stone," *Acta Math. Acad. Sci. Hungar.*, vol. 8, pp. 455–460, 1957.

[4] S.-K. Foo, *Lattice Constructions.* PhD thesis, University of Winnebago, Winnebago, MN, Dec. 1990.

[5] E. T. Moynahan, "Ideals and congruence relations in lattices. II," *Magyar Tud. Akad. Mat. Fiz. Oszt. Közl.*, vol. 7, pp. 417–434, 1957.

ieeetr.bst

Foo, S.-K. (1990). *Lattice Constructions.* PhD thesis, University of Winnebago, Winnebago, MN.

Menuhin, G. A. (1968). *Universal Algebra.* D. van Nostrand, Princeton.

Moynahan, E. T. (1957a). Ideals and congruence relations in lattices. II. *Magyar Tud. Akad. Mat. Fiz. Oszt. Közl.*, 7:417–434.

Moynahan, E. T. (1957b). On a problem of M. Stone. *Acta Math. Acad. Sci. Hungar.*, 8:455–460.

Richardson, F. R. (1982). *General Lattice Theory.* Mir, Moscow, expanded and revised edition.

apalike.bst

10.1 The database

A BIBTEX database is a text file collecting bibliographic entries. To use BIBTEX, you first have to learn how to assemble the databases. This section explains how to do that.

There may be special tools available for your computer system that assist you in building and maintaining your bibliographic data. Such tools make compiling the data easier and may minimize formatting errors.

You can find all the examples in this section in the `template.bib` file in the `samples` directory—see page 4.

10.1.1 Entry types

A bibliographic entry is given in pieces called *fields*. The style (see Section 10.2.2) specifies how these fields will be typeset. Here are two typical entries:

```
@BOOK{gM68,
   author = "George A. Menuhin",
   title = "Universal Algebra",
   publisher = "D.~van Nostrand",
   address = "Princeton",
   year = 1968,
   }

@ARTICLE{eM57,
   author = "Ernest T. Moynahan",
   title = "On a Problem of {M. Stone}",
   journal = "Acta Math. Acad. Sci. Hungar.",
   pages = "455--460",
   volume = 8,
   year = 1957,
   }
```

The start of an entry is indicated with an at sign (`@`) followed by the *entry type*; in the first example, the entry type is `BOOK`, while in the second, it is `ARTICLE`. The entry type is followed by a left brace (`{`). The matching right brace (`}`) indicates the end of the entry. BIBTEX also allows you to use parentheses as delimiters; in this book, however, we will use braces.

The string `@BOOK{` is followed by the *label*, `gM68`, which designates the name of the entry; you will refer to this entry in your document using commands such as `\cite{gM68}`. The label is followed by a comma and a series of fields. In this example, there are five fields: `author`, `title`, `publisher`, `address`, and `year`. Each field starts with the field name, followed by `=` and the value of the field enclosed in double quotes ("). Be sure to use " and *not* LaTeX double quotes (`` or ''). BibTeX also allows you to use braces to enclose the field value; in this book, we will use double quotes.

Numeric field values (consisting entirely of digits) do not need to be enclosed in double quotes or braces (`year` in the examples above, `volume` in the second example, and `number` in some of the examples that follow). Page ranges, such as `455--460`, are not numeric field values since they contain `-`; so they must be enclosed in double quotes or braces.

There *must* be a comma before each field (the comma before the first field is placed after the label).

There are many standard entry types, including

`ARTICLE` an article in a journal or magazine

`BOOK` a book with an author (or editor) and a publisher

`BOOKLET` a printed work without a publisher

`INBOOK` a part of a book, such as a chapter or a page range that, in general, is not titled or authored separately

`INCOLLECTION` a part of a book with its own title (and perhaps author)

`INPROCEEDINGS` an article in a conference proceedings with its own title and author

`MANUAL` technical documentation

`MASTERSTHESIS` a master's thesis

`MISC` an entry that does not fit in any other category

`PHDTHESIS` a Ph.D. thesis

`PROCEEDINGS` the proceedings of a conference

`TECHREPORT` a report published by a school or institution

`UNPUBLISHED` an unpublished paper

Each entry includes a number of *fields* from the following list:

```
address       institution   pages
author        journal       publisher
booktitle     key           school
chapter       language      series
crossref      month         title
edition       note          type
editor        number        volume
howpublished  organization  year
```

The style you choose determines which of the fields within an entry are actually used; all the others are ignored. You may also add fields for your own use. For example, you may want to add a `mycomments` field for personal comments. Such fields will be ignored unless you have a bibliography style that uses them. The `language` field is used by the AMS styles but not by any of the other styles mentioned in this chapter. 

Tip

1. BIBTEX does not care whether you use uppercase or lowercase letters (or mixed) for the names of entry types and fields. In this book, the entry types are shown in uppercase and field names in lowercase.
2. Placing a comma after the last field is optional, but I recommend that you do so that if you append a new field to the entry, the required comma separating the fields will already be there.

For each entry type there are both required and optional fields. Later in this section, I give two examples of each entry type. The first example of an entry type uses a small set of fields, while the second example is a maximal one, showing a large number of optional fields.

10.1.2 Typing fields

Make sure you type the field names correctly; if you misspell one, BIBTEX will ignore the field. BIBTEX will also warn you if a required field is missing.

The `author` and `editor` fields require you to provide a name:

Rule ■ Names

1. Most names can be typed as usual; `"Ernest T. Moynahan"`; or in the form `"Moynahan, Ernest T."`, with one comma separating the family name.
2. Type two or more names separated by `and`. For instance,

```
author = "George Blue and Ernest Brown and Soo-Key Foo",
```

3. The family name of Miguel Lopez Fernandez is Lopez Fernandez, so type it as `"Lopez Fernandez, Miguel"`; doing so will let BIBTEX know that Lopez is not a middle name.
4. Type Orrin Frink, Jr. as `"Frink, Jr., Orrin"`.

Rules 3 and 4 are seldom needed. In a bibliography of about 1500 items,

I found fewer than 10 names that could not be typed as usual. Note that you can type John von Neumann as `"John von Neumann"` or `"von Neumann, John"`. Because BIBTEX knows about `von`, it will handle the name properly.

There are a few rules concerning the `title` field:

Rule ■ Titles

1. You should not put a period at the end of a title; the style will supply the appropriate punctuation.
2. AMS styles convert titles, except for their first letters, to lowercase for all entry types. If you want a letter to appear in uppercase, put it in braces. The same rule applies to the `edition` field. Most other styles—including the standard ones—only do this conversion for the titles of non-book-like entries.
3. To maximize the portability of your database, you should type titles with each important word capitalized:

```
title = "On a Problem of {M. Stone}",
```

The style used in this book, `amsplain.bst`, converts `Problem` to `problem`, so it makes no difference; but some styles do not. To be on the safe side, you should capitalize all words that may have to be capitalized.[1]

In the example above, two letters in the title should not be converted to lowercase, so we enclosed `M. Stone` in braces. (We could also have typed `{M. S}tone` or `{M.} {S}tone`.)

BIBTEX and the style automatically handle a number of things for you that you would have to handle yourself when typing text (as discussed in Chapter 2).

1. You do not have to mark periods in abbreviations (as `.\␣`—see Section 2.2.2) in the names of journals; so

```
journal = "Acta Math. Acad. Sci. Hungar.",
```

will be typeset correctly.

2. You can type a single hyphen for a page range (instead of the usual `--`; see Section 2.4.2) in the pages field; so

```
pages = "455-460",
```

will be typeset correctly (with an en dash).

[1]The full rule for titles: Capitalize (1) the first word; (2) the first word in a subtitle (BIBTEX assumes that a subtitle follows a colon, so it capitalizes the first word after a colon—a colon not introducing a subtitle should be typed in braces); (3) all other words except articles, unstressed conjunctions, and unstressed prepositions. Words that should never be converted to lowercase—for example, proper names such as `Hilbert`—should be enclosed in braces to prevent them from being converted to lowercase.

3. You do not have to type nonbreakable spaces (with ~; see Section 2.4.3) in the author or editor fields:

```
author = "George A. Menuhin",
```

is correct (normally you would type `George~A. Menuhin`).

Finally, a rule about accented characters:[2]

Rule ■ Accents
Put accented characters in braces: `{\"{a}}`

This rule means that

```
author = "Paul Erd\H{o}s",
```

is not recommended; instead, type

```
author = "Paul Erd{\H{o}}s",
```

This rule is, again, about portability. Some styles, (e.g., `alpha` and `amsalpha`) create a citation for an article from the first three letters of the name and the last two digits of the year.

```
author = "Kurt G{\"{o}}del",
year = 1931,
```

will create the citation: [Göd31]. The accent will be used only if the accents rule has been followed.

10.1.3 *Articles*

Entry type: `ARTICLE`
Required fields: `author`, `title`, `journal`, `year`, `pages`
Optional fields: `volume`, `number`, `language`, `note`

Examples:

1. Ernest T. Moynahan, *On a problem of M. Stone*, Acta Math. Acad. Sci. Hungar. **8** (1957), 455–460.
2. Ernest T. Moynahan, *On a problem of M. Stone*, Acta Math. Acad. Sci. Hungar. **8** (1957), no. 5, 455–460 (English), Russian translation available.

typed as

[2] This rule will no longer be needed in BIBTEX 1.0.

```
@ARTICLE{eM57,
   author = "Ernest T. Moynahan",
   title = "On a Problem of {M. Stone}",
   journal = "Acta Math. Acad. Sci. Hungar.",
   pages = "455--460",
   volume = 8,
   year = 1957,
   }

@ARTICLE{eM57a,
   author = "Ernest T. Moynahan",
   title = "On a Problem of {M. Stone}",
   journal = "Acta Math. Acad. Sci. Hungar.",
   pages = "455--460",
   volume = 8,
   number = 5,
   year = 1957,
   note = "Russian translation available",
   language = "English",
   }
```

10.1.4 Books

Entry type: `BOOK`
Required fields: `author` (or `editor`), `title`, `publisher`, `year`
Optional fields: `edition`, `series`, `volume`, `number`, `address`, `month`, `language`, `note`

Examples:

1. George A. Menuhin, *Universal algebra*, D. van Nostrand, Princeton, 1968.
2. George A. Menuhin, *Universal algebra*, second ed., University Series in Higher Mathematics, vol. 58, D. van Nostrand, Princeton, March 1968 (English), no Russian translation.

typed as

```
@BOOK{gM68,
   author = "George A. Menuhin",
   title = "Universal Algebra",
   publisher = "D.~van Nostrand",
   address = "Princeton",
   year = 1968,
   }
```

```
@BOOK{gM68a,
   author = "George A. Menuhin",
   title = "Universal Algebra",
   publisher = "D.~van Nostrand",
   address = "Princeton",
   year = 1968,
   month = mar,
   series = "University Series in Higher Mathematics",
   volume = 58,
   edition = "Second",
   note = "no Russian translation",
   language = "English",
   }
```

Abbreviations, such as `mar`, will be discussed in Section 10.1.9.

A second variant of book has an `editor` instead of an `author`:

15. Robert S. Prescott (ed.), *Universal algebra*, D. van Nostrand, Princeton, 1968.

typed as

```
@BOOK{rP68,
   editor = "Robert S. Prescott",
   title = "Universal Algebra",
   publisher = "D.~van Nostrand",
   address = "Princeton",
   year = 1968,
   }
```

10.1.5 Conference proceedings and collections

Entry type: `INPROCEEDINGS`
Required fields: `author`, `title`, `booktitle`, `year`
Optional fields: `address`, `editor`, `series`, `volume`, `number`, `organization`, `publisher`, `month`, `note`, `pages`, `language`

Examples:

7. Peter A. Konig, *Composition of functions*, Proceedings of the Conference on Universal Algebra, 1970.
8. Peter A. Konig, *Composition of functions*, Proceedings of the Conference on

Universal Algebra (Kingston, ON) (G. H. Birnbaum, ed.), vol. 7, Canadian Mathematical Society, Queen's Univ., December 1970, available from the Montreal office, pp. 1–106 (English).

typed as

```
@INPROCEEDINGS{pK69,
   author = "Peter A. Konig",
   title = "Composition of Functions",
   booktitle = "Proceedings of the Conference on
      Universal Algebra",
   year = 1970,
   }

@INPROCEEDINGS{pK69a,
   author = "Peter A. Konig",
   title = "Composition of Functions",
   booktitle = "Proceedings of the Conference on
    Universal Algebra",
   address = "Kingston, ON",
   publisher = "Queen's Univ.",
   organization = "Canadian Mathematical Society",
   editor = "G. H. Birnbaum",
   pages = "1--106",
   volume = 7,
   year = 1970,
   month = dec,
   note = "available from the Montreal office",
   language = "English",
   }
```

The address field provides the location of the meeting. The address of the publisher, if needed, should be included in the `publisher` field; the address of the organization would be included in the `organization` field.[3]

Entry type: `INCOLLECTION`
Required fields: `author`, `title`, `booktitle`, `publisher`, `year`
Optional fields: `editor`, `series`, `volume`, `number`, `address`, `edition`, `month`, `note`, `pages`, `language`

[3] BIBTEX 1.0 will provide a slightly different set of fields for conference proceedings.

Examples:

1. Henry H. Albert, *Free torsoids*, Current Trends in Lattices, D. van Nostrand, 1970.
2. Henry H. Albert, *Free torsoids*, Current Trends in Lattices (George Burns, ed.), vol. 2, D. van Nostrand, Princeton, January 1970, new edition is due next year, pp. 173–215 (German).

is typed as

```
@INCOLLECTION{hA70,
   author = "Henry H. Albert",
   title = "Free Torsoids",
   booktitle = "Current Trends in Lattices",
   publisher = "D.~van Nostrand",
   year = 1970,
   }

@INCOLLECTION{hA70a,
   author = "Henry H. Albert",
   editor = "George Burns",
   title = "Free Torsoids",
   booktitle = "Current Trends in Lattices",
   publisher = "D.~van Nostrand",
   address = "Princeton",
   pages = "173--215",
   volume = 2,
   year = 1970,
   month = jan,
   note = "new edition is due next year",
   language = "German",
   }
```

The address field contains the address of the publisher.

Cross-referencing

If your database has several articles in conference proceedings and collections, you may prefer to make an entry for the entire volume, and cross-reference the individual articles to that entry. For instance,

```
@PROCEEDINGS{UA69,
   title = "Proceedings of the Conference on Universal Algebra",
```

```
   booktitle = "Proceedings of the Conference on Universal
     Algebra",
   address = "Kingston, ON",
   publisher = "Canadian Mathematical Society",
   editor = "G. H. Birnbaum",
   volume = 7,
   year = 1970,
   }
```

may be the entry for the proceedings volume as a whole, and

```
@INPROCEEDINGS{pK69a,
   author = "Peter A. Konig",
   title = "Composition of Functions",
   booktitle = "Proceedings of the Conference on Universal
     Algebra",
   pages = "1--106",
   crossref = "UA69",
   }
```

is the cross-referencing entry for a specific article. These two entries produce the following:

1. G. H. Birnbaum (ed.), *Proceedings of the conference on universal algebra*, vol. 7, Kingston, ON, Canadian Mathematical Society, 1970.
2. Peter A. Konig, *Composition of functions*, in Birnbaum [1], pp. 1–106.

Rule ■ Cross-references[4]

1. All the required fields of the cross-referencing entry must appear in either that entry or in the cross-referenced entry.
2. The cross-referenced entry should have both a `title` and a `booktitle` field.
3. The cross-referenced entry must appear in the `bib` file later than any entry that cross-references it.

10.1.6 *Theses*

Entry type: `MASTERSTHESIS` or `PHDTHESIS`
Required fields: `author`, `title`, `school`, `year`
Optional fields: `type`, `address`, `month`, `note`, `pages`

[4]This rule will no longer be needed in BIBTEX 1.0.

Examples:

1. Soo-Key Foo, *Lattice constructions*, Ph.D. thesis, University of Winnebago, 1990.
2. Soo-Key Foo, *Lattice constructions*, Ph.D. dissertation, University of Winnebago, Winnebago, MN, December 1990, final revision not yet available, pp. 1–126.

typed as

```
@PHDTHESIS{sF90,
   author = "Soo-Key Foo",
   title = "Lattice Constructions",
   school = "University of Winnebago",
   year = 1990,
   }

@PHDTHESIS{sF90a,
   author = "Soo-Key Foo",
   title = "Lattice Constructions",
   school = "University of Winnebago",
   address = "Winnebago, MN",
   year = 1990,
   month = dec,
   note = "final revision not yet available",
   type = "Ph.D. dissertation",
   pages = "1--126",
   }
```

If the `type` field is present, its content will take the place of the phrase Ph.D. thesis (or Master's thesis).

10.1.7 Technical reports

Entry type: `TECHREPORT`
Required fields: `author`, `title`, `institution`, `year`
Optional fields: `type`, `number`, `address`, `month`, `note`

Examples:

1. Grant H. Foster, *Computational complexity in lattice theory*, tech. report, Carnegie Mellon University, 1986.
2. Grant H. Foster, *Computational complexity in lattice theory*, Research Note

128A, Carnegie Mellon University, Pittsburgh, PA, December 1986, in preparation.

typed as

```
@TECHREPORT{gF86,
   author = "Grant H. Foster",
   title = "Computational Complexity in Lattice Theory",
   institution = "Carnegie Mellon University",
   year = 1986,
   }

@TECHREPORT{gF86a,
   author = "Grant H. Foster",
   title = "Computational Complexity in Lattice Theory",
   institution = "Carnegie Mellon University",
   year = 1986,
   month = dec,
   type = "Research Note",
   address = "Pittsburgh, PA",
   number = "128A",
   note = "in preparation",
   }
```

10.1.8 *Manuscripts and other entry types*

Entry type: UNPUBLISHED
Required fields: author, title, note
Optional fields: month, year

Examples:

1. William A. Landau, *Representations of complete lattices*, manuscript, 55 pages.
2. William A. Landau, *Representations of complete lattices*, manuscript, 55 pages, December 1975.

typed as

```
@UNPUBLISHED{wL75,
   author = "William A. Landau",
   title = "Representations of Complete Lattices",
   note = "manuscript, 55~pages",
   }
```

```
@UNPUBLISHED{wL75a,
   author = "William A. Landau",
   title = "Representations of Complete Lattices",
   year = 1975,
   month = dec,
   note = "manuscript, 55~pages",
   }
```

Other standard entry types include

Entry type: `BOOKLET`
Required field: `title`
Optional fields: `author`, `howpublished`, `address`, `month`, `year`, `note`

Entry type: `INBOOK`
Required fields: `author` or `editor`, `title`, `chapter` or `pages`, `publisher` `year`
Optional fields: `series`, `volume`, `number`, `type`, `address`, `edition`, `month`, `pages`, `language`, `note`

Entry type: `MANUAL`
Required field: `title`
Optional fields: `author`, `organization`, `address`, `edition`, `month`, `year`, `note`

Entry type: `MISC`
Required field: at least one of the optional fields must be present
Optional fields: `author`, `title`, `howpublished`, `month`, `year`, `note`, `pages`

Entry type: `PROCEEDINGS`
Required fields: `title`, `year`
Optional field: `editor`, `series`, `volume`, `number`, `address`, `organization`, `publisher`, `month`, `note`

10.1.9 Abbreviations

You may have noticed the field `month = dec` in some of the examples; it uses an abbreviation. Most BIBTEX styles, including the AMS styles, include abbreviations for the months of the year: `jan`, `feb`, ..., `dec`. When an abbreviation is used, it is not enclosed in quotes (`"`) or braces (`{ }`). The style defines what will actually be typeset. Most styles typeset `dec` as either Dec. or December. 

The name of the abbreviation, such as `dec`, is a string of characters that starts with a letter, does not contain a space, an equal sign (`=`), a comma, or any of the special characters listed in Section 2.4.4.

You may define your own abbreviations using the command `@STRING`. For example,

```
@STRING{au = "Algebra Universalis"}
```

A string definition can be placed anywhere in a `bib` file, as long as it precedes the first use of the abbreviation in an entry.

The AMS supplies the `mrabbrev.bib` file containing the standard abbreviations for many mathematical journals (see Section 13.1; the file is in the `classes` subdirectory). Based on this file, you can make your own `abbrev.bib` file[5] containing entries for all the journals you reference with whatever abbreviations you find easiest to remember.

If you use this scheme, the command you use to specify the `bib` files may look like

```
\bibliography{abbrev,... }
```

(Section 10.2.1 explains the `\bibliography` command.)

10.2 Using BIBTEX

In Section 10.1, you learned how to create database files (the sample `bib` files are `template.bib` and `sampartb.bib` in the `samples` directory; see page 4). In this section, you will learn how to use BIBTEX to process these files to create a bibliography.[6]

We will use the `amsplain` style. To obtain all eight examples of different styles shown on pages 368–369, just change `amsplain` to the appropriate style name in your document and typeset it. The `apalike` style is an exception: It requires that the preamble of your document includes the line

```
\usepackage{apalike}
```

10.2.1 Sample files

Type the following two lines to replace the `thebibliography` environment in the `sampart.tex` sample document:

```
\bibliographystyle{amsplain}
\bibliography{sampartb}
```

Save the new sample article as `sampartb.tex`.

[5] Doing so is a good idea, especially since `mrabbrev.bib` is too large for some systems to handle.

[6] In this section we will illustrate the process of working with BIBTEX with the `sampartb` sample article which uses the `amsart` document class and the `amsplain` bibliography style. We will omit the AMS warnings in the margin.

The first line specifies the `bst` file, `amsplain.bst` (which is part of the AMS distribution—see Section 13.1; you can find this file in the `classes` subdirectory. (As usual, this directory has to be installed by typesetting `ams-c1.ins` with the `LaTeX` format.)

The second line specifies the database files used; in this case there is only one: `sampartb.bib`.

The contents of the `sampartb.bib` bibliographic database file are as follows:

```
@BOOK{gM68,
   author = "George A. Menuhin",
   title = "Universal Algebra",
   publisher = "D.~van Nostrand",
   address = "Princeton",
   year = 1968,
}

@BOOK{fR82,
   author = "Ferenc R. Richardson",
   title = "General Lattice Theory",
   edition = "Expanded and Revised",
   language = "Russian",
   publisher = "Mir",
   address = "Moscow",
   year = 1982,
}

@ARTICLE{eM57,
   author = "Ernest T. Moynahan",
   title = "On a Problem of {M. Stone}",
   journal = "Acta Math. Acad. Sci. Hungar.",
   pages = "455--460",
   volume = 8,
   year = 1957,
}

@ARTICLE{eM57a,
   author = "Ernest T. Moynahan",
   title = "Ideals and Congruence Relations in
      Lattices.~\textup{II}",
   journal = "Magyar Tud. Akad. Mat. Fiz. Oszt. K{\"{o}}zl.",
   language = "Hungarian",
   pages = "417--434",
   volume = 7,
```

```
   year = 1957,
}

@PHDTHESIS{sF90,
   author = "Soo-Key Foo",
   title = "Lattice Constructions",
   school = "University of Winnebago",
   address = "Winnebago, MN",
   year = 1990,
   month = dec,
}
```

Type in `sampartb.bib` or copy it from the `samples` directory to your working directory.

10.2.2 Setup

Before you start BIBTEX, make sure that everything is set up properly as described in this section.

You specify which entries from the database files will appear in the bibliography with the `\cite{`*label*`}` commands; they work as described in Section 6.5.1. If you choose to include an entry that is not cited in the text, you can do so with a `\nocite` command. For example,

```
\cite{pK57}
```

includes and cites the entry with label `pK57`, whereas

```
\nocite{pK57}
```

includes but does not cite the entry. In either case, one of the `bib` files specified in the argument of the `\bibliography` command must contain an entry with the label `pK57`. The `\nocite{*}` command includes *all* the entries from the bibliographic databases you've specified.

Your document must specify the bibliography style and must name the `bib` files to be used. For instance, the `sampartb.tex` sample article contains the lines

```
\bibliographystyle{amsplain}
\bibliography{sampartb}
```

The `\bibliographystyle` command specifies `amsplain.bst` as the style and the `\bibliography` command specifies the database file `sampartb.bib`. Alternatively, you could type

```
\bibliography{abbrev,gg,lattice,sampartb}
```

where

- `abbrev.bib` contains user-defined abbreviations
- `gg.bib` contains personal articles
- `lattice.bib` contains lattice theory articles by other authors
- `sampartb.bib` contains additional references needed for `sampartb.tex`

It is important to make sure that the `bst` file, the `bib` file(s), and the LaTeX document(s) are in subdirectories where BIBTEX can find them. If you are just starting out, you can simply copy all of them into one subdirectory; later, you may want to look for a more permanent solution by keeping the files `abbrev.bib` and `lattice.bib` in one "central" location, while placing `sampartb.bib` in the same directory as its corresponding LaTeX document.

10.2.3 *Four steps of BIBTEXing*

The following steps produce a typeset bibliography in your LaTeX document; we use the `sampartb.tex` sample article as an example:

Step 1. Check that BIBTEX, your LaTeX document, and the `bib` files are placed in the appropriate directories (see the comment at the end of Section 10.2.2).

Step 2. Typeset `sampartb.tex` to get a fresh `aux` file; this step is illustrated in Figure 10.1.

Step 3. Run BIBTEX on the `sampartb.aux` file (by invoking it with the argument `sampartb` or by starting the application and then opening `sampartb.aux`). If BIBTEX cannot find a crucial file—for example, the `bst` file—it will stop. The reason it stopped will be shown on your monitor and will also be written to a `blg` (bibliography log) file, `sampartb.blg`. Correct the error(s) and go back to step 2. A successful run will create a `bbl` (bibliography) file, `sampartb.bbl`, in addition to `sampartb.blg`. This step is illustrated in Figure 10.2.

Step 4. Typeset the LaTeX document `sampartb.tex` *twice*.

10.2.4 *BIBTEX files*

BIBTEX uses and creates a number of files when it is run. To illustrate this process, complete the four steps in Section 10.2.3 using `sampartb.tex`:

Step 1. Start fresh by deleting the `aux`, `blg`, and `bbl` files, if they are present.

Step 2. Typeset the article `sampartb.tex` to get an `aux` file (see Figure 10.1). (Notice that the log file contains warnings about missing references and a number of other lines not relevant to the current discussion.) The lines in the aux file containing bibliographic information are

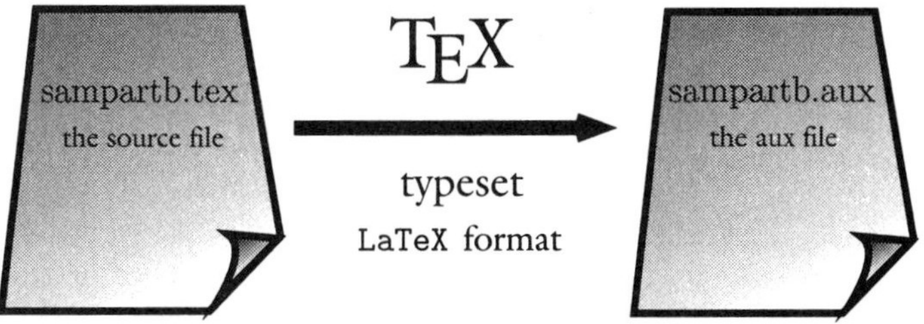

Figure 10.1: Using BibTeX, step 2.

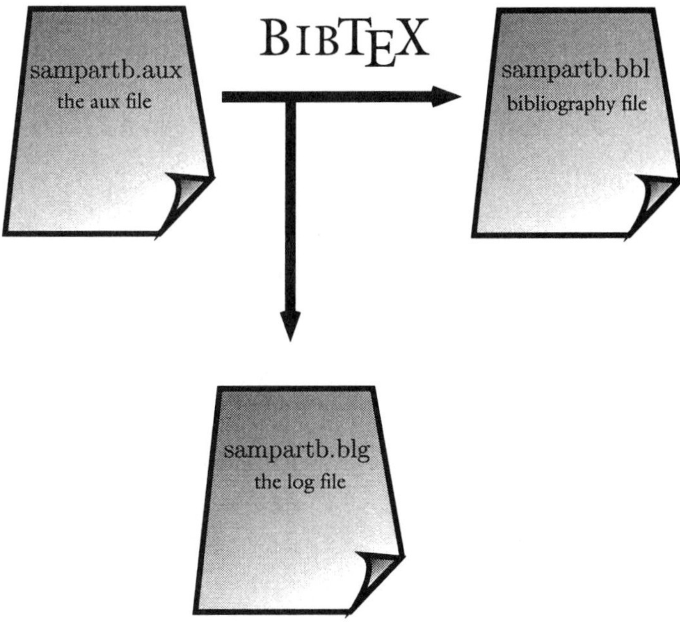

Figure 10.2: Using BibTeX, step 3.

```
\citation{fR82}
\citation{gM68}
\citation{eM57}
\citation{sF90}
\citation{eM57a}
\bibstyle{amsplain}
\bibdata{sampartb}
```

Each `\citation` command in this file corresponds to a `\cite` (or `\nocite`) command in the article. The lines

```
\bibliographystyle{amsplain}
\bibliography{sampartb}
```

in `sampartb.tex` are written as

```
\bibstyle{amsplain}
\bibdata{sampartb}
```

in the `sampartb.aux` file.

Step 3. Now run BIBTEX on the `sampartb.aux` file (see Figure 10.2).

BIBTEX generates two new files: `sampartb.blg` and `sampartb.bbl`. Look at `sampartb.blg` (on some systems, this file may be much longer than the one I show here):

```
This is BibTeX, C Version 0.99c
The top-level auxiliary file: sampartb.aux
The style: amsplain.bst
Database file #1: sampartb.bib
```

At present, this `blg` file does not contain much important information; if there were any warnings or errors, they would be listed in this file.

The `sampartb.bbl` file, in which BIBTEX created a `thebibliography` environment (as described in Section 6.5.1), is more interesting:

```
\providecommand{\bysame}{\leavevmode\hbox to3em%
{\hrulefill}\thinspace}
\begin{thebibliography}{1}

\bibitem{sF90}
Soo-Key Foo, \emph{Lattice constructions}, Ph.D. thesis,
University of Winnebago, Winnebago, MN, December 1990.

\bibitem{gM68}
George~A. Menuhin, \emph{Universal algebra},
D.~van Nostrand, Princeton, 1968.

\bibitem{eM57a}
Ernest~T. Moynahan, \emph{Ideals and congruence relations in
lattices.~\textup{II}}, Magyar Tud. Akad. Mat. Fiz.
Oszt. K{\"{o}}zl. \textbf{7} (1957), 417--434 (Hungarian).
```

```
\bibitem{eM57}
\bysame, \emph{On a problem of {M. Stone}}, Acta
Math. Acad. Sci. Hungar. \textbf{8} (1957), 455--460.

\bibitem{fR82}
Ferenc~R. Richardson, \emph{General lattice theory},
expanded and revised ed., Mir, Moscow, 1982 (Russian).

\end{thebibliography}
```

Observe that the nonbreakable spaces (ties) and the `\bysame` command have been provided in the author fields.

Step 4. Now typeset `sampartb.tex` again. The DVI file now has a REFERENCES section (it was constructed from the `bbl` file), but the new `log` file has warnings about missing entries. The new `aux` file contains five interesting new lines:

```
\bibcite{sF90}{1}
\bibcite{gM68}{2}
\bibcite{eM57a}{3}
\bibcite{eM57}{4}
\bibcite{fR82}{5}
```

These lines identify the cross-reference label `sF90` (see the first line shown—the symbol designates Foo's thesis in `sampartb.bib`) with the number `1`, and so on. Now typeset `sampartb.tex` again, and all the citations will be correctly placed in the typeset article.

Observe:

1. The crucial step 3, running the BIBTEX application, gives different error messages and obeys different rules from LATEX—see Section 10.2.5.
2. The `sampartb.bbl` file was created by BIBTEX. It will not be changed by running LATEX.

10.2.5 BIBTEX rules and messages

Rule ■ BIBTEX and %

You cannot comment out a field with %

For example, the entry

```
@ARTICLE{eM57,
   author = "Ernest T. Moynahan",
   title = "On a Problem of {M. Stone}",
   journal = "Acta Math. Acad. Sci. Hungar.",
   % pages = "455--460",
   volume = 8,
   year = 1957,
   }
```

will cause BIBTEX to generate the error message

```
You're missing a field name---line 23 of file sampartb.bib
 :
 :    % pages = "455--460",
(Error may have been on previous line)
I'm skipping whatever remains of this entry
Warning--missing year in eM57
Warning--missing pages in eM57
(There was 1 error message)
```

Recall that BIBTEX ignores field names it cannot recognize. So changing the field name pages, to say `pages-comment` will not give an error message. However, doing so removes a required field, so you will get a warning message instead:

```
Warning--missing pages in eM57
```

Rule ■ BIBTEX field names
Do not abbreviate field names.

For instance, if you abbreviate `volume` to `vol`, as in

```
@ARTICLE{eM57,
   author = "Ernest T. Moynahan",
   title = "On a Problem of {M. Stone}",
   journal = "Acta Math. Acad. Sci. Hungar.",
   pages = "455--460",
   vol = 8,
   year = 1957,
   }
```

the `vol` field will simply be ignored. This entry will be typeset as

3. Ernest T. Moynahan, *On a problem of M. Stone*, Acta Math. Acad. Sci. Hungar. (1957), 455–460.

instead of

3. Ernest T. Moynahan, *On a problem of M. Stone*, Acta Math. Acad. Sci. Hungar. **8** (1957), 455–460.

Rule ■ BIBTEX field terminations

Make sure that every field of an entry, except possibly the last, is terminated with a comma.

If you drop a comma before a field, you will get an error message such as

```
I was expecting a ',' or a ')'---line 6 of file sampartb.bib
 :
 :    year = 1968,
(Error may have been on previous line)
I'm skipping whatever remains of this entry
Warning--missing year in gM68
```

Rule ■ BIBTEX field value terminations

Make sure that the field value is properly terminated.

You should be careful not to drop a double quote or brace. If you drop the closing quote on line 11 of the `bib` file,

```
   title = "General Lattice Theory
```

you will get the error message

```
I was expecting a ',' or a '}'---line 12 of file sampartb.bib
 :    edition = "
 :               Expanded and Revised",
I'm skipping whatever remains of this entry
Warning--missing publisher in fR82
Warning--missing year in fR82
```

If instead you drop the opening double quote in the same line, you will get the error message

```
Warning--string name "general" is undefined
--line 11 of file sampartb.bib
I was expecting a ',' or a '}'---line 11 of file sampartb.bib
 :    title =  general
 :                        Lattice Theory",
I'm skipping whatever remains of this entry
Warning--missing title in fR82
Warning--missing publisher in fR82
Warning--missing year in fR82
(There was 1 error message)
```

BIBTEX assumed that `general` was an abbreviation, since it was not preceded by a `"`.

The obvious conclusion is that you have to be very careful about typing your bibliographic entries for BIBTEX. If you have access to special tools for maintaining your bibliographic data, use them; otherwise, refer to the `template.bib` file that contains templates of often-used entry types.

10.2.6 Concluding comments

There is a lot more to BIBTEX than what has been covered in this chapter. For example, BIBTEX's algorithm to alphabetize names is fairly complicated. Some names create additional difficulties. Where should John von Neumann be placed, under the "v"-s or the "N"-s? (Answer: it depends on the style.) How do we handle names where the first word is the family name, as in Ho Chi Minh or Grätzer György? (Again, it depends on the style.)

Oren Patashnik's *BIBTEXing* [51] has many helpful hints. It includes a clever hack to order entries correctly even when the style does not do so. Chapter 13 of *The LATEX Companion* [17] has a long discussion of BIBTEX. It also contains a long list of styles.

Sometime after the publication of this book, a new version of BIBTEX is scheduled for release (see Oren Patashnik's article, *BIBTEX 1.0* [52]). It will mostly add new features (using new fields and options to existing fields; for tasks such as handling sorting problems and names such as Grätzer György), but it will be almost completely backward compatible with BIBTEX 0.99.

CHAPTER

11 MakeIndex

Pehong Chen's *MakeIndex* application (described in Pehong Chen and Michael A. Harrison's *Index preparation and processing* [11]) helps LaTeX users create long indexes. For short indexes, you can easily do without it (see Section 6.5.2).

Indexing is a difficult task. Consult the *The Chicago Manual of Style* [12] for help.

11.1 Preparing the document

LaTeX provides the `theindex` environment; see Section 6.5.2. Within this environment, it provides the `\item`, `\subitem`, and `\subsubitem` commands to typeset entries, subentries, and subsubentries, respectively, and the `\indexspace` command for adding vertical space between alphabetical blocks.

The makeidx package provides the `\index` command for specifying the index entry at a particular point in the document; that reference will become a page reference for the entry in the typeset index.

Making an index entry with *MakeIndex* is easy: You simply place the index commands in your source file, and then let LaTeX and *MakeIndex* do the work of gathering the entries and the page numbers for the entries, sorting them, and formatting the typeset index.

There are three steps:

1. In the preamble of your LaTeX document, include the lines

```
\usepackage{makeidx}
\makeindex
```

   (If you use an AMS document class, *do not type the* `\usepackage` *command;* if you do, you will get an error message.) Ⓐ
2. Type the line

```
\printindex
```

   at the point in your document where you want the index to appear. (Usually as part of the back matter (see Section 6.5).
3. Mark all entries in your document with `\index` commands.

We will illustrate this procedure with the `intrarti.tex` article, which modifies `intrart.tex` by inserting a number of index entries (in the `samples` directory; see page 4).

The following 14 `\index` commands create the entries in the index shown in Figure 11.1.

Command 1. Retype the line

```
\begin{theorem}
```

Index	`\index` commands
$\langle \dots, 0, \dots, d, \dots, 0, \dots \rangle$, **1**, 2	4, 9
Foo, Soo-Key, 2	11
lattice, 2	6
distributive, 2	7
complete, 2	8
Main Theorem, 1	1
exposition, 1–2	3, 10
Menuhin, George A., 3	12
Moynahan, Ernest T., 2, 3	5, 13, 14
Π^* construction, 1	2

Figure 11.1: Simple index entries.

to read

```
\begin{theorem}\index{Main Theorem}
```

Commands 2 and 3. Type the commands

```
\index{pistar@$\Pi^{*}$ construction}%
\index{Main Theorem!exposition|(}%
```

following the line

```
\section{The $\Pi^{*}$ construction}\label{S:P*}
```

Command 4. Type

```
\index{<@$\langle\dots,0,\dots,d,\dots,0,\dots\rangle$|textbf}
```

after the line

```
\begin{notation}
```

Command 5. Retype the line

```
See also Ernest~T. Moynahan~\cite{eM57a}.
```

as follows:

```
See also Ernest~T.
\index{Moynahan, Ernest~T.}%
Moynahan~\cite{eM57a}.
```

Commands 6 to 8. The following three index items,

```
\index{lattice}%
\index{lattice!distributive}%
\index{lattice!distributive!complete}%
```

should precede the line

```
\begin{theorem}\label{T:P*}
```

Command 9. Insert the item

```
\index{<@$\langle\dots,0,\dots,d,\dots,0,\dots\rangle$|textbf}
```

following the line

```
we get:
```

Command 10. Type

```
\index{Main Theorem!exposition|)}
```

after the line

```
hence $\Theta = \iota$.
```

Command 11. Retype the line

```
\bibitem{sF90}
```

as follows:

```
\bibitem{sF90}\index{Foo, Soo-Key}%
```

Command 12. Retype the line

```
\bibitem{gM68}
```

as follows:

```
\bibitem{gM68}\index{Menuhin, George~A.}%
```

Command 13. Retype the line

```
\bibitem{eM57}
```

as follows:

```
\bibitem{eM57}\index{Moynahan, Ernest~T.}%
```

Command 14. Retype the line

```
\bibitem{eM57a}
```

as follows:

```
\bibitem{eM57a}\index{Moynahan, Ernest~T.}%
```

These `\index` commands produce the index for the `intrarti.tex` article shown in Figure 11.1. Notice that although you typed 14 index commands, only 13 entries appear in the index. The last two entries for Moynahan (`\index` commands 13 and 14) both occur on the same typeset page, so only one page number shows up in the index.

11.2 Index commands

There are a few major forms of `\index` commands. They are discussed in this section, illustrated by the commands shown in Section 11.1.

- **Simple `\index` commands**

The index entry

Foo, Soo-Key, 2

was created by command 11,

```
\index{Foo, Soo-Key}
```

This entry is an example of the simplest form of an index command:

`\index{`*entry*`}`

The entry

lattice, 2

was created as command 6,

```
\index{lattice}
```

This entry has a subentry,

lattice, 2
    distributive, 2

which was created by command 7,

```
\index{lattice!distributive}
```

There is also a subsubentry,

lattice, 2
    distributive, 2
        complete, 2

which was created by command 8,

```
\index{lattice!distributive!complete}
```

The form of the \index command for subentries is

\index{*entry*!*subentry*}

and for subsubentries it is

\index{*entry*!*subentry*!*subsubentry*}

Modifiers

Command 4,

```
\index{<@$\langle\dots,0,\dots,d,\dots,0,\dots\rangle$|textbf}
```

produces a bold page number in the entry
$\langle\dots,0,\dots,d,\dots,0,\dots\rangle$

The command whose name follows the symbol | (in this case, the command name is textbf) is applied to the page number. For instance, if you wanted a large bold page number, you would define the command \LB as

```
\newcommand{\LB}[1]{\textbf{\Large #1}}
```

and type the \index command as

\index{*entry*|LB}

You can also modify \index commands to indicate *page ranges:*

Main Theorem, 1
    exposition, 1–2

The latter index entry has a page range; it was created with commands 3 and 10,

```
\index{Main Theorem!exposition|(}
\index{Main Theorem!exposition|)}
```

Separate an entry from its modifier with `|`, open the page range with `(`, and close it with `)`.

Modifiers can also be combined. The index commands

```
\index{Main Theorem!exposition|(textbf}
\index{Main Theorem!exposition|)textbf}
```

produce a bold page range.

- **Sorting control**

Observe the `\index` command that occurs twice (once with a `textbf` modifier):

```
\index{<@$\langle\dots,0,\dots,d,\dots,0,\dots\rangle$}
```

This pair of commands produce the entry

$\langle \dots, 0, \dots, d, \dots, 0, \dots \rangle$, **1**, 2

To place this entry at the correct place in the index, use a *sort key*. The general form of an `\index` command with a sort key is

```
\index{sortkey@entry}
```

In this example, the sortkey is `<`. When the entries are sorted, the *`sortkey`* is used to sort the entry. A few typical examples follow:

Example 1 An `\index` command for G.I. Žitomirskiĭ,

```
\index{Zitomirskii@\v{Z}itomirski\u{\i}, G.I.}
```

sorts Žitomirskiĭ with the Z entries.

If you used the command

```
\index{\v{Z}itomirski\u{\i}, G.I.}
```

Žitomirskiĭ would be sorted with the v-s.

Example 2 An `\index` command for the Őrmester lemma,

```
\index{Ormester@\H{O}rmester lemma}
```

would sort Őrmester lemma with the O entries.

If you used the command

```
\index{\H{O}rmester lemma}
```

Őrmester lemma would be sorted with the H-s.

Example 3 An `\index` command for *truncated* lattice,

```
\index{truncated lattice@\emph{truncated} lattice}
```

sorts *truncated* lattice with the t entries.

If you use the command

```
\index{\emph{truncated} lattice}
```

this would sort *truncated* lattice with the e-s.

Example 4 We want to place the symbol Trunc f, typed as `\Trunc f` (see Section 4.7.2) in the index, sorted as Trunc.

```
\index{$\Trunc f$}
```

would place Trunc f near the beginning of the index, sorted with the $ symbols.

If you use the command

```
\index{Trunc@$\Trunc f$}
```

this would sort Trunc f with the T-s.

- **Sorting control and subentries**

If you want to place a subentry under an entry with a sort key, you must include the sort key part of the entry, as well:

`\index{`*sortkey*`@`*entry*`!`*subentry*`}`

For instance,

```
\index{Zitomirskii@\v{Z}itomirski\u{\i}, G.I.!education}
```

You can also use a sort key for subentries (and subsubentries), such as

```
\index{lattice!weakly distributive@\emph{weakly} distributive}
```

or, a more complicated example,

```
\index{Zitomirskii@\v{Z}itomirski\u{\i}, G.I.!elementary
education@\textbf{elementary} education}
```

- **Special characters**

Since the `!`, `@`, and `|` characters have special meanings within an `\index` command, you will need to *quote* those characters if you want them to appear as themselves. *MakeIndex* uses the double quote character (`"`) for this purpose: `"!`, `"@`, and `"|`.

Because this usage makes the double quote a special character itself, it will also have to be quoted if you need to use it in an `\index` command: `""`.

Example 1 To produce the entry Start here!, type the \index command as follows:

```
\index{Start here"!}
```

Example 2 To produce the entry @ symbol, type the \index command as follows:

```
\index{"@ symbol}
```

Example 3 To produce the entry $|A|$, type the \index command as follows:

```
\index{"|A"|@$"|A"|$}
```

- **Cross-references**

It is easy to make a cross-reference to another index entry; for instance, to list distributive lattice by cross-referencing it to lattice, distributive, the command is

```
\index{distributive lattice|see{lattice, distributive}}
```

which produces the following entry:

distributive lattice, *see* lattice, distributive

A command of this form can be placed anywhere in the document.

Tip Put all cross-referencing \index commands in one place in your document, so they are easy to keep track of.

- **Placement of \index commands**

The principle is simple:

Rule ■ Placement of \index commands
An \index command should

1. Reference the correct page
2. Not introduce unwanted space into the typeset document

For example, you should avoid placing \index commands as shown here:

```
Let $L$ be a distributive lattice
\index{lattice}
\index{distributive lattice}
that is strongly complete.
```

This placement may result in unwanted extra space following the word lattice:

Let L be a distributive lattice that is strongly complete.

Note the placement of the \index commands in Section 11.1; in each case I have placed them as close to the referenced item as I could. If you place an index entry on a separate line, use % to comment out unwanted spaces (including the end-of-line character; see Section 2.5), as in

```
Let $L$ be a distributive lattice
\index{lattice}%
\index{distributive lattice}%
that is strongly complete.
```

Read also Section 12.5 on page breaks and index entries.

- **Listing the forms of the `\index` command.**

We have discussed the following forms:

```
\index{entry}
\index{entry!subentry}
\index{entry!subentry!subsubentry}
\index{entry|modifier}
\index{entry|open/close modifier}
\index{sortkey@entry}
\index{sortkey@entry!subentry}
\index{sortkey@entry!subsortkey@subentry}
```

Of course, more combinations are possible; the following may be the longest form:

```
\index{sortkey@entry!subsortkey@subentry
!subsubsortkey@subsubentry|open/close modifier}
```

11.3 Processing the index entries

Once you are pleased with the \index commands, the index is ready to be created.

Step 1 Typeset `intrarti.tex` (see Figure 11.2).

Step 2 Run the *MakeIndex* application on `intrarti.idx` (see Figure 11.3); depending on your system, you will either be asked to open the document or will have to supply the name of the document as an argument of `makeindex`.

Step 3 Typeset `intrarti.tex` again.

You will find the index on page 3 of the typeset document.

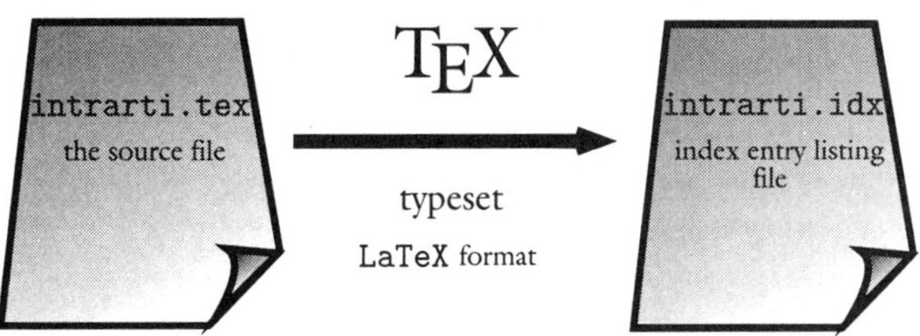

Figure 11.2: Using *MakeIndex*, step 1.

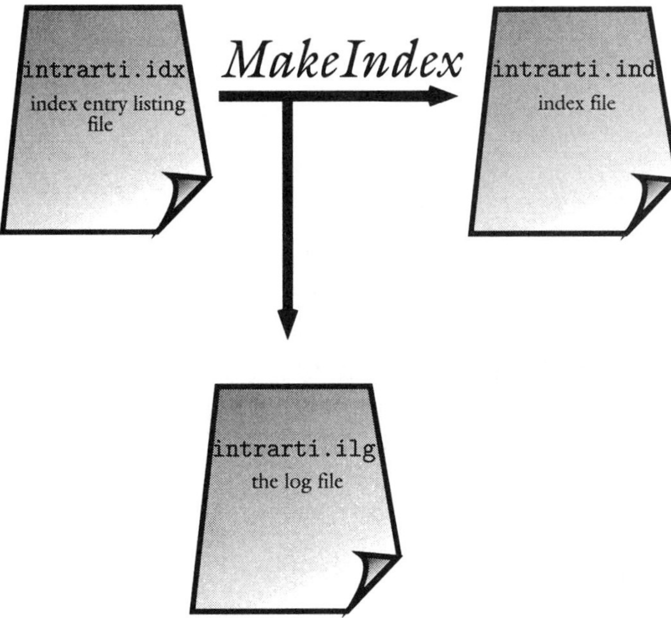

Figure 11.3: Using *MakeIndex*, step 2.

Let us look at this process in detail. In step 1 (see Figure 11.2), LaTeX creates the intrarti.idx file:

```
\indexentry{Main Theorem}{1}
\indexentry{pistar@$\Pi^{*}$ construction}{1}
\indexentry{Main Theorem!exposition|(}{1}
\indexentry{<@$\langle \dots,0,\dots,d,\dots,0,\dots\rangle$|textbf}{1}
\indexentry{Moynahan, Ernest~T.}{2}
\indexentry{lattice}{2}
\indexentry{lattice!distributive}{2}
\indexentry{lattice!distributive!complete}{2}
\indexentry{<@$\langle\dots,0,\dots,d,\dots,0,\dots\rangle$}{2}
\indexentry{Main Theorem!exposition|)}{2}
\indexentry{Foo, Soo-Key}{2}
\indexentry{Menuhin, George~A.}{2}
\indexentry{Moynahan, Ernest~T.}{2}
\indexentry{Moynahan, Ernest~T.}{2}
```

In step 2 (see Figure 11.3), *MakeIndex* processes intrarti.idx (*MakeIndex* is invoked with the argument intrarti) and creates the index file intrarti.ind, which contains a theindex environment with all the index entries:

```
\begin{theindex}

  \item $\langle\dots,0,\dots,d,\dots,0,\dots\rangle$,\textbf{1}, 2

  \indexspace

  \item Foo, Soo-Key, 2

  \indexspace

  \item lattice, 2
    \subitem distributive, 2
      \subsubitem complete, 2

  \indexspace

  \item Main Theorem, 1
    \subitem exposition, 1--2
  \item Menuhin, George~A., 2
  \item Moynahan, Ernest~T., 2

  \indexspace
```

```
  \item $ \Pi^{*} $ construction, 1

\end{theindex}
```

The \printindex command reads in intrarti.ind during the next typesetting cycle.

MakeIndex also produces the index log file intrarti.ilg:

```
This is MakeIndex, portable version 2.12 [26-May-1993].
Scanning input file intrarti.idx....done
(14 entries accepted, 0 rejected).
Sorting entries....done (53 comparisons).
Generating output file intrarti.ind....done
(27 lines written, 0 warnings).
Output written in intrarti.ind.
Transcript written in intrarti.ilg.
```

It is important to understand that in step 1, LaTeX does not process the index entries; it simply writes the arguments of the \index commands in the source file to the idx file as arguments of \indexentry commands verbatim (that is, with no change). *MakeIndex* then processes the idx file by removing the double quote marks for the special characters, sorting the entries, and collating the page numbers. The resulting ind file is a normal LaTeX source file (you can edit it, if necessary) that is included in the original document by the \printindex command the next time you run LaTeX.

11.4 Rules

There are some simple rules to keep in mind when entering index items.

Rule ■ Spaces in \index

Do not leave unnecessary spaces in the argument of an \index command.

\index{item}, \index{␣item}, and \index{item␣}

will produce three different entries.

There are options that instruct *MakeIndex* to ignore such spaces, but you are better off typing the \index commands correctly in the first place.

Rule ■ Spacing rules for *MakeIndex*
LaTeX's spacing rules (Section 2.2.1) do not apply; *MakeIndex* does not follow these rules when it sorts the index items. While LaTeX ignores spaces, *MakeIndex* does not.

Rule ■ Sort keys
In \index{*sortkey*@*item*}, the *sortkey* is both space and case sensitive.

For instance,

```
\index{alpha@$\alpha$}
\index{Alpha@$\alpha$}
\index{ALPHA@$\alpha$}
```

represent three different items.

Rule ■ amsmath
If you use the amsmath package, do not place \index commands inside displayed math environments. Ⓐ

If you violate this rule, you may get an error message such as

```
! TeX capacity exceeded, sorry [input stack size=200].
\restorecounters@ ...ecounters@
                                \@empty
l.9      \end{equation}

If you really absolutely need more capacity,
you can ask a wizard to enlarge me.
```

Rule ■ Braces
In every entry, the braces must be balanced.

Normally, balancing braces is not a problem. The braces within a math formula or a TeX expression should always be balanced. However, the \index command that creates the entry for { with the sort key leftbrace cannot be typed as

```
\index{leftbrace@\{}
```

because LaTeX would give the error message

```
Runaway argument?
{leftbrace@\{}
! Paragraph ended before \@wrindex was complete.
```

There are many ways to correct this `\index` command. Perhaps the simplest is to define

```
\newcommand{\printleftbrace}{\{}
```

and rewrite the `\index` command

```
\index{leftbrace@\printleftbrace}
```

This produces the entry

{, 1

There is, of course, a lot more to *MakeIndex* than what we have discussed in this short introduction, but what we have covered here will do for most documents. See Pehong Chen and Michael A. Harrison's *Index preparation and processing* [11] for more detail. Chapter 12 of *The LaTeX Companion* [17] covers *MakeIndex* in great detail, including the creation of multiple indexes and customizing indexes.

11.5 Glossary

Using the glossary commands is very similar to using the corresponding index commands.

Instead of the `\index` and `\makeindex` commands, use the `\glossary` and `\makeglossary` commands, respectively. Glossary entries are written in the `glo` file, which corresponds to the `idx` file. LaTeX gives you no further assistance in making a glossary file: there is no `\printglossary` command, `theglossary` environment, or *MakeGlossary* application. There is, however, Thomas Henlich's makeglos package, see the
`/tex-archive/macros/latex/contrib/supported/makeglos/`
directory on CTAN (see Section 13.1).

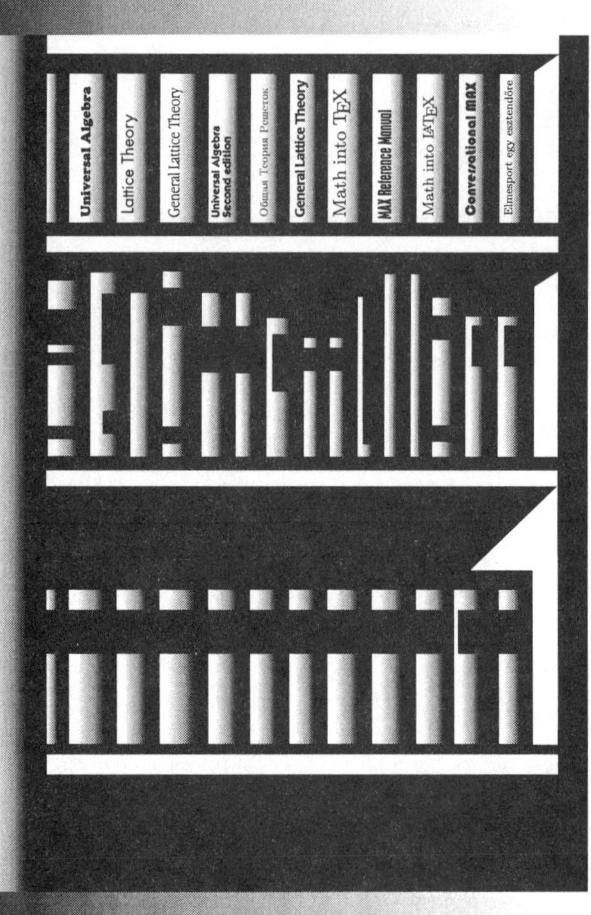
Universal Algebra
Lattice Theory
General Lattice Theory
Universal Algebra Second edition
Общая Теория Решеток
General Lattice Theory
Math into TEX
MAX Reference Manual
Math into LATEX
Conversational MAX
Elmesport egy esztendőre

CHAPTER

12

Books in LaTeX

Since the introduction of LaTeX, the visual quality of articles published in mathematical journals has improved dramatically. Unfortunately, the same cannot be said of books published using LaTeX: A record number of very ugly books have appeared.

It is easy to understand why. While the article document classes (`article` and, especially, `amsart`) have been designed to produce high-quality printed output, the standard book document classes do not produce attractive books without additional work.

LaTeX provides the `book` document class and the AMS offers the `amsbook` document class to serve as a foundation for well-designed books. However, better quality books (or book series) have to be *individually designed*, a task that has to be left to the professionals.

We briefly discussed logical and visual design in Section 1.11. The book document classes give you the foundation for proper logical design, but you should leave the visual design to your publisher. Many publishers offer their own book document classes. As a rule, they are not all that different from the two standard ones: They offer the standard sectioning commands. See Appendix F for an illustration.

So this chapter is not about how to produce a finished book using LATEX. Our goal is much more modest: Discussing how to prepare a book manuscript for your publisher. In Section 12.1 we describe the book document classes `book` and `amsbook`. The table of contents and lists of figures and tables are discussed in Section 12.2. It is usually necessary to write a LATEX book in several pieces; on the other hand, when you e-mail a project to an editor, coauthor, or colleague, you may want to combine a number of files into one large file; these two topics are discussed in Section 12.3. Section 12.4 covers logical design. Section 12.5 deals with the final preparation of your edited manuscript for your publisher. Finally, Section 12.6 suggests a few more things to do before your book is printed. Ⓐ

12.1 Book document classes

In this section, we briefly discuss the way in which `book` and `amsbook`, the two standard book document classes, differ from the corresponding article document classes. Ⓐ

12.1.1 Sectioning

Both `book` and `amsbook` document classes have a high-level sectioning unit that the article document classes do not have: the chapter unit is invoked with the `\chapter` command. Ⓐ

There is also one more sectioning unit, the *part*, invoked with the `\part` command, which has no effect on other sectioning commands. It is generally placed between groups of chapters in longer documents; see the present book for an example. Both `\chapter` and `\part` take a title as an argument. The `\chapter` command has an optional argument that works just like the optional argument of the `\section` command:

```
\chapter[short_title]{title}
```

The optional *short_title* argument is used in the running head and table of contents. Protect any fragile commands in *short_title* with the `\protect` command; see Section 2.3.3.

Here is the whole hierarchy:

```
\part

\chapter
   \section
      \subsection
         \subsubsection
            \paragraph
               \subparagraph
```

Part V of this book is introduced by the command

```
\part{Long documents}\label{P:long}
```

Note that `\ref{P:long}` typesets as V. The present chapter starts with

```
\chapter{Books in \LaTeX}\label{C:Books}
```

`\ref{C:Books}` is typeset as 12 and not V.12 because part numbers do not affect chapter numbers.

Book document classes, as a rule, do not number subsubsections (or any of the sectioning divisions below that level).

Equations in chapters

By default, equations are numbered from 1 within chapters; so in Chapter 1, the equations will be numbered (1), (2), and so forth.

Ⓐ The amsmath package provides the

```
\numberwithin{equation}{chapter}
```

command, to be placed in the preamble. This command will cause equations in Chapter 2 to be numbered as (2.1), (2.2), and so on.

12.1.2 *Division of the body*

The book document classes formalize the division of the body into three parts:

Front matter The material that appears in the front of the document, including the title pages (normally four), table of contents, preface, introduction, and so on. LaTeX numbers these pages using roman numerals. The front matter is introduced with the `\frontmatter` command.

Main matter The main part of the book, including the appendices (if any). Page numbering starts from 1 using arabic numerals. The main matter is introduced with the `\mainmatter` command.

Back matter Material that appears in the back of the book, including the bibliography, index, and various other sections, such as the colophon, afterword, and so on. The back matter is introduced with the `\backmatter` command.

In the front and back matter, the `\chapter` command does not produce a chapter number but the title is listed in the table of contents. So you can start your introduction with

```
\chapter{Introduction}
```

Within such a chapter, you should use the *-ed forms of the other sectioning commands (`\section`, `\subsection`, and so on); otherwise you will have sections with numbers such as 0.1 and 0.2 (unless you explicitly reformat the section numbers; see Section 9.5.1).

In the main matter, the `\appendix` command marks the beginning of the appendices. Each subsequent chapter becomes a new appendix. For example,

```
\appendix
\chapter{A geometric proof of the Main Theorem}\label{A:geom}
```

produces an appendix with the given title.

Note that appendices may be labeled and cross-referenced like any other sectioning command. In Appendix A, sections are numbered A.1, A.2, and so on; subsections in A.1 are numbered A.1.1, A.1.2, and so on. The precise form these numbers take, of course, depends on the document class, packages, and user-specific changes (see Section 9.5.1).

12.1.3 Document class options

The options (and defaults) for the book document classes are the same as those of other document classes (see Sections 7.1.1 and 8.5) with a few exceptions:

Two-sided printing

Options: `twoside`
`oneside`

Default: `twoside`

The `twoside` option formats the output for printing on both sides of a page (duplexing). The default for the book document classes is `twoside`.

Titlepage

Options: `titlepage`
`notitlepage`

Default: `titlepage`

The `titlepage` option creates a separate title page. The `notitlepage` option creates no separate pages. For the book document classes the default is `titlepage`.

Chapter start

Options: `openright`
`openany`

Default: `openright`

A chapter always starts on a new page. The `openright` option starts each chapter on an odd page, while the `openany` option starts each chapter on the first available new page.

12.1.4 Title pages

The `book` document class supports the `\title`, `\author`, `\date`, and `\maketitle` commands, as described in Section 1.7. The default visual design, however, is completely different.

Ⓐ The `amsbook` document class supports the same commands as `amsart`; see Section 8.2 for specifics.

You can design your own title page within the `titlepage` environment, which does not require the use of the `\maketitle` command. Title pages for publications, of course, should be created by a book designer and the publisher.

12.2 Tables of contents, lists of tables and figures

A long document, as a rule, has a table of contents. It may also include a list of figures and a list of tables.

12.2.1 Tables of contents

When you typeset your document, LaTeX creates a file with the `toc` extension. The next time the document is typeset, the `toc` file is also typeset and included in your typeset document at the point where the command

```
\tableofcontents
```

appears in the source file, usually in the front matter. If your source file is named `myart.tex`, the `toc` file will be named `myart.toc`. This file lists all the sectioning units (parts, chapters, sections, appendices, and so on), as well as their titles and page numbers.

If you already have a `toc` file, the `\tableofcontents` command typesets a table of contents using the previously created `toc` file and creates a new `toc` file.

LaTeX will add a line to the table of contents formatted like a section title if you include the command

```
\addcontentsline{toc}{section}{text_to_be_added}
```

in your source file. There are three arguments:

1. The first argument informs LaTeX that a line, the third argument, should be added to the `toc` file.
2. The second argument specifies how the line should be formatted in the table of contents. In our example, the second argument is `section`, so the line will be

formatted as a section title in the table of contents. The second argument must be the name of a sectioning command (`part`, `chapter`, `section`, `subsection`, `subsubsection`, `paragraph`, or `subparagraph`).

3. The third argument is the text to be added.

You can add an unformatted line to the table of contents with the command

```
\addtocontents{toc}{text_to_be_added}
```

Such a command can also be used to add vertical spaces to the table of contents. For instance, if you wanted to add some vertical space before a part, you could insert the following line before the sectioning command for the part:

```
\addtocontents{toc}{\protect\vspace{10pt}}
```

The `toc` file is easy to read; you will find that the lines within it are self-explanatory. The following are typical lines from the table of contents file for a document using the `book` document class (they would look different if the document used an AMS document class): 

```
\contentsline {section}{\numberline {5-4.}Top matter}{119}
\contentsline {subsection}{\numberline {5-4.1.}Article info}{119}
\contentsline {subsection}{\numberline {5-4.2.}Author info}{121}
```

Section 9.5.1 explains how you can specify which levels of sectioning will appear in the table of contents. Section 2.4 of *The LaTeX Companion* [17] lists the style parameters for the table of contents. It also shows you how to define new `toc`-like files and use multiple tables of contents in a single document (for instance, adding a mini table of contents for each chapter).

Tip You may have to typeset the document three times to get the table of contents and the rest of the document right.

---

1. The first typesetting creates the `toc` file.
2. The second inserts the table of contents with the old page numbers into the typeset document, re-records the page numbers (which may have changed as a result of the insertion) and cross-references in the `aux` file, and generates a new `toc` file with the correct page numbers.
3. The third typesetting uses these new `aux` and `toc` files to typeset the document correctly (and creates a new `toc` file).

Recall from Section 2.3.3 that fragile commands in a movable argument must be `\protect`-ed. Here is a simple example using the table of contents: If the document contains the `\section` command

```
\section{The function \( f(x^{2}) \)}
```

(see Section 4.1 for the `\(` and `\)` commands), the section title will be stored in the `toc` file as

```
\contentsline {section}{\numberline
{1}The function \relax $ f(x^{2}) \relax \GenericError { }{LaTeX
Error: Bad math environment delimiter}{See the LaTeX manual or
LaTeX Companion for explanation.}{Your command was
ignored.\MessageBreak Type I <command> <return> to replace it
with another command,\MessageBreak or <return> to continue
without it.}}{1}
```

and the log file will contain the message

```
! LaTeX Error: Bad math environment delimiter.

See the LaTeX manual or LaTeX Companion for explanation.
Type  H <return>  for immediate help.
 ...

l.1 ...continue without it.}}{1}
```

Error messages usually refer to a line in the source file, but in this case the error message refers to a line in the `toc` file.

The correct form for this section title is

```
\section{The function \protect\( f(x^{2}) \protect\)}
```

or, even simpler,

```
\section{The function $f(x^{2})$}
```

Note that this example is merely an illustration of unprotected fragile commands in movable arguments. As a rule, avoid using formulas in (sectioning) titles.

12.2.2 *Lists of tables and figures*

If you place a `\listoftables` command in the document, LaTeX will store information for the list of tables in a `lot` file. The list of tables is inserted into the body of your document at the point where the command appears (normally in the front matter, following the table of contents).

A list of figures (similar to a list of tables) can be compiled with the command `\listoffigures`. This command creates an auxiliary file with the extension `lof`.

An optional argument of the `\caption` commands in your tables and figures can replace the argument in the list of tables and figures. Typically, the optional argument is used to specify a shorter caption for the list of tables or list of figures. There are other uses. For instance, you may notice that, as a rule, captions should be terminated by periods. If the book style you use fills the space between the text and the page number with dots, the extra period will look bad. This problem goes away if you use the following form of the `\caption` command:

```
\caption[title]{title.}
```

There are analogs of the table of contents commands discussed in Section 12.2 for use with tables and figures. The command

```
\addtocontents{lot}{line_to_add}
```

adds a line to the list of tables (or figures with the first argument `lof`).

12.3 Splitting and combining files

It is often convenient to write a LaTeX document in several pieces. There are two commands that can be used to combine separate files into one document; we will discuss them in Section 12.3.1. To e-mail a project, you can combine a number of files into one large file; see Section 12.3.3.

12.3.1 `\input` and `\include`

You can piece together a long document with the `\input` and `\include` commands. For example,

```
\input{subfile}
```

will insert the contents of the file `subfile.tex` as if its contents had been typed at that place in the document (the end-of-file provides no spacing, so be careful). You can also use the `\include` command for the same purpose, however, an `\include`-ed file will always start on a new page.

As an example, if your document contains five chapters (for another simple example, see Appendix F), in files named `chapter1.tex` and so on, and an appendix in the file named `appendix.tex`, you could assemble the document with the following commands:

```
\include{chapter1}
\include{chapter2}
\include{chapter3}
\include{chapter4}
\include{chapter5}
\include{appendix}
```

The \include command has some advantages over \input, the most important of which is that it allows you to use the \includeonly command. If you are currently working on Chapter 4, you can put the command

```
\includeonly{chapter4}
```

in the preamble, and Chapter 4 will be the only chapter that is typeset but it will still have the correct page numbers, section numbers, and cross-references (more precisely, this information is derived from the last typesetting of the other chapters—see Section C.2.4). You could also have

```
\includeonly{chapter2,chapter5}
```

to typeset only Chapters 2 and 5.

You may place the lines

```
\includeonly{%
%chapter1,
 chapter2,
%chapter3,
%chapter4,
%chapter5,
%appendix,
}
```

in the preamble of your document and uncomment the lines corresponding to the chapters you want to typeset; in this example, only Chapter 2 would be typeset.

Rule ■ File termination
I recommend that you terminate every file that you \input or \include with an \endinput command.

If you terminate an \include-ed file with \end{document}, the typesetting of the document will terminate with a warning such as:

```
(\end occurred when \iftrue on line 6 was incomplete)
(\end occurred when \ifnum on line 6 was incomplete)
```

Remember that each included file starts on a new page. If this does not suit your needs, merge the source files into one large file for the final printing; alternatively, you could change all \include commands to \input commands.

Tip In the preamble, place the line

```
% \renewcommand{\include}{\input}
```

When you want to change all `\include` commands to `\input`, simply uncomment the above line (that is, remove the `%`).

For interactive inclusion of `\include`-ed files, use the askinclude package; you can find this package on CTAN (see Section 13.1), in the directory

```
/tex-archive/macros/latex/contrib/other/misc/
```

12.3.2 *Organizing your files*

Typesetting a longer document, such as this book, involves dozens of files. If they are not carefully organized, they will be hard to maintain.

In Appendix F, I present a very simple example of the files of a book. In this section, I will describe a "real-life" example: How are the files for this book organized.

The directory containing the files of this book contains only a few files: the master document, `LaTeXB3.tex`; the command file `LaTeXB3.sty`; and of course, all the auxiliary files that LaTeX creates.

The master document, `LaTeXB3.tex`, reads as follows:

```
% Math into LaTeX, third edition master document
\documentclass[leqno]{book}
\usepackage{LaTeXB3}
\makeindex

% For Macintosh:
\newcommand{\dirsep}{:}
\newcommand{\dirprefix}{:}
% For Unix
%\newcommand{\dirprefix}{}
%\newcommand{\dirsep}{/}

\includeonly{
%\dirprefix chapters\dirsep fm,% Front matter
%\dirprefix chapters\dirsep qf,% Quick Finder
%\dirprefix chapters\dirsep pr,% Preface
%\dirprefix chapters\dirsep intro,% Introduction
%\dirprefix chapters\dirsep sc,% Short course, Ch. 1
```

```
%\dirprefix chapters\dirsep tx,% text, Ch. 2
%\dirprefix chapters\dirsep dt,% displayed text, Ch. 3
%\dirprefix chapters\dirsep m,% math, Ch. 4
%\dirprefix chapters\dirsep mm,% multiline math, Ch. 5
%\dirprefix chapters\dirsep ld,% LaTeX docs and LaTeX,
                              % Chs. 6 and 7
%\dirprefix chapters\dirsep amsp,% AMS packages, Ch. 8
%\dirprefix chapters\dirsep cust,% customizing LaTeX, Ch. 9
%\dirprefix chapters\dirsep long,% BibTeX and Makeindex,
                                % Chs. 10 and 11
\dirprefix chapters\dirsep book,% writing books, Ch. 12
%\dirprefix chapters\dirsep web,% Web, Chs. 13 and 14
%\dirprefix chapters\dirsep apt,% tables, Appendices A and B
%\dirprefix chapters\dirsep apo,% Appendices C-G
                               % and bibliography
}

\begin{document}
\frontmatter
\include{\dirprefix chapters\dirsep fm}%Front matter
\shorttableofcontents
\tableofcontents
\listoftables
\listoffigures

\include{\dirprefix chapters\dirsep qf}% Quick Finder
\include{\dirprefix chapters\dirsep pr}% Preface
\include{\dirprefix chapters\dirsep intro}% Introduction

\mainmatter
\include{\dirprefix chapters\dirsep sc}% Short course, Ch. 1
\include{\dirprefix chapters\dirsep tx}% text, Ch. 2
\include{\dirprefix chapters\dirsep dt}% displayed text, Ch. 3
\include{\dirprefix chapters\dirsep m}% math, Ch. 4
\include{\dirprefix chapters\dirsep mm}% multiline math, Ch. 5
\include{\dirprefix chapters\dirsep ld}% LaTeX docs and LaTeX,
                                      % Chs. 6 and 7
\include{\dirprefix chapters\dirsep amsp}% AMS packages, Ch. 8
\include{\dirprefix chapters\dirsep cust}% customizing LaTeX,
                                        % Ch. 9
\include{\dirprefix chapters\dirsep long}% BibTeX and Makeindex,
                                        % Chs. 10 and 11
```

```
\include{\dirprefix chapters\dirsep book}% writing books,
                                         % Ch. 12
\include{\dirprefix chapters\dirsep web}% Web,
                                         % Chs. 13 and 14

\appendix
\include{\dirprefix chapters\dirsep apt}% tables,
                                         % Appendices A and B
\include{\dirprefix chapters\dirsep apo}% Appendices C-G
                                         % and bibliography

\backmatter
\renewcommand{\indexname}{Index}
\printindex
\end{document}
```

The `chapters` subdirectory contains the 16 files `\include`-ed in the master document. For every `\include`-ed file, such as `amsp.tex`, there is a corresponding subdirectory in `chapters` containing the graphics files for that chapter. There are more than 50 files in these subdirectories.

The `\includeonly` block is set up so that adding and removing a single `%` specifies whether a particular the chapter(s) will be typeset. To use this setup on a UNIX computer, you should comment out the two lines following `For Macintosh` and uncomment the two lines following `For Unix`. See Section 9.1.1 for a more detailed discussion.

Unfortunately, this organization makes typing `\includegraphics` commands very cumbersome. For instance, to include the EPS graphics file for Figure 5.2, you would have to type the command

```
\includegraphics{\dirprefix chapters\dirsep sc%
                \dirsep aligndouble.eps}
```

The `\graphicspath` command, provided by the graphics package, comes to the rescue (see Section 6.4.3). This command lists all the directories that should be searched for graphics files. For this book, we included the following command in `LaTeXB3.sty` (we reproduce only a few lines of the command):

```
\graphicspath{...
{\dirprefix chapters\dirsep sc\dirsep}%
{\dirprefix chapters\dirsep tx\dirsep}%
{\dirprefix chapters\dirsep m\dirsep}
...}
```

Note that if you use the `\graphicspath` command, then you must make sure that each graphics file has a unique name.

12.3.3 *Combining files*

If you want to e-mail or FTP your LaTeX document to someone, you often have to send a number of additional files, such as command files, document class files, EPS graphics files, and so on. LaTeX makes it easy to package all your files into one large file. Let us assume that along with your main document, you want to send the `lattice.sty` command file and the `myart.cls` document class file.

To do so, you would place *before* the `\documentclass` command in your main document file the following commands:

```
\begin{filecontents}{lattice.sty}
% Command file for lattice papers
   ....
   ....
\end{filecontents}

\begin{filecontents}{myart.cls}
% Document class myart.cls
% Use it with all Proceedings submissions
   ....
   ....
\end{filecontents}
```

When the document is typeset, the lines in each `filecontents` environment are written to a file with the name given as the environment's argument, provided that such a file does not already exist. LaTeX informs you when it creates a file by writing an entry in the log file,

```
LaTeX Warning: Writing file 'lattice.sty'.
```

On the other hand, if the file `lattice.sty` already exists, you would get the warning

```
LaTeX Warning: File 'lattice.sty' already exists on the system.
               Not generating it from this source.
```

When LaTeX gets to the lines

```
\documentclass{myart}
\usepackage{lattice}
```

in the main document, the `myart.cls` document class and the lattice package are already available for input.

12.4 *Logical design*

The discussion of logical and visual design in Section 1.11 applies to books even more than to articles. Since books are long and complex documents, errors in the logical design are much harder to correct.

Let us review some common-sense rules:

Rule 1 ■ Stick with the sectioning commands provided by the document class. Define the nonstandard structures you wish to use as environments.

Here is an obvious bad example:

```
\vspace{18pt}

\noindent \textbf{Theorem 1.1.}
\textit{This is bad.}

\vspace{18pt}
```

And a good way to achieve the same result:

```
\begin{theorem}\label{T:Goodtheorem}
This is a good theorem.
\end{theorem}
```

The bad example creates a number of difficulties:

- You have to number the theorems yourself. Adding, deleting, and rearranging theorems becomes difficult; updating cross-references is even harder.
- It is difficult to keep such constructs consistent.
- If the publisher decides to increase the white space before and after the theorems to 20 points, finding and changing all the appropriate commands becomes a tedious task.

Rule 2 ■ Define frequently used constructs as commands.

Rather than

```
\textbf{Warning! Do not exceed this amount!}
```

define

```
\newcommand{\important}[1]{\textbf{#1}}
```

and type your warnings as

```
\important{Warning! Do not exceed this amount!}
```

You or your editor can then change all the warnings to a different style with ease.

Rule 3 ■ Avoid text style commands.

If you use small caps for acronyms, do not type

```
\textsc{ibm}
```

but rather define

```
\newcommand{\ibm}{\textsc{ibm}}
```

and then

```
\ibm
```

or more generally

```
\newcommand{\acronym}[1]{\textsc{#1}}
```

and then

```
\acronym{ibm}
```

Rule 4 ■ Avoid white space commands.

Occasionally, you may feel that there should be some white space separating two paragraphs, so you do the following:

```
paragraph 1

\medskip

paragraph 2
```

It would be better to define a new command, say `\separate`, as

```
\newcommand{\separate}{\medskip}
```

and type the previous example as

```
paragraph 1

\separate

paragraph 2
```

Now such white space can be adjusted throughout the entire document by simply redefining one command. Note that redefining `\medskip` itself may have unintended side effects:

- Many environments depend on LaTeX's definition of `\medskip`
- You may have used `\medskip` in other situations as well

Here is a short list of commands you should try not to use:

```
\bigskip  \hfil   \hspace   \parskip    \vfill  \vspace
\break    \hfill  \kern     \smallskip  \vglue
\eject    \hglue  \medskip  \vfil       \vskip
```

12.5 Final preparations for the publisher

While reading this book, you have come across a number of "don't"-s. Most are practices you should avoid while writing articles. When writing a book, it is even more important not to violate these rules.

When the editors (including the copy editor) are finished with your manuscript and you have the document class designed for the book, then you can start on the final preparations.

Step 1 ■ Eliminate all TeX macros.

TeX macros—that is, Plain TeX macros that are not part of LaTeX (not listed as LaTeX commands in the index of this book)—may interfere with LaTeX in unexpected ways; they may also cause problems with the style file that is created for your book. See also Section G.1.1 on specific TeX commands to absolutely avoid using in a LaTeX document: These commands are TeX macros redefined by LaTeX.

Step 2 ■ Collect all of your user-defined commands and environments together in one place, preferably in a separate command file (see Section 9.3).

Step 3 ■ Make sure that user-defined commands for notations and user-defined environments for structures are used consistently throughout your document.

This book uses the command `\doc` for document names; so `intrart` is typed as `\doc{intrart}`. Of course, `\texttt{intrart}` gives the same result, but if you intermix `\doc{intrart}` and `\texttt{intrart}` commands, you lose the ability to easily change the way document names are displayed.

Step 4 ■ Watch out for vertical white space adding up:

- Do not directly follow one displayed math environment with another. Multiple adjacent lines of displayed mathematics should all be in the same environment.
- If your style file uses interparagraph spacing, avoid beginning paragraphs with displayed math.

For instance,

```
\[
   x=y
\]
\[
   x=z
\]
```

is wrong. Use, instead, an `align` or `gather` environment.

Step 5 ■ If possible, do not place "tall" mathematical formulas inline; all formulas that might change the interline spacing, as a rule, should be displayed.

You can find examples on pages 17 and 318. One more example is double hat accents used inline: $\hat{\hat{A}}$.

Step 6 ■ Read the log file.

- Watch for line-too-wide warnings (see Section 1.1.3).
- Check for font substitutions (see Section 2.6.8).

If you find lines that are too wide:

- Fix wide lines by rewording the sentence or adding optional hyphens (see Section 2.4.9).
- Break displayed formulas so that they fit comfortably within the line.

Font substitutions can also cause problems:

- A font that was used in typesetting the document may not be the font you intended. Missing fonts are substituted and the substitute fonts are rarely satisfactory.
- A special trap: Your publisher may have more (or maybe fewer) fonts than you do! As a result, the font substitutions on your publisher's system may be different from those on yours. Make sure that the fonts you use are not substituted.

Step 7 ■ Do not assume that gray boxes or color illustrations will appear when published exactly the way that they look on your monitor or printer.

Color work requires calibration of monitors and printers; it is often best left to the experts at the publisher.

Step 8 ■ Do not assume that the application that created your EPS files (see Section 6.4.3) can create high-quality EPS files.

Many applications can create EPS files or convert files to EPS format. Very few do it right. Ask your publisher what applications they recommend you use.

12.6 Final preparations for printing

Many publishers will take your manuscript, prepared as described in Section 12.5, and guide it through the final steps for printing. Some books are, however, prepared by the authors for printing. If your book falls into this category, there are a few more things you should do before you print your book.

Break the book into pages

Make sure that you are satisfied with the way the document is broken into pages by LaTeX and with the placement of the `figure` and `table` environments (see Section 6.4.3). If necessary, you should make last-minute changes to adjust pagebreaks. You may find the `\enlargethispage` command (see Section 2.7.3) very helpful at this stage; just be sure to apply it on both facing pages.

Now break the book into pages, taking care to ensure that

- Page numbers in the index are correct
- \pageref references (see Section 6.4.2) are correct
- Marginal comments (see Section 2.9.3) are properly placed
- Tables and figures are properly placed

Move the figure and table environments (see Section 6.4.3) physically close to the text they appear near in the typeset version, and change the optional argument of the figure and table environments to h!.

Where pages break, add the three commands \linebreak, \pagebreak, and \noindent.

Here is an example. The bottom of page 3 and the top of page 4 of my book *General Lattice Theory* [29] are shown in Figure 12.1.

The paragraph split by the page break is

```
In other words, lattice theory singles out a special type of
poset for detailed investigation. To make such a definition
worthwhile, it must be shown that this class of posets is
a very useful class, that there are many such posets in
various branches of mathematics (analysis, topology, logic,
algebra, geometry, and so on), and that a general study of
these posets will lead to a better understanding of the behavior
of the examples. This was done in the first edition of
G.~Birkhoff's \emph{Lattice Theory} \cite{gB40}. As we go along,
we shall see many examples, most of them in the exercises.
For a general survey of lattices in mathematics, see
```

In other words, lattice theory singles out a special type of poset for detailed investigation. To make such a definition worthwhile, it must be shown that this class of posets is a very useful class, that there are many such posets in various branches of mathematics (analysis, topology, logic, algebra, geometry, and so on), and that a general study of these posets will lead to a better understanding of the behavior of the examples. This was done in the first edition of G. Birkhoff's

---

4 I. First Concepts

Lattice Theory [1940]. As we go along, we shall see many examples, most of them in the exercises. For a general survey of lattices in mathematics, see G. Birkhoff [1967] and H. H. Crapo and G.-C. Rota [1970].

Figure 12.1: A page break.

```
G.~Birkhoff \cite{gB67} and H.~H. \index{Crapo, H. H.}Crapo
and G.-C.~\index{Rota, G.-C.}Rota \cite{CR70}.
```

When typesetting this paragraph, LaTeX inserts a page break following
`This was done in the first edition of G.~Birkhoff's.`
So this paragraph is edited as follows:

```
In other words, lattice theory singles out a special type of
poset for detailed investigation. To make such a definition
worthwhile, it must be shown that this class of posets is
a very useful class, that there are many such posets in
various branches of mathematics (analysis, topology, logic,
algebra, geometry, and so on), and that a general study of
these posets will lead to a better understanding of the behavior
of the examples. This was done in the first edition of
G.~Birkhoff's \linebreak

\pagebreak

\noindent \emph{Lattice Theory} \cite{gB40}. As we go along,
we shall see many examples, most of them in the exercises.
For a general survey of lattices in mathematics, see G.~Birkhoff
\cite{gB67} and H.~H. \index{Crapo, H. H.}Crapo and
G.-C.~\index{Rota, G.-C.}Rota \cite{CR70}.
```

This change will not affect the appearance of the typeset page, but now pages 3 and 4 are separated by a command. Of course, if the page break is between paragraphs, only the `\pagebreak` command is needed. If the break occurs in the middle of a word, use `\-\linebreak` to add a hyphen.

This method works about 95 percent of the time. Occasionally, you will have to drop either the `\linebreak` or the `\pagebreak` command.

Make sure that any `\index` or `\label` commands are moved to the appropriate half of the paragraph.

Balance the white space on each page as necessary.

Generate the index after the document is broken into pages.

Polish the auxiliary files

Typeset the document one last time, and then place the `\nofiles` command in the preamble (see Section C.2.4) to make sure that the auxiliary files will not be overwritten.

Normally, you should not have to edit the table of contents (`toc`) file (or the `lot` and `lof` files); see Section 12.2. Your style file should take care of the formatting. Sometimes, however, an unfortunate page break makes editing necessary.

Finally, create the index (`ind`) file from the new `aux` file, as described in Section 11.3.

The Chicago Manual of Style [12] has a section on bad breaks, remedies, and *Continued* lines in the index. Break the `ind` file into pages; to minimize bad breaks, use the `\enlargethispage` command where necessary (see Section 2.7.3). Add any *Continued* entries. See the index of this book for examples.

Finally, add `\markboth` commands to each page to create headers that show the item ranges.

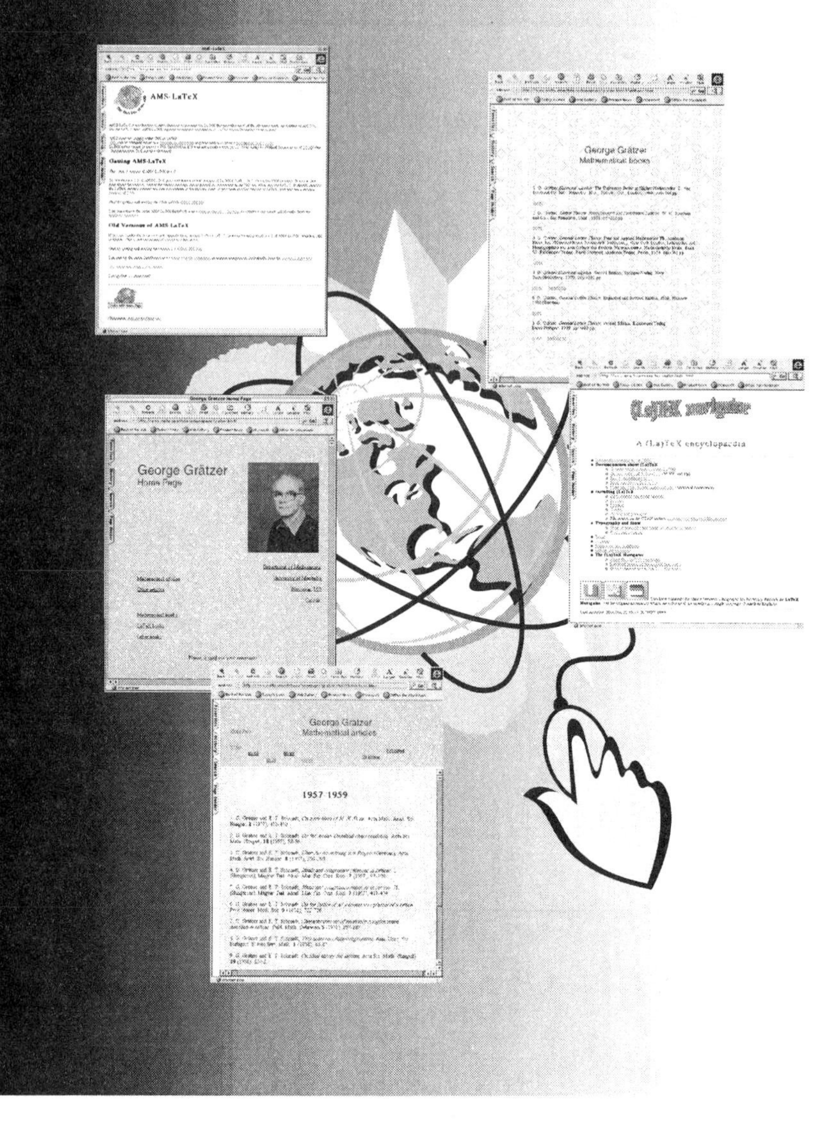

AMS-LaTeX
Getting AMS-LaTeX
Old Versions of AMS-LaTeX
George Grätzer
Mathematical books
George Grätzer
Home Page
A (La)TeX encyclopaedia
George Grätzer
Mathematical articles
1957–1959

PART VI

Math and the Web

CHAPTER

13

TEX, LATEX, and the Internet

The world around us is changing very fast: The Internet is playing an ever larger role in our lives. While a few years back, for most of us, the Internet was no more than e-mail and FTP, today we have electronic journals, World Wide Web pages, and math on the Web. These developments make LATEX all the more important as the main tool for getting high-quality typeset math onto the Internet. This chapter deals with the Internet as a useful source of LATEX information. We shall discuss math on the Internet in Chapter 14.

The Internet is clearly the main depository of all matters LATEX, and the Comprehensive TEX Archive Network (CTAN) is the preeminent collection of TEX-related material available. Section 13.1 discusses how and where to find the LATEX distribution, AMS and LATEX packages, and the sample files for this book on CTAN.

There are many different implementations of TEX available: I briefly list some commercial, free, and shareware versions in Sections 13.2 and 13.3. Various international TEX user groups (especially TUG, the TEX Users Group) and the American Mathematical Society play a significant role in supporting LATEX. I discuss some of the major user groups in Section 13.4.

Finally, you will find a great deal of useful information on the Internet concerning LATEX. I provide some pointers in Section 13.5.

13.1 Obtaining files from the Internet

In general, there are two types of Internet sites from which you can download files:

- FTP sites (using the file transfer protocol)
- Web (World Wide Web) sites (using the HTTP protocol)

To access them, use a *client* application on your computer to connect to a *server* on another machine. Today, most *Web browsers*, which are designed to connect to Web sites, also handle FTP transfers.

PCs and UNIX computers include an FTP client as part of the system distribution. On a Macintosh, use Fetch from Dartmouth College
`http://www.dartmouth.edu/pages/softdev/fetch.html`
or Anarchie Pro, by Peter Lewis
`http://www.anarchie-pro.com/anarchie.html`

Throughout this book, I have told you where you can find some files on CTAN. Many of those files, in fact, are probably already on your computer; they came with your LATEX distribution. Before you go to CTAN to fetch a file, you should first check to see if you already have it. Go to CTAN if you do not or if you want to update it.

The Comprehensive TEX Archive Network

The Comprehensive TEX Archive Network (CTAN) is the preeminent collection of TEX-related material on the Internet. There are three main CTAN hosts:

- U.S.
  - FTP address: `ftp://ctan.tug.org/`
  - Web address: `http://www.ctan.org/`
- U.K.
  - FTP address: `ftp://ftp.tex.ac.uk/`
  - Web address: `http://www.tex.ac.uk/`
- Germany
  - FTP address: `ftp://ftp.dante.de/`
  - Web address: `http://www.dante.de/`

It is easier to search for a file or package using the Web sites, but if you know exactly what you want and where it is, downloading from an FTP site can be faster.

There are many *full mirrors* (exact duplicates) of CTAN and many *partial mirrors*—more than 50 as of this writing. To reduce network load, you should try to use a mirror located near you. You can get a list of mirrors by retrieving (from any CTAN site) the document
`/tex-archive/CTAN.sites`

The LaTeX distribution

The main LaTeX directory on CTAN is /tex-archive/macros/latex/. It has a number of subdirectories, including

- base—the current LaTeX distribution
- required—packages that all LaTeX installations should have, such as the AMS packages, the LaTeX tools, Babel, graphics, and PSNFSS (for using PostScript fonts)
- contrib—user-contributed packages
- unpacked—the base LaTeX distribution in a form that can be downloaded and placed directly in your TEX input directory

The AMS packages

Ⓐ Chances are that you received the AMS packages with your LaTeX distribution. If you did not, or if you want to update them, go to a CTAN site:

- /tex-archive/fonts/amsfonts/latex/
- /tex-archive/macros/latex/required/amslatex/

or to the AMS site:

http://www.ams.org/tex/amslatex.html

Sample files

The sample files for this book are available from CTAN sites in the directory
/tex-archive/info/MiL3/
You can also download the directory MiL3 from
ftp://server.maths.umanitoba.ca/pub/gratzer/

13.2 Commercial TEX implementations

Some commercial TEX implementations are *integrated:* The application provides an editor, DVI viewer (video driver), and DVI printer driver, as well as the TEX engine. Commercial TEX implementations are also more likely to provide technical support; for a novice, this may be an important consideration.

Two popular integrated implementations are

- PCTEX for a PC: http://www.pctex.com/
- TEXTURES for a Macintosh: http://www.bluesky.com/

Scientific Word incorporates a LaTeX preprocessor, making LaTeX similar to a WYSIWYG experience; see

http://www.mackichan.com/

Some users prefer a *nonintegrated* setup, which allows them to use the editor of their choice and the best tools for viewing and printing available for their platform. These configurations also allow you to run TEX and the printing application in batch mode, which can be useful for automatically creating documents that change frequently (e.g., price lists, schedules). One such package (for the PC) is Y&Y TEX (`http://www.yandy.com/`).

When producing documents with diagrams that contain formulas, it is important that you be able to copy typeset TEX formulas to Adobe Illustrator (or a similar application), so that the formulas look the same in your diagrams as in your typeset document. All of the above packages have this feature. (Of course, you must use the PostScript CM and AMS fonts; see Section D.1.)

The AMS maintains a list of commercial implementations—see
`http://www.ams.org/tex/commercial-tex-vendors.html`

13.3 *Free and shareware implementations*

The most popular TEX implementations are emTEX (running on DOS), MiKTEX (on all flavors of Windows), and teTEX (UNIX, Linux), all of which are available from CTAN.

The TEXLive CD is distributed free to all TUG members, and is also available from many other user groups. TEXLive includes TEX implementations for several UNIX variants, Windows 95/NT, and Macintosh. It also includes some of the files available on CTAN.

The 4allTEX (for Windows) CD-ROM is available from the Dutch user group:

`http://4tex.ntg.nl/`
e-mail: `ntg@ntg.nl`

The most popular shareware implementations on the Macintosh are OzTEX,
`http://www.trevorrow.com/oztex/`
and CMacTEX, which is available on CTAN in the directory
`/tex-archive/nonfree/systems/mac/cmactex/`

Most Linux distributions include teTEX as an optional package; if not, you can find the source code on CTAN in the directory
`/tex-archive/systems/unix/linux/tetex/`

The AMS has a full list of freeware and shareware TEX implementations—see
`http://www.ams.org/tex/public-domain-tex.html`

13.4 *TEX user groups and the* AMS

There are many user groups around the world that encourage and help people to use TEX and LATEX.

The TeX Users Group

The TeX Users Group (TUG) does a tremendous job of supporting and promoting TeX, publishing a quarterly journal (*TUGboat*), and organizing an annual international conference. TUG also helps support the LaTeX3 team in maintaining LaTeX and developing LaTeX3.

Consider joining TUG if you have an interest in TeX or LaTeX. TUG's contact information is:

1466 NW Naito Parkway
Suite 3141
Portland, OR 97209–2820

Telephone: (503) 223-9994
E-mail: `office@tug.org`
Web page: `http://www.tug.org/`

International TeX user groups

There are also many TeX user groups that are geographic or linguistic in nature. Some of the main groups include

- Dante (Germany)
- GUTenberg (France)
- NTG (Netherlands)
- UK TUG (U.K.)

Links to all of these groups, and many more, can be found on TUG's Web site, at `http://www.tug.org/lugs.html`

The American Mathematical Society

The AMS provides excellent technical advice for using the AMS packages and AMSFonts. You can reach the AMS technical staff by e-mail at `tech-support@ams.org`, or by telephone at (800) 321-4267 or (401) 455-4080. You will also find a great deal of helpful TeX information on the AMS Web site, at `http://www.ams.org/tex/`

13.5 Some useful sources of LaTeX information

You may find the Frequently Asked Questions (FAQ) documents maintained on CTAN (in the `/tex-archive/help/` directory) useful. The UK TeX Users Group maintains its own FAQ list at
`http://www.tex.ac.uk/cgi-bin/texfaq2html?introduction=yes`

You can also ask most TEX-related questions in the Usenet newsgroup `comp.text.tex`.

Other useful places to start browsing include:

- LATEX Navigator
  `http://www.loria.fr/services/tex/index.html` (French)
  `http://www.loria.fr/services/tex/english/index.html` (English)
  `http://www.loria.fr/services/tex/german/index.html` (German)
- Sebastian Rahtz's Interesting TEX-related URLs
  `http://www.tug.org/interest.html`
- CTAN Catalogue
  `/help/Catalogue/ctfull.html`

All of these sites contain many links to other useful sites. The last is a Web index of many of the packages that have been developed for use with LATEX.

CHAPTER

14

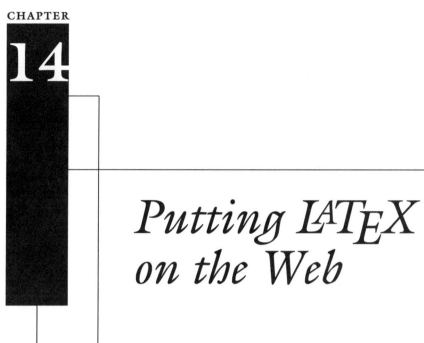

Putting LaTeX on the Web

The popularity and ease of use of the World Wide Web makes it one of the best ways to share your LaTeX articles, reports, and books.

To understand how best to proceed with this task, you have to learn a bit about file formats (especially PDF, PostScript, and Encapsulated PostScript) and another markup language, HTML.

Here we are entering a very technical field, full of acronyms,[1] most of them covering specifications running to hundreds of pages. Every section of this chapter deals with topics which are often treated by entire books. But by staying focused on our task—publishing LaTeX on the Web—we can keep this chapter short and practical.

The definitive book on this subject is *The LaTeX Web Companion: Integrating TeX, HTML and XML* by Michel Goossens and Sebastian Rahtz (with Eitan Gurari, Ross Moore, and Robert Sutor), which we will refer to as *The LaTeX Web Companion* [19].

[1] CGI, DSSSL, DTD, HTTP, MIME, SGML, XHTML, and XML, to name a few.

14.1 File formats

Publications on the Web are predominantly presented in one of the following three formats:

- Hypertext Markup Language, HTML
- PostScript language, PS
- Portable Document Format, PDF

and for LaTeX,

- Device Independent Format, DVI

14.1.1 HTML

Web pages are written in the markup language HTML (or some extension of it). It is a simple, yet powerful language for creating structured documents, providing headings, paragraphs, and listings. The final appearance of a document, that is, the appearance and positioning of the elements, is provided by the browser, the application with which you view the document.[2]

Here is the HTML code for a simple Web page:

```
<html>
   <head>
      <title>HTML can do math (a little)</title>
   </head>
   <body>
   <h1>A simple example
   </h1>
   <p>
   Hello, <i>new users</i>!
   <p>
   We link to my Web site:
   <a href="http://www.maths.umanitoba.ca/homepages/gratzer/">
   Gratzer Homepage</a>
   <p>
   And here is a list:
   <ul>
      <li>We do a squared<br>
          a <sup>2</sup><p>
          <!-- Do not try to do square root! -->
```

[2]While this lack of control makes the life of Web page designers difficult, it is also inevitable; a Web page may be displayed on a variety of hardware, ranging from a two-page monitor to a hand-held communication device such as a cellular phone.

```
      <li>and a umlaut<br>
          George Gr&auml;tzer
   </ul>
   </body>
</html>
```

Type this code in as a text file (or use the `sample.html` file from the `samples` directory; see page 4) and open it as a file in your browser; you should see something close to Figure 14.1 in your browser (the title is shown above the example):

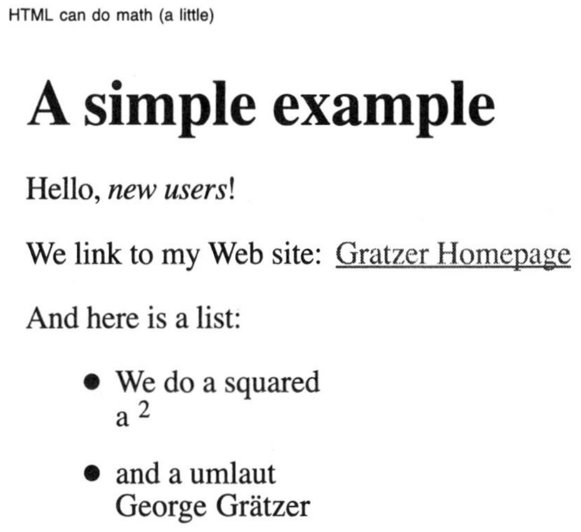

HTML can do math (a little)

A simple example

Hello, *new users*!

We link to my Web site: Gratzer Homepage

And here is a list:

- We do a squared
  a ^{2}
- and a umlaut
  George Grätzer

Figure 14.1: A simple Web page and its title.

We use this example to illustrate several points.

Tags There is a great deal of similarity between LaTeX and HTML. LaTeX commands and environments correspond to HTML *tags*:

- `<body>`, corresponding to `\begin{document}`
- `</body>`, corresponding to `\end{document}`
- The `<title>` and `</title>` construct is like a `\chapter` command; it provides a title that appears in the title bar of the Web page
- The `<h1>` and `</h1>` construct is like a `\section` command in an article
- The text within `<i>` and `</i>` is italicized, just like the argument of the `\textit` command in LaTeX
- The text within `<sup>` and `</sup>` is set as a superscript, as in the LaTeX construct `${}^{}$`
- `<p>` is a new paragraph, corresponding to the LaTeX command `\par`
- `<br>` forces a new line; it corresponds to the LaTeX command `\newline`
- The special character ä is typed in HTML as `ä`

Display A LaTeX user should easily accept that HTML leaves it up to the browser to determine the appearance of the section head; after all, in LaTeX, the document class determines how to typeset a section title. But HTML goes far beyond LaTeX: All display decisions are left to the browser. HTML markup is primarily for structure. (We are not going to discuss some newer extensions of HTML—such as Cascading Style Sheets—that allow you to specify some pretty significant aspects of visual appearance.)

Links If you click on the underlined Gratzer Homepage, your browser will load my Web page. Apart from the structural description of a document, links are the most important feature of HTML: the ability to link to another part of the same document, to another document on the same computer, or to any resource having a URL (Uniform Resource Locator, a Web address)—provided, of course, that your computer is connected to the Internet.

Many people use graphical authoring tools to create Web pages; those applications write the HTML code for the user. So while you do not have to learn HTML to create Web pages, you should still learn the basics so that you can help out your authoring tool should it run into trouble.

Even a limited knowledge of HTML is sufficient to allow you to edit the Web pages created by graphical authoring tools. Most tags should be easy to understand from their context by comparing the displayed Web page and the HTML source code. A table of special characters can be useful; you can find one in most books on HTML.

The most authorative source of information on HTML and its extensions is the World Wide Web Consortium's Web site. The W^{3}C is in charge of the existing Web standards and is responsible for developing new ones. Visit them at

```
http://www.w3c.org/
```

for lots of useful guides and reference material such as Dave Raggett's *Getting started with HTML* at

```
http://www.w3.org/MarkUp/Guide/
```

This guide links to his *More advanced features* and *Adding a touch of style.*

I would also recommend Chuck Musciano and Bill Kennedy's *HTML: The Definitive Guide* [49] and Ed Tittel and Steve James' *HTML4 for Dummies* [59]. (Online bookstores list a few hundred HTML titles.)

Unfortunately, HTML is not capable of displaying complex math. It has subscripts and superscripts, but lacks the hundreds of special symbols and math constructs provided by LaTeX. Some people have tried to overcome these limitations by converting math formulas into images and including the images in the Web pages, with varying degrees of success; see *The LaTeX Web Companion* [19] for a detailed review of LaTeX2HTML and TeX4ht.

Equation generation by Java applets can give much better results. WebEQ (from Geometry Technologies, Inc.), which processes a LaTeX-like markup language called WebTeX, uses this approach. See their Web site at `http://www.WebEQ.com/`.

MathML

In 1998, the World Wide Web Consortium published a recommendation describing the mathematical markup language MathML, for coding both high-quality visual display and semantic coding for mathematical content; the specification is currently in the final stages of development; see
`http://www.w3.org/TR/REC-MathML/`

For an introduction to MathML, see Robert Miner and Jeff Schaefer's *Gentle Introduction to MathML* [42]. The following simple example, based on an example in Miner and Schaefer's exposition, will give you a taste of how it works. We represent the equation $a^3 + 7b - c$, first using presentational tags, then using semantic tags. The presentational tags generally start with `m`, operator tags with `o`, identifier tags with `i`, and number tags with `n`. The `mrow` tags organize the code into groups.

```
<mrow>
   <msup>
      <mi>a</mi>
      <mn>3</mn>
   </msup>
   <mo>+</mo>
   <mrow>
      <mn>7</mn>
      <mo>&invisibletimes;</mo>
      <mi>b</mi>
   </mrow>
   <mo>-</mo>
   <mi>c</mi>
</mrow>
```

There is also a semantic—by meaning—coding using tags such as `minus`, `power`:

```
<apply>
   <minus/>
   <apply>
       <power/>
       <ci>a</ci>
       <cn>3</cn>
   </apply>
```

```
    <apply>
        <times/>
        <cn>7</cn>
        <ci>b</ci>
     </apply>
     <ci>c</ci>
</apply>
```

You can see that the first coding is quite appropriate if you want to display the formula. The second coding might be more appropriate if our goal is to pass the formula to a math application (such as Mathematica or Maple V) to carry out the computations or to a voice synthesizer.

This example also illustrates that you will not be expected to code formulas in MathML; most coding will be done by applications.

There are indications that the standard browsers may soon support MathML, at which point serious math could finally be displayed directly in a Web browser. This development will presumably be accompanied by applications that translate from LATEX to MathML.

14.1.2 *PostScript*

Adobe PostScript is the preeminent page-description language. Unlike the markup language HTML, which describes the structure of a document, PostScript describes how a page appears, including (normally) the fonts and the placement and shapes of all the elements in the document. Documents placed on the Web in PostScript format can be downloaded to any computer and print identically on all PostScript printers. Until the appearance of PDF, PostScript was the format of choice for sharing LATEX articles with diagrams or complex forms.

The PostScript version of a LATEX document is generally created using a DVI to PostScript converter. See Adobe Systems' *PostScript Language Reference Manual* [2] for a complete description of the PostScript programming language.

14.1.3 *PDF*

There are a number of disadvantages to using PostScript files on the Web:

- The files tend to be very large and cannot contain proprietary fonts unless those fonts are licensed for such use.
- They cannot be viewed until the whole file has been downloaded.
- If a PostScript file does not include a particular font and you do not have that font installed on your computer, then the font will be substituted (usually by Courier) causing graphically unacceptable rendering.

All of these concerns have been addressed by Adobe's Portable Document Format (PDF); see Adobe Systems' *Portable Document Format Reference Manual* [3] for a complete description of this file format.

PDF is based on the PostScript language, with some important differences:

- PDF is much more concise than PostScript; a PDF file normally is about 10 percent of the size of the corresponding PostScript file (the relative size range is 1–30 percent).
- Missing fonts are substituted by fonts with the same metrics, so that the size of the substituted text is the same as that of the original; in particular, there are no incorrect line breaks caused by the substitution.
- PDF files allow *partial downloading of fonts;* as a result, it is much easier to obtain permission to include proprietary fonts in PDF documents.
- PDF files can be downloaded and viewed in a Web browser one page at a time, without having to wait for the whole file to download first—provided that
  - The file was optimized (save the PDF file with `Save as...` and click on the optimized option)
  - The Web server cooperates
  - Your Web browser is properly configured (see below)

Like PostScript files, PDF files are created with special software.[3] You will need Adobe's Acrobat Distiller (or a similar application), which converts PostScript files to PDF. When downloaded, a PDF file can be read and printed using Acrobat Reader (or another PDF viewer). Acrobat Reader is available free of charge for PCs, Macs, and many UNIX computers from Adobe's Web site:
`http://www.adobe.com/prodindex/acrobat/readstep.html#reader`

You can create a PDF file on a Mac or PC in one step using Adobe's PDF Writer printer driver. By choosing this driver, the `Print` command will create a PDF file. But simplicity has its price:

- Many of the options you can set in Distiller are not available
- There are some quality limitations on the output
- You cannot include graphics

PDF files and Acrobat offer many nice features, including

- Efficient navigational tools—previous page, next page, previous view, next view, first page, last page, find, search (collections of documents), index, and lots of others
- Bookmarks
- Thumbnails of pages
- Editing (very limited)

[3]Hán Thế Thán's pdfTEX project provides a version of TEX that can create a PDF file instead of a DVI file. It is in development; see *The LATEX Web Companion* [19].

- Annotations (notes, text, and voice)
- Hypertext links to the same document or to another document

See Adobe Systems' *Adobe Acrobat 4.0 Classroom in a Book* [4] and Ted Padova's *Acrobat* PDF *Bible* [50] for the full set of features.

PDF files can also be used to make legacy documents available on the Web. For instance, if you go to my homepage on the Web,
`http://www.maths.umanitoba.ca/homepages/gratzer/`
and click on Mathematical articles, then 80–89, in the bottom frame you will find entry 102, which links to a PDF file. I created that PDF file by scanning the original article, saving the pages as PostScript files, converting them to PDF files, and finally stringing the pages together into a single document(using Acrobat Exchange).[4] The scanned PostScript files totalled 32 MB, the PDF file is 320 KB. The printed version of the PDF file is somewhat lower in quality than that of the original, but it is still quite satisfactory.

With the appropriate plug-in, your Web browser can view PDF files as they are downloaded:

- Your browser has a directory containing the plug-in files; make sure that the `PDF-Viewer` plug-in is there. (Acrobat Reader 4.0 or higher includes this plug-in; you obtain the plug-in when you install the application.)
- Go to the `Preferences` of your browser and find the application listing (`Helper applications`, `File helpers`, or a similar name). Find `Portable Document Format` and edit/change the application to `View with Plug-in` (or equivalent) and make sure that the plug-in selected is `PDFViewer` in the `Plug-ins` directory.

14.1.4 *Graphics file formats*

Of the hundred or so image formats on various computer platforms, publishing on the Web requires familiarity with the following four formats:

GIF GIF files compress solid areas of (8-bit) color while preserving sharp detail. GIFs use a lossless compression method, in which no data is discarded.

JPEG The JPEG format, designed for use with photographic images, uses 24-bit color and preserves the broad range and subtle variations in brightness and hue found in photographs. Sharp detail in images containing type or vector art created in illustration applications such as Illustrator can be degraded by the compression method used by JPEG.

PNG The PNG format supports color. Like GIFs, PNGs compress solid areas of color while preserving sharp detail, such as that in line art, logos, or illustrations with type.

[4] Adobe Capture now automates this process.

EPS An Encapsulated PostScript (EPS) file represents a single illustration to be placed in a LaTeX document. The file contains a PostScript illustration, with the following differences:

- At the beginning of the document, the size of the illustration (called its *bounding box*) is specified
- A bitmap version of the illustration may be included, for use by a display application
- There are some PostScript operators whose use is forbidden

Most graphics applications (such as Illustrator) can save (export) pictures in all four formats. All current computer platforms have utilities for converting one graphics format to another.

The standard browsers support GIF, JPEG, and PNG images. If you want to include an image in a Web page, these are your options.

The preferred mode of including illustrations in a LaTeX document is with the `\includegraphics` command; see Section 6.4.3. This command accepts EPS files but not PostScript files.

14.2 Choosing a file format

To publish a LaTeX document on the Web, you have to choose the file format for the document. Your choice depends on two factors:

1. How do you intend your audience to use your article?
   (a) Download only
   (b) View only
   (c) View and download
2. What tools are available to your intended audience?

14.2.1 Downloading only

Publishing a LaTeX document on the Web used to mean that you uploaded your document to your Web site, and anyone interested in reading it could download and print it.

There were a number of ways to achieve this goal:

TeX files

The easiest solution would seem to be to put your TeX source file on the Web; those who want it would download, typeset, and print it. So why is it that so few documents are posted as TeX files? The answer is that there are too many TeX variants:

- Plain TeX
- LaTeX 2.09
- The standard LaTeX (LaTeX 2_ε)
- $\mathcal{AMS}$-LaTeX 1.x
- $\mathcal{AMS}$-TeX
- REVTeX (for physics journals)

If you use one variant and the person downloading your document uses another, there is a good chance that there will be difficulties in typesetting your document. There are many other sources of problems:

- Incompatibilities between some LaTeX variants and some packages.
- Incompatibilities among packages.
- Some packages you use may be unavailable to the user.
- You use a complicated set of files and directories to arrange the parts of your LaTeX document; the user would have to reproduce that structure (and make any necessary changes to directory names and references because they are platform-dependent).
- You may use a package that works only with some types of DVI printer drivers.

Finally, most of us are not particularly proud of the way we write a LaTeX source file; we are satisfied so long as the typeset version looks nice. Few of us are ready to let the world see our LaTeX source. This leads us to the next file format: the typeset LaTeX document.

DVI files

Typesetting a LaTeX document produces a "Device Independent" or DVI file; see Sections 1.13 and C.2.2. The DVI format is device and computer-platform independent, so it seems like an ideal candidate for downloading from Web pages.

DVI files work well if the following conditions are met:

- The intended audience for your LaTeX documents is comprised of TeX users who have access to the same fonts you have used.
- Your documents contain no graphics.
- Your documents do not use LaTeX packages that make special assumptions about the DVI printer driver used.

If an article uses graphics (diagrams, graphs, and so on), this approach is awkward because all the graphics files will have to be separately downloaded along with the DVI file (and unless the graphics files are in EPS format, you may also have to worry about their platform independence).

DVI and LaTeX files also cannot be directly displayed by your browser; the IBM techexplorer may change that for LaTeX files, see
`http://www.software.ibm.com/network/techexplorer/`

PostScript files

When you convert your LaTeX document to PostScript format (see Section 14.1.2), you should include all the fonts you use in your document in the PostScript file (except for the standard 13 built into every PostScript printer). The PostScript file then will contain everything your document needs: the DVI file, any illustrations, and the fonts. So there is only one file to download and the document can be printed with complete accuracy on any PostScript printer[5] (or any other printer with an appropriate rasterizing application). Unfortunately, PostScript files are bulky. My lattice theory book of 600 pages turns into a 10.1 MB PostScript file. The size of these files can be quite an obstacle to downloading them with a modem.

PDF files

If you create a PDF file from your PostScript file as discussed in Section 14.1.3, you have the best of both worlds: typographically perfect printing and reasonable file size. Moreover, your Web publication can be read and printed with Acrobat Reader, which is available free of charge; see Section 14.1.3.

This perfect scheme also has one drawback: You must make certain that your intended audience has (the appropriate version of) Acrobat Reader installed.

14.2.2 *Viewing only*

If you go to my homepage on the Web,
`http://www.maths.umanitoba.ca/homepages/gratzer/`
and click on Mathematical articles, then 1991–2000, and in the bottom frame find entry 172, and click on abstract, the abstract of the article will appear in the bottom frame.

This abstract is an image. As we mentioned in Section 13.2, many TeX implementations allow you to transfer a typeset page into Illustrator (or a similar application) and export it as a GIF. The resulting GIF image can be included in a Web page and viewed in a browser.

It should be obvious from the discussion in Section 14.1.4 that a typeset page image should be saved as a GIF or PNG file.

Viewing such an image on the monitor is fine; printing, however, will produce poor results because the image uses fonts rendered to screen resolution (between 72 and 100 dpi), whereas most printers print at 300, 600, or 1200 dpi.

You can even use this method to display a whole article, converting it into images one page at a time and then linking them together. This method is time consuming and, again, the printed version is quite unsatisfactory, though readable.

Scanned images and similar illustrations should be converted to JPEG format.

[5] Assuming, of course, that all the included fonts are PostScript fonts and the graphics are not fixed at a particular resolution.

14.2.3 *Viewing and downloading*

The file formats available for viewing are poor candidates for downloading, and vice versa. Recent developments make PDF files ideal for both purposes. With the appropriate plug-in, your browser can even view PDF files as they are downloaded; see Section 14.1.3.

With this setup, when you click on a link to a PDF document, it will be displayed *in the browser window* by the Acrobat Reader application. You can then use the paging commands of the plug-in to look at the document and, if desired, print it.

14.3 *Hyperlinks and PDF files*

It is tedious to set hyperlinks one at a time in your PDF file. Would it not be nice if hyperlinks corresponding to cross-references were set automatically? For instance, clicking on Lemma 6 in

> This follows from Lemma 6 and the relevant definitions.

would cause the display to jump to the page containing Lemma 6.

Sebastian Rahtz's hyperref package does just that. You can find it on CTAN in the directory
`/tex-archive/macros/latex/contrib/supported/hyperref/`
The downloaded directory contains the `hyperref.ins` document, which must be typeset with the `LaTeX` format to unpack the package. There is a user guide included, `manual.pdf`, but for a more detailed exposition you should turn to *The LaTeX Web Companion* [19].

14.3.1 *Using* hyperref

To use the hyperref package, put the unpacked package in your TeX input directory, add

```
\usepackage[driver]{hyperref}
```

as the *last* `\usepackage` line in the preamble of your LaTeX document.

`driver` is the name of the DVI printer driver, which is one of

- `dvips` for the DVI printer driver `dvips`, used by many UNIX implementations and OzTeX
- `hypertex` for HyperTeX-compliant printer drivers (this is the default—used, for example, by TEXTURES)
- `dvipsone` for the DVI printer driver of the same name for Y&Y TeX; see Section 13.2

Figure 14.2 shows a page fragment with hyperlinks to some sections, theorems, and citations.

14.3.2 backref *and* colorlinks

A delightful addition to hyperref is David Carlisle's backref package; invoke it as an option of hyperref:

```
\usepackage[driver,backref]{hyperref}
```

The items in your bibliography will be followed by a list of sections in which the bibliographic reference is cited; each number is a hyperlink to the section. Alternatively, you can use the `pagebackref` option, which produces a list of page numbers. Figure 14.3 shows a page fragment from a bibliography displaying lists of section numbers.

The proof of the Main Theorem relies on several results in the literature. In Section 2, we recall a construction—due to M.E. Adams and J. Sichler [1]—of the lattice Ind **G** from a graph **G**. Section 3 introduces $\mathcal{C}$-*extensions*, a special case of *reduced free products of lattices* of C.C. Chen and G. Grätzer [3] that generalizes some of the techniques originally introduced in R.P. Dilworth [4]. The most important new result in this section is Theorem 11, stating that any sublattice of a reduced free product that contains neither the zero nor the unit is naturally isomorphic to a sublattice of the free product on the same factors; this allows us to apply a result of H. Lakser [13] on simple sublattices in free products to $\mathcal{C}$-extensions.

The construction of the uniquely complemented lattice representing a given monoid is introduced in Section 4. It is based on V. Koubek and J. Sichler [12]. Section 5 proves that this construct has many simple sublattices. Finally, in Section 6, we put all these pieces together to construct the lattice L for the Main Theorem.

To prove Theorem 1, we need a different construction, which is presented in Section 7.

Figure 14.2: The hyperref package with the `\autoref` command.

[9] ———, *General Lattice Theory. Second Edition,* Birkhäuser Verlag, Basel, 1998. xix+663 pp. 1

[10] G. Grätzer and J. Sichler, *On the endomorphism semigroup (and category) of bounded lattices*, Pacific J. Math. **35** (1970), 639–647. 1, 1

[11] ———, *On the endomorphism monoid of complemented lattices*, AMS Abstract 97T-06-98. 1

[12] V. Koubek and J. Sichler, *Universality of small lattice varieties*, Proc. Amer. Math. Soc. **91** (1984), 19–24. 1, 2, 4, 4.2, 4.3, 4.3, 4.3, 7

[13] H. Lakser, *Simple sublattices of free products of lattices*, Abstract, Notices Amer. Math. Soc. **19** (1972), A 509. 1, 3, 3

Figure 14.3: The hyperref package with the backref option.

Another popular option is colorlinks, which colors the text of links instead of putting boxes around them.

14.3.3 Bookmarks

A major navigational feature of Acrobat is the ability to set and use bookmarks. If you click on the Show/Hide Navigation Pane icon (the fourth from the left on the Acrobat Reader toolbar), the navigation pane opens up, optionally showing one of four navigational aids; the default is bookmarks.

For a typical example, view the Acrobat Guide (look for it on the Help menu), where the bookmarks form a table of contents. Clicking on a chapter title bookmark, displays the first page of the chapter in the main pane. Clicking on the triangle next to a chapter title bookmark opens up the chapter title to show the sections within the chapter.

The hyperref package option `bookmarks=true` makes bookmarks from the table of contents of a LaTeX document (even if the document had none). You can invoke all the options we have discussed together:

```
\usepackage[backref,colorlinks,bookmarks=true]{hyperref}
```

Typesetting your LaTeX document with the `bookmarks=true` option of hyperref produces an `out` file, which contains entries such as

```
\BOOKMARK [1]{section.4}{ 4.1emThe lattice}{}
\BOOKMARK [2]{subsection.4.1}{ 4.1.1emThe category}{section.4}
```

You should edit this file to make sure that there it contains no LaTeX code. hyperref does its best to convert internal encodings for accented characters to the encoding used by Acrobat Reader, but it is still best to avoid accented characters. Once this file has been edited, add the line

```
\let\WriteBookmarks\relax
```

at the start of the file to prevent it from being overwritten.

14.3.4 Additional commands

The hyperref package has dozens of commands and parameters, but we will discuss only four more commands.

Preventing links

If you do not want a `\ref` or `\pageref` command to appear as a link, you can use their `*`-ed forms, `\ref*` and `\pageref*`, which are provided by the hyperref package.

Long links

An often heard complaint is that in the link Theorem 6, only the 6 can be clicked on to activate the link, and it is too small on some monitors. hyperref provides the `\autoref` command to help out. Instead of

```
Theorem~\ref{T:new}
```

you can simply type

```
\autoref{T:new}
```

and hyperref will provide the word Theorem so that the link becomes Theorem 6. The list of names supported by the `\autoref` command is shown in Table 14.1.

Command	Meaning
`\figurename`	Figure
`\tablename`	Table
`\partname`	Part
`\appendixname`	Appendix
`\equationname`	Equation
`\Itemname`	item
`\chaptername`	chapter
`\sectionname`	section
`\subsectionname`	subsection
`\paragraphname`	subsubsection
`\Hfootnotename`	footnote
`\AMSname`	Equation
`\theoremname`	Theorem

Table 14.1: hyperref `\autoref` names.

For my own use, I redefine:

```
\renewcommand{\chaptername}{Chapter}
\renewcommand{\sectionname}{Section}
\renewcommand{\subsectionname}{Section}
\renewcommand{\subsubsectionname}{Section}
```

External links

Use the

```
\href{address}{text}
```

command to typeset *text* and make it into a link to the Web address (URL) to be substituted for *address*.

For instance, in your references, you may have

```
 Robert Miner and Jeff Schaefer,
 \emph{Gentle intoduction to MathML.}\\
 \href{http://www.webeq.com/mathml/gitmml/}%
{http://www.webeq.com/mathml/gitmml/}
```

Then the last line of the reference will appear as

http://www.webeq.com/mathml/gitmml/

and clicking on it links to the Web site. An even fancier example, using the AMS document class, amsart is to write the \urladdr command (see Section 8.2.2) in the form (A)

```
\urladdr{\href{http://www.maths.umanitoba.ca/homepages/gratzer/}%
{http://www.maths.umanitoba.ca/homepages/gratzer/}}
```

Then, as part of my address, you will find

http://www.maths.umanitoba.ca/homepages/gratzer/

Now clicking on my Web address will link to my Web page.

hyperref, of course, offers a lot more than I have presented here. For more detail, see the user manual, manual.pdf, and *The LaTeX Web Companion* [19]. For technical information about PDF files, see Thomas Merz's *Web Publishing With Acrobat* PDF [41].

APPENDIX

Math symbol tables

References to AMS sources are marked by Ⓐ.

A.1 Hebrew and Greek letters

A.1.1 Hebrew letters

Source	Type	Typeset
LaTeX		
	\aleph	$\aleph$
amssymbⒶ		
	\beth	$\beth$
	\daleth	$\daleth$
	\gimel	$\gimel$

A.1.2 Greek letters

Lowercase

Source	Type	Typeset	Type	Typeset	Type	Typeset
LaTeX						
	\alpha	α	\iota	ι	\sigma	σ
	\beta	β	\kappa	κ	\tau	τ
	\gamma	γ	\lambda	λ	\upsilon	υ
	\delta	δ	\mu	μ	\phi	ϕ
	\epsilon	ϵ	\nu	ν	\chi	χ
	\zeta	ζ	\xi	ξ	\psi	ψ
	\eta	η	\pi	π	\omega	ω
	\theta	θ	\rho	ρ		
LaTeX variants						
	\varepsilon	ε	\varpi	ϖ	\varsigma	ς
	\vartheta	ϑ	\varrho	ϱ	\varphi	φ
amssymbⒶ						
	\digamma	$\digamma$	\varkappa	$\varkappa$		

Uppercase

Source	Type	Typeset	Type	Typeset	Type	Typeset
LaTeX						
	\Gamma	Γ	\Xi	Ξ	\Phi	Φ
	\Delta	Δ	\Pi	Π	\Psi	Ψ
	\Theta	Θ	\Sigma	Σ	\Omega	Ω
	\Lambda	Λ	\Upsilon	Υ		
amsmathⒶ						
	\varGamma	$\varGamma$	\varXi	$\varXi$	\varPhi	$\varPhi$
	\varDelta	$\varDelta$	\varPi	$\varPi$	\varPsi	$\varPsi$
	\varTheta	$\varTheta$	\varSigma	$\varSigma$	\varOmega	$\varOmega$
	\varLambda	$\varLambda$	\varUpsilon	$\varUpsilon$		

A.2 Binary relations

A.2.1 LaTeX binary relations

Source	Type	Typeset	Type	Typeset
LaTeX				
	<	$<$	>	$>$
	=	$=$	:	$:$
	\in	$\in$	\ni or \owns	$\ni$
	\leq or \le	$\leq$	\geq or \ge	$\geq$
	\ll	$\ll$	\gg	$\gg$
	\prec	$\prec$	\succ	$\succ$
	\preceq	$\preceq$	\succeq	$\succeq$
	\sim	$\sim$	\approx	$\approx$
	\simeq	$\simeq$	\cong	$\cong$
	\equiv	$\equiv$	\doteq	$\doteq$
	\subset	$\subset$	\supset	$\supset$
	\subseteq	$\subseteq$	\supseteq	$\supseteq$
	\sqsubseteq	$\sqsubseteq$	\sqsupseteq	$\sqsupseteq$
	\smile	$\smile$	\frown	$\frown$
	\perp	$\perp$	\models	$\models$
	\mid	$\mid$	\parallel	$\parallel$
	\vdash	$\vdash$	\dashv	$\dashv$
	\propto	$\propto$	\asymp	$\asymp$
	\bowtie	$\bowtie$		
latexsym				
	\sqsubset	$\sqsubset$	\sqsupset	$\sqsupset$
	\Join	$\Join$		

A.2.2 AMS binary relations

Source	Type	Typeset	Type	Typeset
amssymb(A)				
	\leqq	$\leqq$	\geqq	$\geqq$
	\leqslant	$\leqslant$	\geqslant	$\geqslant$
	\eqslantless	$\eqslantless$	\eqslantgtr	$\eqslantgtr$
	\lesssim	$\lesssim$	\gtrsim	$\gtrsim$
	\lessapprox	$\lessapprox$	\gtrapprox	$\gtrapprox$
	\approxeq	$\approxeq$		
	\lessdot	$\lessdot$	\gtrdot	$\gtrdot$
	\lll	$\lll$	\ggg	$\ggg$
	\lessgtr	$\lessgtr$	\gtrless	$\gtrless$
	\lesseqgtr	$\lesseqgtr$	\gtreqless	$\gtreqless$
	\lesseqqgtr	$\lesseqqgtr$	\gtreqqless	$\gtreqqless$
	\doteqdot	$\doteqdot$	\eqcirc	$\eqcirc$
	\circeq	$\circeq$	\triangleq	$\triangleq$
	\risingdotseq	$\risingdotseq$	\fallingdotseq	$\fallingdotseq$
	\backsim	$\backsim$	\thicksim	$\thicksim$
	\backsimeq	$\backsimeq$	\thickapprox	$\thickapprox$
	\preccurlyeq	$\preccurlyeq$	\succcurlyeq	$\succcurlyeq$
	\curlyeqprec	$\curlyeqprec$	\curlyeqsucc	$\curlyeqsucc$
	\precsim	$\precsim$	\succsim	$\succsim$
	\precapprox	$\precapprox$	\succapprox	$\succapprox$
	\subseteqq	$\subseteqq$	\supseteqq	$\supseteqq$
	\Subset	$\Subset$	\Supset	$\Supset$
	\vartriangleleft	$\vartriangleleft$	\vartriangleright	$\vartriangleright$
	\trianglelefteq	$\trianglelefteq$	\trianglerighteq	$\trianglerighteq$
	\vDash	$\vDash$	\Vdash	$\Vdash$
	\Vvdash	$\Vvdash$		
	\smallsmile	$\smallsmile$	\smallfrown	$\smallfrown$
	\shortmid	$\shortmid$	\shortparallel	$\shortparallel$
	\bumpeq	$\bumpeq$	\Bumpeq	$\Bumpeq$
	\between	$\between$	\pitchfork	$\pitchfork$
	\varpropto	$\varpropto$	\backepsilon	$\backepsilon$
	\blacktriangleleft	$\blacktriangleleft$	\blacktriangleright	$\blacktriangleright$
	\therefore	$\therefore$	\because	$\because$

A.2.3 Negated binary relations

Source	Type	Typeset	Type	Typeset
LaTeX				
	`\neq` or `\ne`	$\neq$	`\notin`	$\notin$
amssymb(A)				
	`\nless`	$\nless$	`\ngtr`	$\ngtr$
	`\nleq`	$\nleq$	`\ngeq`	$\ngeq$
	`\nleqslant`	$\nleqslant$	`\ngeqslant`	$\ngeqslant$
	`\nleqq`	$\nleqq$	`\ngeqq`	$\ngeqq$
	`\lneq`	$\lneq$	`\gneq`	$\gneq$
	`\lneqq`	$\lneqq$	`\gneqq`	$\gneqq$
	`\lvertneqq`	$\lvertneqq$	`\gvertneqq`	$\gvertneqq$
	`\lnsim`	$\lnsim$	`\gnsim`	$\gnsim$
	`\lnapprox`	$\lnapprox$	`\gnapprox`	$\gnapprox$
	`\nprec`	$\nprec$	`\nsucc`	$\nsucc$
	`\npreceq`	$\npreceq$	`\nsucceq`	$\nsucceq$
	`\precneqq`	$\precneqq$	`\succneqq`	$\succneqq$
	`\precnsim`	$\precnsim$	`\succnsim`	$\succnsim$
	`\precnapprox`	$\precnapprox$	`\succnapprox`	$\succnapprox$
	`\nsim`	$\nsim$	`\ncong`	$\ncong$
	`\nshortmid`	$\nshortmid$	`\nshortparallel`	$\nshortparallel$
	`\nmid`	$\nmid$	`\nparallel`	$\nparallel$
	`\nvdash`	$\nvdash$	`\nvDash`	$\nvDash$
	`\nVdash`	$\nVdash$	`\nVDash`	$\nVDash$
	`\ntriangleleft`	$\ntriangleleft$	`\ntriangleright`	$\ntriangleright$
	`\ntrianglelefteq`	$\ntrianglelefteq$	`\ntrianglerighteq`	$\ntrianglerighteq$
	`\nsubseteq`	$\nsubseteq$	`\nsupseteq`	$\nsupseteq$
	`\nsubseteqq`	$\nsubseteqq$	`\nsupseteqq`	$\nsupseteqq$
	`\subsetneq`	$\subsetneq$	`\supsetneq`	$\supsetneq$
	`\varsubsetneq`	$\varsubsetneq$	`\varsupsetneq`	$\varsupsetneq$
	`\subsetneqq`	$\subsetneqq$	`\supsetneqq`	$\supsetneqq$
	`\varsubsetneqq`	$\varsubsetneqq$	`\varsupsetneqq`	$\varsupsetneqq$

A.3 Binary operations

Source	Type	Typeset	Type	Typeset
LaTeX				
	+	$+$	-	$-$
	\pm	$\pm$	\mp	$\mp$
	\times	$\times$	\cdot	$\cdot$
	\circ	$\circ$	\bigcirc	$\bigcirc$
	\div	$\div$	\bmod	$\bmod$
	\cap	$\cap$	\cup	$\cup$
	\sqcap	$\sqcap$	\sqcup	$\sqcup$
	\wedge or \land	$\wedge$	\vee or \lor	$\vee$
	\triangleleft	$\triangleleft$	\triangleright	$\triangleright$
	\bigtriangleup	$\bigtriangleup$	\bigtriangledown	$\bigtriangledown$
	\oplus	$\oplus$	\ominus	$\ominus$
	\otimes	$\otimes$	\oslash	$\oslash$
	\odot	$\odot$	\bullet	$\bullet$
	\dagger	$\dagger$	\ddagger	$\ddagger$
	\setminus	$\setminus$	\uplus	$\uplus$
	\wr	$\wr$	\amalg	$\amalg$
	\ast	$\ast$	\star	$\star$
	\diamond	$\diamond$		
latexsym				
	\lhd	$\lhd$	\rhd	$\rhd$
	\unlhd	$\unlhd$	\unrhd	$\unrhd$
amssymbⒶ				
	\dotplus	$\dotplus$	\centerdot	$\centerdot$
	\ltimes	$\ltimes$	\rtimes	$\rtimes$
	\leftthreetimes	$\leftthreetimes$	\rightthreetimes	$\rightthreetimes$
	\circleddash	$\circleddash$	\smallsetminus	$\smallsetminus$
	\barwedge	$\barwedge$	\doublebarwedge	$\doublebarwedge$
	\curlywedge	$\curlywedge$	\curlyvee	$\curlyvee$
	\veebar	$\veebar$	\intercal	$\intercal$
	\doublecap or \Cap	$\Cap$	\doublecup or \Cup	$\Cup$
	\circledast	$\circledast$	\circledcirc	$\circledcirc$
	\boxminus	$\boxminus$	\boxtimes	$\boxtimes$
	\boxdot	$\boxdot$	\boxplus	$\boxplus$
	\divideontimes	$\divideontimes$	\vartriangle	$\vartriangle$
amsmathⒶ				
	\And	$\And$		

A.4 Arrows

A.4.1 LaTeX arrows

Source	Type	Typeset	Type	Typeset
LaTeX				
	`\leftarrow`	$\leftarrow$	`\rightarrow` or `\to`	$\rightarrow$
	`\longleftarrow`	$\longleftarrow$	`\longrightarrow`	$\longrightarrow$
	`\Leftarrow`	$\Leftarrow$	`\Rightarrow`	$\Rightarrow$
	`\Longleftarrow`	$\Longleftarrow$	`\Longrightarrow`	$\Longrightarrow$
	`\leftrightarrow`	$\leftrightarrow$	`\longleftrightarrow`	$\longleftrightarrow$
	`\Leftrightarrow`	$\Leftrightarrow$	`\Longleftrightarrow`	$\Longleftrightarrow$
	`\uparrow`	$\uparrow$	`\downarrow`	$\downarrow$
	`\Uparrow`	$\Uparrow$	`\Downarrow`	$\Downarrow$
	`\updownarrow`	$\updownarrow$	`\Updownarrow`	$\Updownarrow$
	`\nearrow`	$\nearrow$	`\searrow`	$\searrow$
	`\swarrow`	$\swarrow$	`\nwarrow`	$\nwarrow$
	`\iff`	$\iff$	`\mapstochar`	$\mapstochar$
	`\mapsto`	$\mapsto$	`\longmapsto`	$\longmapsto$
	`\hookleftarrow`	$\hookleftarrow$	`\hookrightarrow`	$\hookrightarrow$
	`\leftharpoonup`	$\leftharpoonup$	`\rightharpoonup`	$\rightharpoonup$
	`\leftharpoondown`	$\leftharpoondown$	`\rightharpoondown`	$\rightharpoondown$
latexsym				
	`\leadsto`	$\leadsto$		

A.4.2 AMS arrows

Source	Type	Typeset	Type	Typeset
amssymb(A)				
	`\leftleftarrows`	$\leftleftarrows$	`\rightrightarrows`	$\rightrightarrows$
	`\leftrightarrows`	$\leftrightarrows$	`\rightleftarrows`	$\rightleftarrows$
	`\Lleftarrow`	$\Lleftarrow$	`\Rrightarrow`	$\Rrightarrow$
	`\twoheadleftarrow`	$\twoheadleftarrow$	`\twoheadrightarrow`	$\twoheadrightarrow$
	`\leftarrowtail`	$\leftarrowtail$	`\rightarrowtail`	$\rightarrowtail$
	`\looparrowleft`	$\looparrowleft$	`\looparrowright`	$\looparrowright$
	`\upuparrows`	$\upuparrows$	`\downdownarrows`	$\downdownarrows$
	`\upharpoonleft`	$\upharpoonleft$	`\upharpoonright`	$\upharpoonright$
	`\downharpoonleft`	$\downharpoonleft$	`\downharpoonright`	$\downharpoonright$
	`\leftrightsquigarrow`	$\leftrightsquigarrow$	`\rightsquigarrow`	$\rightsquigarrow$
	`\multimap`	$\multimap$		
	`\nleftarrow`	$\nleftarrow$	`\nrightarrow`	$\nrightarrow$
	`\nLeftarrow`	$\nLeftarrow$	`\nRightarrow`	$\nRightarrow$
	`\nleftrightarrow`	$\nleftrightarrow$	`\nLeftrightarrow`	$\nLeftrightarrow$
	`\dashleftarrow`	$\dashleftarrow$	`\dashrightarrow`	$\dashrightarrow$
	`\curvearrowleft`	$\curvearrowleft$	`\curvearrowright`	$\curvearrowright$
	`\circlearrowleft`	$\circlearrowleft$	`\circlearrowright`	$\circlearrowright$
	`\leftrightharpoons`	$\leftrightharpoons$	`\rightleftharpoons`	$\rightleftharpoons$
	`\Lsh`	$\Lsh$	`\Rsh`	$\Rsh$

A.5 Miscellaneous symbols

Source	Type	Typeset	Type	Typeset
LaTeX				
	`\hbar`	$\hbar$	`\ell`	ℓ
	`\imath`	$\imath$	`\jmath`	$\jmath$
	`\wp`	$\wp$	`\partial`	∂
	`\Im`	$\Im$	`\Re`	$\Re$
	`\infty`	∞	`\prime`	$\prime$
	`\emptyset`	$\emptyset$	`\neg` or `\lnot`	$\neg$
	`\forall`	$\forall$	`\exists`	$\exists$
	`\smallint`	$\smallint$	`\triangle`	$\triangle$
	`\top`	$\top$	`\bot`	$\bot$
	`\P`	¶	`\S`	§
	`\dag`	†	`\ddag`	‡
	`\flat`	$\flat$	`\natural`	$\natural$
	`\sharp`	$\sharp$	`\angle`	$\angle$
	`\clubsuit`	$\clubsuit$	`\diamondsuit`	$\diamondsuit$
	`\heartsuit`	$\heartsuit$	`\spadesuit`	$\spadesuit$
	`\surd`	$\surd$	`\nabla`	∇
	`\pounds`	£		
latexsym				
	`\Box`	$\Box$	`\Diamond`	$\Diamond$
	`\mho`	$\mho$		
amssymb(A)				
	`\hslash`	$\hslash$	`\complement`	$\complement$
	`\backprime`	$\backprime$	`\nexists`	$\nexists$
	`\Bbbk`	$\Bbbk$	`\varnothing`	$\varnothing$
	`\diagup`	$\diagup$	`\diagdown`	$\diagdown$
	`\blacktriangle`	$\blacktriangle$	`\blacktriangledown`	$\blacktriangledown$
	`\triangledown`	$\triangledown$	`\Game`	$\Game$
	`\square`	$\square$	`\blacksquare`	$\blacksquare$
	`\lozenge`	$\lozenge$	`\blacklozenge`	$\blacklozenge$
	`\measuredangle`	$\measuredangle$	`\sphericalangle`	$\sphericalangle$
	`\circledS`	$\circledS$	`\bigstar`	$\bigstar$
	`\Finv`	$\Finv$	`\eth`	$\eth$

A.6 Delimiters

<table>
<tr><th>Source</th><th>Name</th><th>Type</th><th>Typeset</th></tr>
<tr><td>LaTeX</td><td></td><td></td><td></td></tr>
<tr><td></td><td>left parenthesis</td><td>(</td><td>$($</td></tr>
<tr><td></td><td>right parenthesis</td><td>)</td><td>$)$</td></tr>
<tr><td></td><td>left bracket</td><td>[or \lbrack</td><td>$[$</td></tr>
<tr><td></td><td>right bracket</td><td>] or \rbrack</td><td>$]$</td></tr>
<tr><td></td><td>left brace</td><td>\{ or \lbrace</td><td>$\{$</td></tr>
<tr><td></td><td>right brace</td><td>\} or \rbrace</td><td>$\}$</td></tr>
<tr><td></td><td>backslash</td><td>\backslash</td><td>$\backslash$</td></tr>
<tr><td></td><td>forward slash</td><td>/</td><td>$/$</td></tr>
<tr><td></td><td>left angle bracket</td><td>\langle</td><td>$\langle$</td></tr>
<tr><td></td><td>right angle bracket</td><td>\rangle</td><td>$\rangle$</td></tr>
<tr><td></td><td>vertical line</td><td>| or \vert</td><td>$\vert$</td></tr>
<tr><td></td><td>double vertical line</td><td>\| or \Vert</td><td>$\Vert$</td></tr>
<tr><td></td><td>left floor</td><td>\lfloor</td><td>$\lfloor$</td></tr>
<tr><td></td><td>right floor</td><td>\rfloor</td><td>$\rfloor$</td></tr>
<tr><td></td><td>left ceiling</td><td>\lceil</td><td>$\lceil$</td></tr>
<tr><td></td><td>right ceiling</td><td>\rceil</td><td>$\rceil$</td></tr>
<tr><td></td><td>upward</td><td>\uparrow</td><td>$\uparrow$</td></tr>
<tr><td></td><td>double upward</td><td>\Uparrow</td><td>$\Uparrow$</td></tr>
<tr><td></td><td>downward</td><td>\downarrow</td><td>$\downarrow$</td></tr>
<tr><td></td><td>double downward</td><td>\Downarrow</td><td>$\Downarrow$</td></tr>
<tr><td></td><td>up-and-down</td><td>\updownarrow</td><td>$\updownarrow$</td></tr>
<tr><td></td><td>double up-and-down</td><td>\Updownarrow</td><td>$\Updownarrow$</td></tr>
<tr><td>amsmath Ⓐ</td><td></td><td></td><td></td></tr>
<tr><td></td><td>upper-left corner</td><td>\ulcorner</td><td>$\ulcorner$</td></tr>
<tr><td></td><td>upper-right corner</td><td>\urcorner</td><td>$\urcorner$</td></tr>
<tr><td></td><td>lower-left corner</td><td>\llcorner</td><td>$\llcorner$</td></tr>
<tr><td></td><td>lower-right corner</td><td>\lrcorner</td><td>$\lrcorner$</td></tr>
</table>

A.7 Operators

A.7.1 "Pure" operators, with no limits

Type	Typeset	Type	Typeset	Type	Typeset	Type	Typeset
`\arccos`	arccos	`\cot`	cot	`\hom`	hom	`\sin`	sin
`\arcsin`	arcsin	`\coth`	coth	`\ker`	ker	`\sinh`	sinh
`\arctan`	arctan	`\csc`	csc	`\lg`	lg	`\tan`	tan
`\arg`	arg	`\deg`	deg	`\ln`	ln	`\tanh`	tanh
`\cos`	cos	`\dim`	dim	`\log`	log		
`\cosh`	cosh	`\exp`	exp	`\sec`	sec		

A.7.2 Operators with limits

Source	Type	Typeset	Type	Typeset
LaTeX				
	`\det`	det	`\limsup`	lim sup
	`\gcd`	gcd	`\max`	max
	`\inf`	inf	`\min`	min
	`\lim`	lim	`\Pr`	Pr
	`\liminf`	lim inf	`\sup`	sup
amsmathⒶ				
	`\injlim`	inj lim	`\projlim`	proj lim
	`\varliminf`	$\underline{\lim}$	`\varlimsup`	$\overline{\lim}$
	`\varinjlim`	$\varinjlim$	`\varprojlim`	$\varprojlim$

A.7.3 Large operators

Type	Inline	Displayed
`\int_{a}^{b}`	$\int_{a}^{b}$	$\displaystyle\int_{a}^{b}$
`\oint_{a}^{b}`	$\oint_{a}^{b}$	$\displaystyle\oint_{a}^{b}$
`\prod_{i=1}^{n}`	$\prod_{i=1}^{n}$	$\displaystyle\prod_{i=1}^{n}$
`\coprod_{i=1}^{n}`	$\coprod_{i=1}^{n}$	$\displaystyle\coprod_{i=1}^{n}$
`\bigcap_{i=1}^{n}`	$\bigcap_{i=1}^{n}$	$\displaystyle\bigcap_{i=1}^{n}$
`\bigcup_{i=1}^{n}`	$\bigcup_{i=1}^{n}$	$\displaystyle\bigcup_{i=1}^{n}$
`\bigwedge_{i=1}^{n}`	$\bigwedge_{i=1}^{n}$	$\displaystyle\bigwedge_{i=1}^{n}$
`\bigvee_{i=1}^{n}`	$\bigvee_{i=1}^{n}$	$\displaystyle\bigvee_{i=1}^{n}$
`\bigsqcup_{i=1}^{n}`	$\bigsqcup_{i=1}^{n}$	$\displaystyle\bigsqcup_{i=1}^{n}$
`\biguplus_{i=1}^{n}`	$\biguplus_{i=1}^{n}$	$\displaystyle\biguplus_{i=1}^{n}$
`\bigotimes_{i=1}^{n}`	$\bigotimes_{i=1}^{n}$	$\displaystyle\bigotimes_{i=1}^{n}$
`\bigoplus_{i=1}^{n}`	$\bigoplus_{i=1}^{n}$	$\displaystyle\bigoplus_{i=1}^{n}$
`\bigodot_{i=1}^{n}`	$\bigodot_{i=1}^{n}$	$\displaystyle\bigodot_{i=1}^{n}$
`\sum_{i=1}^{n}`	$\sum_{i=1}^{n}$	$\displaystyle\sum_{i=1}^{n}$

A.8 Math accents and fonts

A.8.1 Math accents

LaTeX		amsmath(A)		amsxtra(A)	
Type	Typeset	Type	Typeset	Type	Typeset
\acute{a}	$\acute{a}$				
\bar{a}	$\bar{a}$				
\breve{a}	$\breve{a}$			\spbreve	$\breve{}$
\check{a}	$\check{a}$			\spcheck	$\vee$
\dot{a}	$\dot{a}$			\spdot	$\cdot$
\ddot{a}	$\ddot{a}$			\spddot	$\cdot\cdot$
		\dddot{a}	$\dddot{a}$	\spdddot	$\cdots$
		\ddddot{a}	$\ddddot{a}$		
\grave{a}	$\grave{a}$				
\hat{a}	$\hat{a}$				
\widehat{a}	$\widehat{a}$			\sphat	$\widehat{}$
\mathring{a}	$\mathring{a}$				
\tilde{a}	$\tilde{a}$				
\widetilde{a}	$\widetilde{a}$			\sptilde	$\sim$
\vec{a}	$\vec{a}$				

A.8.2 Math fonts

Source	Type	Typeset
LaTeX		
	`\mathbf{A}`	$\mathbf{A}$
	`\mathcal{A}`	$\mathcal{A}$
	`\mathit{A}`	A
	`\mathnormal{A}`	$\mathnormal{A}$
	`\mathrm{A}`	A
	`\mathsf{A}`	A
	`\mathtt{A}`	$\mathtt{A}$
amsmathⒶ		
	`\boldsymbol{\alpha}`	$\boldsymbol{\alpha}$
amssymbⒶ		
	`\mathbb{A}`	$\mathbb{A}$
	`\mathfrak{A}`	$\mathfrak{A}$
eucalⒶ (with `mathscr` option)		
	`\mathscr{a}`	$\mathscr{A}$

A.9 Math spacing commands

		LaTeX		amsmathⒶ	
Name	Width	Short	Long	Short	Long
Positive space					
1 mu (math unit)	ı				`\mspace{1mu}`
thinspace	␣	`\,`	`\thinspace`		
medspace	␣	`\:`			`\medspace`
thickspace	␣	`\;`			`\thickspace`
1 em	␣		`\quad`		
2 em	␣		`\qquad`		
Negative space					
1 mu	ı				`\mspace{-1mu}`
thinspace	␣	`\!`	`\negthinspace`		
medspace	␣				`\negmedspace`
thickspace	␣				`\negthickspace`

APPENDIX

B

Text symbol tables

B.1 Some European characters

Name	Type	Typeset	Type	Typeset
a-ring	\aa	å	\AA	Å
aesc	\ae	æ	\AE	Æ
ethel	\oe	œ	\OE	Œ
eszett	\ss	ß	\SS	SS
inverted question mark	?‘	¿		
inverted exclamation mark	!‘	¡		
slashed L	\l	ł	\L	Ł
slashed O	\o	ø	\O	Ø

B.2 Text accents

Name	Type	Typeset	Name	Type	Typeset
acute	`\'{o}`	ó	macron	`\={o}`	ō
breve	`\u{o}`	ŏ	overdot	`\.{g}`	ġ
caron/haček	`\v{o}`	ǒ	ring	`\r{u}`	ů
cedilla	`\c{c}`	ç	tie	`\t{oo}`	o͡o
circumflex	`\^{o}`	ô	tilde	`\~{n}`	ñ
dieresis/umlaut	`\"{u}`	ü	underdot	`\d{m}`	ṃ
double acute	`\H{o}`	ő	underbar	`\b{o}`	o̲
grave	`` \`{o} ``	ò			
dotless i	`\i`	ı	dotless j	`\j`	ȷ
	`\'{\i}`	í		`\v{\j}`	ǰ

B.3 Text font commands

B.3.1 Text font family commands

Command with Argument	Command Declaration	Switches to
`\textnormal{...}`	`{\normalfont ...}`	document font family
`\emph{...}`	`{\em ...}`	*emphasis*
`\textrm{...}`	`{\rmfamily ...}`	roman font family
`\textsf{...}`	`{\sffamily ...}`	sans-serif font family
`\texttt{...}`	`{\ttfamily ...}`	`typewriter-style font family`
`\textup{...}`	`{\upshape ...}`	upright shape
`\textit{...}`	`{\itshape ...}`	*italic shape*
`\textsl{...}`	`{\slshape ...}`	*slanted shape*
`\textsc{...}`	`{\scshape ...}`	SMALL CAPITALS
`\textbf{...}`	`{\bfseries ...}`	**bold**
`\textmd{...}`	`{\mdseries ...}`	normal weight and width

B.3.2 Text font size changes (LaTeX and AMS)

Command	LaTeX sample text	AMS sample text(A)
`\Tiny`	[not available]	sample text
`\tiny`	sample text	sample text
`\SMALL` or `\scriptsize`	sample text	sample text
`\Small` or `\footnotesize`	sample text	sample text
`\small`	sample text	sample text
`\normalsize`	sample text	sample text
`\large`	sample text	sample text
`\Large`	sample text	sample text
`\LARGE`	sample text	sample text
`\huge`	sample text	sample text
`\Huge`	sample text	sample text

B.4 *Additional text symbols*

Name	Type	Typeset
ampersand	\&	&
asterisk bullet	\textasteriskcentered	∗
backslash	\textbackslash	\
bar (caesura)	\textbar	|
brace left	\{	{
brace right	\}	}
bullet	\textbullet	•
circled a	\textcircled{a}	ⓐ
circumflex	\textasciicircum	ˆ
copyright	\copyright	©
dagger	\dag	†
double dagger (diesis)	\ddag	‡
dollar	\$	$
double quotation left	\textquotedblleft or ``	“
double quotation right	\textquotedblright or ''	”
em dash	\textemdash or ---	—
en dash	\textendash or --	–
exclamation down	\textexclamdown or !`	¡
greater than	\textgreater	>
less than	\textless	<
lowline	_	_
midpoint	\textperiodcentered	·
octothorp	\#	#
percent	\%	%
pilcrow (paragraph)	\P	¶
question down	\textquestiondown or ?`	¿
registered trademark	\textregistered	®
section	\S	§

Additional text symbols, *continued*

Name	Type	Typeset
single quote left	`\textquoteleft` or ‘	‘
single quote right	`\textquoteright` or ’	’
sterling	`\pounds`	£
superscript	`\textsuperscript{a}`	ª
tilde	`\textasciitilde`	˜
trademark	`\texttrademark`	™
visible space	`\textvisiblespace`	␣

B.5 Additional text symbols with T1 encoding

B.5.1 Accents

Name	Type	Typeset
ogonek	`\k{e}`	ę

B.5.2 European characters

Name	Type	Typeset	Type	Typeset
eth	`\dh`	ð	`\DH`	Ð
dyet	`\dj`	đ	`\DJ`	Đ
eng	`\ng`	ŋ	`\NG`	Ŋ
thor n	`\th`	þ	`\TH`	Þ

B.5.3 Quotation marks

Name	Type	Typeset	Type	Typeset
single guillemet	`\guilsinglleft`	‹	`\guilsinglright`	›
double guillemet	`\guillemotleft`	«	`\guillemotright`	»
single quotation	`\quotesinglbase`	‚	`\textquoteright`	’
double quotation	`\quotedblbase`	„	`\textquotedbl`	"

B.6 Text spacing commands

		LaTeX		amsmath Ⓐ	
Name	Width	Short	Long	Short	Long
Positive Space					
Normal	varies	␣			
Intersentence	varies	`\@.␣`			
Interword	varies	`\␣`			
Italic Corr.	varies	`\/␣`			
Tie	varies	~			
Thinspace	␣	`\,`	`\thinspace`		
Medspace	␣			`\:`	`\medspace`
Thickspace	␣			`\;`	`\thickspace`
1 em	␣		`\quad`		
2 em	␣		`\qquad`		
Negative Space					
Thinspace	␣			`\!`	`\negthinspace`
Medspace	␣				`\negmedspace`
Thickspace	␣				`\negthickspace`

APPENDIX

C

Background

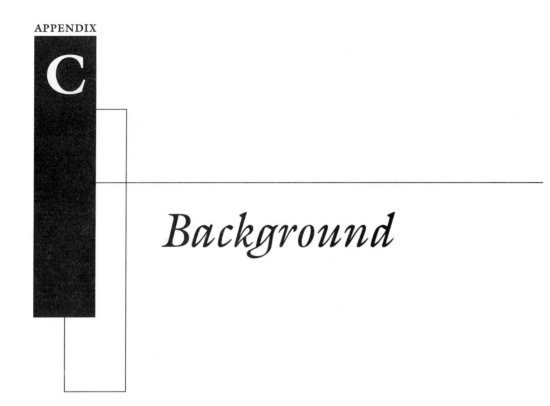

While you do not need to know anything about LaTeX's structure and history to use it, such knowledge may help you understand how and why LaTeX works the way it does.

C.1 A short history

Donald E. Knuth's multivolume work, *The Art of Computer Programming* [33], caused its author a great deal of frustration because it was very difficult to keep the volumes typographically uniform. To solve this problem, Knuth decided to create his own typesetting language; the result is described in *The TeXbook* [34].[1]

A mathematical typesetting language takes care of the multitude of details that are so important in mathematical typesetting, including

- Spacing formulas properly
- Breaking text into pleasingly typeset lines and paragraphs
- Hyphenating words where necessary
- Providing hundreds of symbols for typesetting mathematics

[1]In Software Practice and Experience **19** (1989), 607–685, Knuth writes that "[I] realized that a central aspect of printing has been reduced to bit manipulation. As a computer scientist, I could not resist the challenge of improving print quality by manipulating bits better."

TeX does all this and more on almost any computer: PC, Macintosh, Atari, Amiga, UNIX, workstation, minicomputer, or mainframe. You can write your document on a PC and e-mail it to a coworker who makes corrections on a Macintosh. The final manuscript might be sent to a publisher who uses a minicomputer to prepare the document for printing.

Knuth realized that typesetting is only half the solution to the manuscript production problem. You also need a style designer—a specialist who determines what fonts will be used, how large a vertical space to put before and after a theorem, and numerous other design issues.

Knuth also realized that typesetting a complex document in TeX requires a very knowledgeable user. So TeX was designed as a platform on which *convenient work environments*—macro packages—could be built, which would be more suitable for the average user to work with. It is somewhat unfortunate that *two* such macro packages were made available to the mathematical community in the early 1980s: AMS-TeX and LaTeX.

AMS-TeX was written by Michael D. Spivak for the American Mathematical Society, whereas LaTeX was developed by Leslie Lamport. The strengths of the two systems were somewhat complementary. AMS-TeX provided many features needed by mathematical articles, including

- Extensive options for formatting aligned and other multiline formulas
- Flexible bibliographic references

LaTeX also provided many features, including

- The use of logical units to separate the logical and the visual design of an article
- Automatic numbering and cross-referencing
- Bibliographic databases

Both AMS-TeX and LaTeX became very popular, causing a split in the mathematical community as some chose one system over the other.

C.1.1 LaTeX3

When Lamport decided not to develop LaTeX any further, the *LaTeX3 team*[2] took over with the aim of actively supporting, maintaining, and updating LaTeX.

The goals for LaTeX3 are very ambitious; LaTeX3 will

- Provide high-quality typesetting for a wide variety of document types and typographic requirements

[2] A talented group of mathematicians and programmers, Frank Mittelbach, Chris Rowley, and Rainer Schöpf. The group has since expanded with the addition of Johannes Braams, David Carlisle, Michael Downes, Denys Duchier, Robin Fairbairns, Alan Jeffrey, and Martin Schröder; many volunteers have also contributed to the project.

- Support direct formatting commands for editors and designers, which are essential to the fine-tuning of document layout and page design
- Process complex structured documents and support a document syntax that allows automatic translation of documents conforming to the international document-type definition standard SGML (Standard Generalized Markup Language, ISO 8879)
- Provide a common foundation for a number of incompatible LaTeX variants that have been developed, including LaTeX with the New Font Selection Scheme and the AMS packages

See two articles by Frank Mittelbach and Chris Rowley, *LaTeX 2.09 → LaTeX3* [44] and *The LaTeX3 Project* [46], for a complete statement of goals and a progress report.

A number of projects have already been completed that will be part of LaTeX3, including the following:

The New Font Selection Scheme. LaTeX uses Knuth's Computer Modern fonts. In 1989, Frank Mittelbach and Rainer Schöpf wrote the New Font Selection Scheme, NFSS, which allows the ***independent changing*** of font attributes and the integration of new font families into LaTeX. With the proliferation of PostScript fonts and printers, more and more users want to use PostScript fonts in their LaTeX documents.

AMS-TeX as a LaTeX package. Frank Mittelbach, Rainer Schöpf, and Michael Downes recoded AMS-TeX so that it would work as a LaTeX package.

Proclamations with style. All proclamations in LaTeX were typeset in the same style, whether they were a **Main Theorem** or a lowly *Comment.* Mittelbach and Schöpf created a sophisticated scheme that allowed proclamation styles to be specified.

New and improved environments. Rainer Schöpf improved the `verbatim` and `comment` environments and Frank Mittelbach wrote a new multicolumn environment. There have also been several improvements made to the `tabular` and `array` environments.

The first interim solution

In 1990, the AMS released AMS-LaTeX, version 1.0. This release contained

- AMS-TeX recoded to work with LaTeX
- The NFSS styles for proclamations
- The new `verbatim` environment

AMS-LaTeX, version 1.0, was a LaTeX *dialect,* incompatible with the then current LaTeX (version 2.09).

While the LaTeX3 team wanted to unify the mathematical community, their first attempt split it even further apart. Many AMS-TeX users simply refused to switch. Even the LaTeX community was split into users of the old LaTeX, those whose LaTeX incorporated the NFSS, and AMS-LaTeX users.

The second interim solution

When it became obvious that the LaTeX3's goals could not be fulfilled any time soon, the LaTeX3 team decided to issue a new version of LaTeX, version 2e (also called LaTeX 2_ε) in June of 1994. This version replaced LaTeX 2.09; see the two Mittelbach and Rowley articles cited above. This interim release accomplished some of LaTeX3's goals, including the projects listed previously. Since then, LaTeX 2_ε (called LaTeX in this book) has become accepted as the standard LaTeX.

In February of 1995, the AMS released version 1.2 of AMS-LaTeX (which I call the AMS packages in this book) built on top of LaTeX. Michael Downes was the project leader.

The changes in AMS-LaTeX were substantial. The `align` environment, for example, was completely rewritten by David M. Jones. The recoded AMS-TeX had now become a LaTeX package, amsmath.

It is extremely important to note that while AMS-LaTeX 1.1, was a monolithic structure, versions 1.2 and 2.0 (see Section C.1.2) are just collections of packages that fit nicely into the LaTeX model. You can use one AMS package or all, by themselves or mixed with other LaTeX packages. This book uses a LaTeX document class (`book`) and the AMS packages, version 2.0, along with a number of other LaTeX (non-AMS) packages.

C.1.2 Recent developments

Since 1996, changes to LaTeX have been minor. A few new symbols have been added. Much work has been done to extend LaTeX to languages other than American English (character encoding and the EM fonts; see Appendixes D and E); all file names used by LaTeX were made lowercase.

In 1999, the American Mathematical Society has released version 2.0 of the AMS packages. This third edition covers the changes made in that release.

The big news was that a consortium (made up of the AMS, Blue Sky Research, and Y&Y) released free PostScript versions of the CM and AMS fonts, discussed in Section D.1.

Interestingly, there are still those who argue that the AMS packages are not part and parcel of LaTeX and typesetting math. In life, almost everything is a compromise; in software design, even more so. Using the AMS packages to typeset math is an exception. It costs you nothing—if you do not need their features for a document, then you don't have to use them. You need not sacrifice anything in order to have the power of the AMS packages available when you need them.

I trust that this attitude will also change in time, just as LaTeX 2.09 won out over Plain TeX, and LaTeX has taken the place of LaTeX 2.09. Maybe this third edition will help this process along.

C.2 How does LaTeX work?

In this section, I present a very simplified overview of the inner workings of LaTeX.

C.2.1 The layers

TeX and LaTeX consist of many layers. These include

`virtex` TeX's core, containing about 350 primitive commands such as `\input`, `\accent`, and `\hsize`. `virtex` can also read *format files,* which are precompiled sets of macros. LaTeX is nothing more than `virtex` reading in a large set of macros, built layer upon layer.

`plain.tex` The most basic layer built on `virtex`, written by Donald E. Knuth. It adds about 600 commands to `virtex`. When you type the `tex` command, `virtex` loads the `plain` format, which is the default; the core TeX commands combined with the commands defined by the `plain` format are called Plain TeX.

`plain.tex` is described in detail in Appendix B of Knuth's *The TeXbook* [34]. You can also read `plain.tex`, a text file in the TeX distribution. Plain TeX is powerful enough that you could do all your work in it. This approach is advocated by many, including Michael Doob in his book, *TeX Starting from* 1 [14].

`virtex` cannot build (compile) format files. For that you need another version of TeX called `initex`, which loads the most basic information a format needs, such as the hyphenation tables and `plain.tex`, and creates a format file.

LaTeX

LaTeX is a format file containing a compiled set of macros written by Leslie Lamport and others. It provides tools for logical document design, automatic numbering and cross-referencing, tables of contents, and many other features.

Document classes

The document class forms the next layer. You may choose to use a standard LaTeX document class, such as `article`, `book`, `letter`, `proc`, `report`, or `slides`; one provided by the AMS, such as `amsart`, `amsbook`, or `amsproc`; or any one of a large (and growing) number of other document classes provided by publishers of books and journals, universities, and other interested parties.

Packages

The next layer is made up of the packages loaded by the document. You can use standard LaTeX packages, AMS packages, or any of hundreds of other packages in the LaTeX universe, mixed together as necessary. Any package may require other packages, or may automatically load other packages.

Documents

At the top of this hierarchy sit your documents, with their user-defined commands and environments, utilizing all the power derived from the layers below.

C.2.2 *Typesetting*

When typesetting, TeX uses two basic types of files: the source files and the font metric files.

A font metric file is designed to hold the information for a font of a given size and style. Each TeX font metric file, called a `tfm` file, contains the size of each character, the kerning (the space placed between two adjacent characters), the length of the italic correction, the size of the interword space, and so on. A typical `tfm` file is `cmr10.tfm`, which is the TeX font metric file for the font `cmr` (CM roman) at 10-point size.

TeX reads the source file one line at a time. It converts the characters of each line into a *token sequence;* a token is either a character (together with an indication of what role the character plays) or a macro. The argument of a macro is the token following the macro unless a group enclosed in braces follows the macro, in which case the contents of the group becomes the argument.[3] (An example of this behavior can be seen when you specify an exponent; TeX looks for the next token as the exponent unless a group enclosed in braces follows the ^ symbol. Now you should understand why `$2^3$` and `$2^\alpha$` work, but `$2^\mathfrak{m}$` does not: 3 and `\alpha` each become a single token but `\mathfrak{m}` becomes more than one (four, in fact). Of course, if you *always* use braces, as in

```
$ 2^{3}$, $2^{\alpha}$, $2^{ \mathfrak{m} }$
```

then you will never have to think about tokens in order to type such expressions.)

After tokenizing the text, TeX hyphenates it and attempts to split the paragraph into lines of the required width. The measurements of the characters (also called glyphs) are absolute, as are the distances between characters (kerning). The spaces (interword space, intersentence space, and so on) are made of *glue* (rubber length in Section 9.5.2). Glue has three parameters: the length of the space, stretchability (the amount by which it can be made longer), and shrinkability (the

[3]Delimited commands work somewhat differently; see Section 9.1.8.

amount by which it can be made shorter). TeX will stretch and shrink glue to do its best to form lines of equal length.

TeX employs a formula to measure how much stretching and shrinking is necessary in a line. The result is called badness. A badness of 0 is perfect; a badness of 10,000 is very bad. Lines that are too wide are reported with messages such as

```
Overfull \hbox (5.61168pt too wide) in paragraph at lines 49--57
```

The badness of a line that is stretched too much is reported as follows:

```
Underfull \hbox (badness 1189) in paragraph at lines 93--93
```

Once enough paragraphs are put together, TeX composes a page from the typeset paragraphs using vertical glue. A short page will generate a warning message such as

```
Underfull \vbox (badness 10000) has
occurred while \output is active
```

The typeset file is stored as a `dvi` (Device Independent) file.

C.2.3 *Viewing and printing*

Viewing and printing TeX's typeset output are not really part of TeX proper, but they are obviously an important part of your work environment. The DVI printer driver prints the `dvi` files, and the DVI video driver lets you view them on your monitor.

C.2.4 *LaTeX's files*

LaTeX is a *one-pass compiler,* that is, it reads the source file only once for typesetting. As a result, LaTeX must use auxiliary files to store information it generates during a run. For each typesetting run, LaTeX uses the auxiliary files compiled during the *last* typesetting run. This mechanism explains why you have to typeset twice (or more—see Section 12.2) to make sure that changes you have made to the source files are reflected in the typeset document. These auxiliary files have the same base name as the source file; their extensions indicate their types.

The most important auxiliary file, the aux file, contains a great deal of information about the document, most importantly, the data needed for symbolic referencing. Here are two typical entries:

```
\newlabel{struct}{{5}{2}}
\bibcite{eM57a}{4}
```

The first entry indicates that a new symbolic reference was introduced on page 2 of the typeset document in Section 5 using the command

```
\label{struct}
```

The command `\ref{struct}` produces 5, while `\pageref{struct}` yields 2.

The second entry indicates that the bibliographic entry with label `eM57a` has been assigned the number 4, so `\cite{eM57a}` produces [4].

There is an `aux` file for the source file being processed, and another one for each file included in the main file by an `\include` command.

No auxiliary file will be written if the `\nofiles` command is given. The message

```
No auxiliary output files.
```

in the log file reminds you that `\nofiles` is in effect.

The log file contains all the information shown on your monitor during the typesetting. The `dvi` file contains the typeset version of the source file.

There are five auxiliary files that store information for special tasks. They are written only if that special task is invoked by a command and there is no `\nofiles` command. The additional auxiliary files are

`glo` Contains the glossary entries produced by `\glossary` commands. A new file is written only if there is a

```
\makeglossary
```

command in the source file (see Section 11.5).

`idx` Contains the index entries produced by `\index` commands. A new file is written only if there is a

```
\makeindex
```

command in the source file (see Section 11.3).

`lof` Contains the entries used to compile a list of figures. A new file is written only if there is a

```
\listoffigures
```

command in the source file (see Section 6.4.3).

`lot` Contains the entries used to compile a list of tables. A new file is written only if there is a

```
\listoftables
```

command in the source file (see Section 6.4.3).

`toc` Contains the entries used to compile a table of contents. A new file is written only if there is a

```
\tableofcontents
```

command in the source file (see Section 12.2).

For information about the auxiliary files created by BibTeX and *MakeIndex*, see Sections 10.2.4 and 11.3, respectively. Some classes and packages create additional auxiliary files (see Section 14.3.3 for an example).

APPENDIX

D

PostScript fonts

As we mentioned in Section C.1.2, the big news of the last few years was that a consortium (the AMS, Blue Sky Research, and Y&Y) released a free PostScript version of the CM and AMS fonts, so everyone could switch to PostScript fonts. Section D.1 discusses these PostScript fonts.

The Computer Modern fonts were originally "hardwired" into LaTeX. Many users liked LaTeX but disliked Computer Modern, and with the spread of personal computers and PostScript laser printers, it was imperative that PostScript fonts be integrated into LaTeX. In Section D.2, I illustrate how easy it is to use standard PostScript fonts, such as Times, with LaTeX with two examples. Finally, in Section D.3, I show you how to replace the CM and AMS fonts in a LaTeX document with the Lucida Bright fonts.

And now an apology: "PostScript fonts" is the terminology that lay people, like myself, use. The proper terminology is *Adobe Type 1 format fonts.* PostScript has provisions for a wide range of fonts including Type 3 and Type 1 (as well as Type 42 and Type 5, and so on). The Type 3 font category is very general and includes bitmap fonts, grayscaled fonts, and so on. Type 1 fonts are tightly constrained *outline* fonts, which can be accurately rendered at almost any resolution, and have special purpose code that deals only with Type 1 fonts.

D.1 CM, AMS, and EM PostScript Fonts

The CM and AMS fonts are available in PostScript format from the CTAN FTP servers in the directories
`/tex-archive/fonts/amsfonts/ps-type1/`
`/tex-archive/fonts/cm/ps-type1/bluesky/`
on the CTAN Web servers in the directories
`http://ctan.tug.org/tex-archive/fonts/cm/ps-type1/bluesky/`
`http://ctan.tug.org/tex-archive/fonts/amsfonts/ps-type1/`
on the AMS FTP server (`ftp.ams.org`) in the directories
`/pub/tex/psfonts/cm/`
`/pub/tex/psfonts/ams/`
and on the AMS Web server from
`http://www.ams.org/tex/type1-fonts.html`

The advantages of using PostScript fonts include

Size Traditionally, CM and AMS fonts were distributed rasterized as pk fonts; the size of the distribution goes up geometrically as the printer resolution increases. For instance, the AMS fonts as bitmaps at 300 dpi occupy 4.7 MB, at 600 DPI they occupy 8.8 MB. Today, many laser printers are 1200 dpi, and the size of the bitmap fonts would be excessive. In contrast, the PostScript font set occupies less than 1 MB.

Illustrations As we discussed in Section 13.2, you need PostScript fonts to be able to copy formulas from the typeset document to illustrations.

PDF files If you use pk fonts, PDF files can be read easily on your monitor or print well—but not both.

Flexibility Bitmapped fonts are made for one resolution and when printed or displayed at another resolution they look bad; hence a PostScript file using pk fonts must be made for a specific resolution. When sending a PostScript job to a printer or service bureau, you may not know what resolution device will be used.

There is only one disadvantage to using the PostScript fonts: the AMS font set does not include some of the small font sizes required by LaTeX and the AMS packages. There are several remedies:

- If you use an AMS document class, use the `psamsfonts` option of the document class.
- As we discussed in Section 8.5.1, if you use a non-AMS document class with the
  - amsmath package, use the `cmex10` option of the package
  - amsfonts package, use the `psamsfonts` option of the package

  and use the exscale package if necessary.

- At the LaTeX level, use David Carlisle's type1cm package, available from CTAN in the directory
/tex-archive/macros/latex/contrib/supported/type1cm/
- Buy Y&Y's complete AMS font set, which provides the missing fonts.
- Most TeX implementations support virtual fonts; you can provide the missing fonts as virtual fonts. The correction is then made at the Plain TeX level. Gary L. Gray's Macintosh TeX/LaTeX software page
http://www.esm.psu.edu/mac-tex/
contains a number of AMS virtual metrics provided by Arthur Ogawa, Simon Mang Cao, and Uwe Schmock; these virtual metrics can be used for all platforms.

You can buy the European Modern (EM) PostScript font set from Y&Y; it is based on the CM font set but has many more glyphs, including over 90 ready-made accented and composite characters.

D.2 *The Times font and MathTime*

In this section, we step through the process of incorporating the Adobe Times font into a LaTeX document to replace the Computer Modern text fonts, and, optionally, of using the *MathTime* math fonts to replace the Computer Modern math fonts. To do so, we use the PSNFSS packages; see Section 13.1.

Recall from Section 2.6.2 that a document class specifies three standard font families:

- A roman (or serif) font family
- A sans-serif font family
- A typewriter-style font family

The times package (in the PSNFSS distribution) makes Times the roman font family, Helvetica the sans-serif font family, and Courier the typewriter-style font family.

Setting up Times First install the Adobe Times, Helvetica, and Courier PostScript fonts and their TeX font metric files.

Now typeset the `psfonts.ins` file (in the PSNFSS distribution)—using the `LaTeX` format, of course. Doing so will produce style (`sty`) files for the standard PostScript fonts. The Times style file is called times.sty. Copy it into your TeX input directory.

To use the times package, you must have the *font definition* (`fd`) files for the fonts specified. By checking the `times.sty` file, you will see that you need three files for the three fonts: Times, Helvetica, and Courier. In the `times` package these are named `ptm`, `phv`, and `pcr`, respectively; these are the font names in the naming scheme devised by Karl Berry. In `ptm`, `p` stands for the foundry's name (in this case, Adobe), `tm` stands for Times, `hv` for Helvetica, and `cr` for Courier. The corresponding font definition files are named `ot1ptm.fd`, `ot1phv.fd`, and `ot1pcr.fd`, respectively. (`OT1` designates the old TEX font encoding scheme, which is not discussed here.) You can get these files from CTAN (see Section 13.1). Place all these font files in your TEX input directory.

Using Times In the preamble of your document, type

```
\usepackage{times}
```

after the `\documentclass` line. Then Times will become the roman, Helvetica the sans-serif, and Courier the typewriter-style document font family.

That is all there is to it.

Using the times package changes the document font family throughout your document. To switch to Times only occasionally, type

```
{\fontfamily{ptm}\selectfont
phrase}
```

The text preceding and following this construct will not be affected. For example,

```
{\fontfamily{ptm}\selectfont
This text is typeset in the Times font.}
```

will typeset as

This text is typeset in the Times font.

Similarly,

```
\fontfamily{ptm}\selectfont
This text is typeset in the Times font.
\normalfont
```

will also typeset the same phrase in Times. (The `\normalfont` command restores the document font family—see Section 2.6.2.)

Setting up *MathTime* Looking at a mathematical article typeset with the Times text font, you may find that the Computer Modern math symbols look too thin. To more closely match Times (and other PostScript fonts) Michael Spivak modified the CM math symbols, calling these modified fonts *MathTime*. You can purchase the *MathTime* fonts from Y&Y; e-mail: `sales@YandY.com`; Web address: `http://www.YandY.com`.

Install the *MathTime* PostScript fonts and the TEX font metric files for the *MathTime* fonts. From PSNFSS, copy the `mathtime.ins`, `mathtime.dtx` files, and `mtfonts.fdd` into your TEX input directory. Typeset `mathtime.ins` with the `LaTeX` format to produce the necessary `fd` files and the `mathtime.sty` file.

Using *MathTime* If you want to use Times as the document font family and *MathTime* as the default math font, specify

```
\usepackage[LY1]{fontenc}             %specify font encoding
\usepackage[LY1,mtbold]{mathtime}  %switch math fonts
\usepackage{times}                    %switch text fonts
```

in the preamble of your document. With TEXTURES, you should specify `LM1` instead of `LY1`.

The mathtime package has many of options; see its documentation for more information—typeset mathtime.dtx to get it.

D.3 *Lucida Bright fonts*

Another alternative to Computer Modern fonts is *Lucida Bright* for both text and math fonts. You can purchase the Lucida Bright fonts from Y&Y.

Copy `lucidabr.ins`, `lucidabr.dtx`, `lucidabr.fdd`, `lucidabr.yy` into your TeX input directory. Typeset `lucidabr.yy` with the `LaTeX` format, producing the `lucidabr.sty` file and a large number of `fd` files.

Now add the lines

```
\usepackage[LY1]{fontenc}      %specify font encoding
\usepackage[LY1]{lucidabr}    %switch text and math fonts
```

in the preamble of your document. With TEXTURES, you should specify `LM1` rather than `LY1`. The lucidabr package has many options; see its documentation (typeset lucidabr.dtx to get it).

D.4 *More PostScript fonts*

You can obtain PostScript fonts from a wide variety of sources. You will find many free PostScript fonts on CTAN. Table D.1 is a short list of the more prominent commercial vendors.

See also the Web page at `http://www.microsoft.com/typography/` for a lot of useful information and links.

Foundry	URL
Adobe	`http://www.adobe.com/type/`
Agfa/Monotype	`http://www.agfamonotype.com/`
Berthold	`http://www.bertholdtypes.com/`
Bitstream	`http://www.bitstream.com/`
Coniglio	`http://www.conigliotype.com/`
Emigre	`http://www.emigre.com/`
Hoefler	`http://www.typography.com/`
ITC	`http://www.itcfonts.com/`
Linotype	`http://www.linotypelibrary.com/`
Monotype	`http://www.monotype.com/`
P22	`http://www.p22.com/`
Scriptorium	`http://www.ragnarokpress.com/`
Tiro	`http://www.tiro.com/`
URW	`http://www.urwpp.de/home_e.htm`
Vintage	`http://www.vintagetype.com/`
Y&Y	`http://www.yandy.com/products.htm#fonts`

Table D.1: Some type foundries on the World Wide Web.

APPENDIX

E

LaTeX localized

Many of the improvements to LaTeX in recent years have been related to the increased ability to localize LaTeX; that is, to adapt LaTeX for use with languages other than American English. The babel, fontenc, and inputenc packages are the major players, along with new font-encoding schemes, including the T1 encoding. You will find fontenc and inputenc in the `base` directory and babel in the `required` directory of the standard LaTeX distribution (see Section 13.1).

The babel package is described in detail in Chapter 9 of *The LaTeX Companion* [17], and although much has happened since 1994, that description is still quite up-to-date.

If you are interested in using a localized LaTeX, you should turn to the TeX user group for that linguistic group to find out what is available. You should also consult the babel user guide.

At a minimum, a supported language has translated redefinable names (see Table 9.1), and a localized variant of the `\today` command. Two very advanced language adaptations are German and French.

We illustrate the use and installation of the babel package with the German language, which gives you a rich set of features, including

- Allows you to type `"a` for `\"{a}`
- Introduces `"s` for sharp s (eszett)
- Introduces `"ck` for ck-s that becomes k-k when hyphenated

To install babel

1. Start with a system with no TeX fonts installed.
2. Install the EC fonts (from CTAN: `/tex-archive/fonts/ec/`). A complete set of pk fonts is almost 90 MB in size.
3. Rename `hyphen.tex` (in your TeX inputs directory) to, say, `ushyphen.tex`.
4. Get the German hyphenation patterns, `dehypht.tex`, from CTAN's `/tex-archive/languages/hyphenation/` directory and put it in the TeX inputs directory.
5. Put the babel package in your TeX input directory and install it.
6. Modify the `language.dat` file in the babel package to indicate that you want to use German as the primary language.
7. Create a new `LaTeX` format by typesetting `latex.ltx` with `initex`.
8. Typeset the following test file (in the `samples` directory):

```
\documentclass{article}
\usepackage[german]{babel}
\usepackage[T1]{fontenc}

\begin{document}
\section{H"ullenoperatoren}
Es sei $P$ eine teilweise geordnete Menge. Wir
sagen, da"s in $P$ ein \emph{H"ullenoperator}
$\lambda$ erkl"art ist, wenn sich jedem $a \in  P$
ein eindeuting bestimmtes $\lambda(a) \in P$
zuordnen l"a"st, so  da"s die folgenden
Bedingungen erf"ullt sind.
\end{document}
```

If you see the same material shown in Figure E.1, your setup works!

1 Hüllenoperatoren

Es sei P eine teilweise geordnete Menge. Wir sagen, daß in P ein *Hüllenoperator* λ erklärt ist, wenn sich jedem $a \in P$ ein eindeuting bestimmtes $\lambda(a) \in P$ zuordnen läßt, so daß die folgenden Bedingungen erfüllt sind.

Figure E.1: German test for Babel.

APPENDIX

A book document class

To produce an attractive looking book, you should follow the instructions in Chapter 12 (especially, Section 12.5) and choose a well-designed book document class.

By way of an example, in this appendix, we utilize the Springer-Verlag book class, `svsing6.cls`. To produce a book with this document class, you first create a "master document," let us call it `master.tex` (in the `samples` directory; see page 4), which may read as follows:

```
%Master document for svsing6
\documentclass{svsing6}
\usepackage{author}
\makeindex

\begin{document}
\frontmatter
\include{frontmatter}
\tableofcontents
\include{introduction}

\mainmatter
```

```
\include{chapter1}
\include{chapter2}
\include{chapter3}
\include{chapter4}
\include{chapter5}

\appendix
\include{appendix1}
\include{appendix2}

\backmatter
\include{references}
\include{afterword}

\printindex
```

The `author.sty` command file collects the packages and commands utilized by the author. It contains lines like

```
\RequirePackage{amsmath}
\RequirePackage{amssymb}
\RequirePackage{latexsym}
```

to instruct LaTeX to load the named packages.

`frontmatter.tex` will be provided by Springer-Verlag, and it will produce the first four pages of the book. This is followed by `introduction.tex`, the introduction. These pages are numbered with lower case roman numerals (because the `\frontmatter` command was given).

The `\mainmatter` command starts the page numbering from 1, using arabic numerals. `chapter1.tex`, ..., `chapter5.tex` are the five chapters.

The `\appendix` command introduces the appendices, there are two in this example, named `appendix1.tex` and `appendix2.tex`.

Finally, the `\backmatter` command introduces the references, in the document `references.tex`, and the afterword, in the document `afterword.tex`.

To illustrate what such a book document class can do for your book, in this appendix, you find the first four pages of the first chapter and the first page of the bibliography from Gabriel P. Paternain's *Geodesic Flows*, published by Birkhäuser Boston in 1999. These pages illustrate the formatting of

- The first page of a chapter (using the `\chapter` command)
- A section, a subsection, and a definition (using the `\section` and `\subsection` commands and the `definition` proclamation)
- A list (using the `enumerate` environment)
- A lemma with its proof (using the `lemma` proclamation and the `proof` environment)

- The bibliography (using the `thebibliography` environment)

The facing pages show the corresponding source code.

In the `samples` directory (see page 4), you will find the Springer-Verlag book class, `svsing6.cls`, and svsing2e.sty, a package that can be used with LaTeX's standard `book` document class.

1

Introduction to Geodesic Flows

Our aim in this chapter is to introduce the geodesic flow on the tangent bundle of a complete Riemannian manifold from several points of view. Geodesic flows have the remarkable property of being at the intersection of various branches in mathematics; this gives them a rich structure and makes them an exciting subject of research with a long tradition.

In Section 1.1 we define the geodesic flow of a complete Riemannian manifold. We also recall that geodesics can be obtained as solutions of the Euler-Lagrange equation of a Lagrangian given by the kinetic energy. In Section 1.2 we define symplectic and contact manifolds. In Section 1.3 we set up the basic geometry of the tangent bundle: we introduce the connection map, horizontal and vertical subbundles, the Sasaki metric, the symplectic form and the contact form. We describe the main properties of these objects, and we show that the geodesic flow is a Hamiltonian flow and that when we restrict it to the unit sphere bundle of the manifold we then obtain a contact flow. The contact form naturally induces a probability measure that is invariant under the geodesic flow and is called the Liouville measure. In Section 1.4 we describe the canonical symplectic form of the cotangent bundle and, using the musical isomorphisms, we shall describe its relations with the symplectic form defined in Section 1.3. In Section 1.5 we write the differential of the geodesic flow in terms of Jacobi fields. In the last section we define the asymptotic cycle of an invariant probability measure and the stable norm. We show that the asymptotic cycle of the Liouville measure vanishes and that the same holds for the measure of maximal entropy if the latter is unique. Finally we show that the unit

```
\chapter{Introduction to Geodesic Flows}\label{C:Introduction}

Our aim in this  chapter is to introduce the geodesic flow on the
tangent bundle of a complete Riemannian manifold from several
points of view. Geodesic flows have the remarkable property of
being at the intersection of various branches in mathematics;
this gives them a rich structure and makes them an exciting
subject of research with a long tradition.

In Section~\ref{S:Riemannian} we define the geodesic flow of a
complete Riemannian manifold. We also recall that geodesics can
be obtained as solutions of the Euler-Lagrange equation of a
Lagrangian given by the kinetic energy. In
Section~\ref{S:Sym_con} we define symplectic and
contact manifolds. In Section~\ref{S:geometry} we set up the
basic geometry of the tangent bundle: we introduce the
connection map, horizontal and vertical subbundles, the Sasaki
metric, the symplectic form and the contact form. We describe
the main properties of these objects,  and we  show that the
geodesic flow is a Hamiltonian flow and that when we restrict it
to the unit sphere bundle of the manifold we then obtain a
contact flow. The contact form naturally induces a probability
measure that is invariant under the geodesic flow and is called
the Liouville measure. In Section~\ref{S:cotangent_bundle} we
describe the canonical symplectic form  of the cotangent bundle
and,  using the musical isomorphisms, we shall describe its
relations with the symplectic form  defined in
Section~\ref{S:geometry}. In Section~\ref{S:geodesic_flow} we
write the differential of the geodesic  flow in terms of Jacobi
fields. In the last section we define the asymptotic cycle of an
invariant probability measure and the stable norm. We show that
the asymptotic cycle of the Liouville measure vanishes and that
the same holds for the measure of maximal entropy if the latter
is unique. Finally we show that the unit
```

ball of the stable norm coincides with the set of asymptotic cycles of all invariant probability measures.

Chapter 1 of Besse's book [Be], Chapter 3 of Klingenberg's book [Kl1], Chapter II of Sakai's book [Sa] and Chapter IV in Ballmann's lecture notes [Ba] also contain introductions to the geometry of the tangent and unit tangent bundles as well as some basic facts about geodesic flows.

1.1 Geodesic flow of a complete Riemannian manifold

Let M be a complete Riemannian manifold and let $\gamma_{(x,v)}(t)$ be the unique geodesic with initial conditions as follows:

$$\begin{cases} \gamma_{(x,v)}(0) = x; \\ \dot{\gamma}_{(x,v)}(0) = v. \end{cases}$$

Definition 1.1. For a given $t \in \mathbb{R}$, we define a diffeomorphism of the tangent bundle TM

$$\phi_t : TM \to TM,$$

as follows

$$\phi_t(x,v) := \left(\gamma_{(x,v)}(t), \dot{\gamma}_{(x,v)}(t)\right).$$

The family of diffeomorphisms ϕ_t is in fact a *flow*, that is, it satisfies $\phi_{t+s} = \phi_t \circ \phi_s$. This last property is an easy consequence of the uniqueness of the geodesic with respect to the initial conditions. Let SM be the *unit tangent bundle* of M, that is, the subset of TM given by those pairs (x,v) such that v has norm one. Since geodesics travel with constant speed, we see that ϕ_t leaves SM invariant, that is, given $(x,v) \in SM$, for all $t \in \mathbb{R}$ we have that $\phi_t(x,v) \in SM$.

1.1.1 Euler-Lagrange flows

Let $L : TM \to \mathbb{R}$ be a smooth function and let Ω_{xy} be the space

$$\Omega_{xy} := \{u : [0,1] \to M, \text{piecewise differentiable and } u(0) = x, u(1) = y\}.$$

The *action* A of L over a path from x to y is the map,

$$A : \Omega_{xy} \to \mathbb{R}, \quad A(u) := \int_0^1 L(u(t), \dot{u}(t))dt.$$

Let us try to find the critical points or extremals of A. Consider a variation $s \mapsto u_s \in \Omega_{xy}$ with $s \in (-\varepsilon, \varepsilon)$ such that $\frac{d}{ds}A(s)|_{s=0} = 0$. If we set $W(t) := \frac{\partial u_s}{\partial s}(t)|_{s=0}$, then a computation in local coordinates shows that u is a critical point if and only if

```
ball of the stable norm coincides with the set of asymptotic
cycles of all invariant probability measures.

Chapter 1 of Besse's book \cite{Be}, Chapter 3 of Klingenberg's
book \cite{K1}, Chapter II of Sakai's book \cite{Sakai} and
Chapter IV in Ballmann's lecture notes \cite{Ball} also contain
introductions to the geometry of the tangent and unit tangent
bundles as well as some basic facts about geodesic flows.

\section{Geodesic flow of a complete Riemannian
manifold}\label{S:Riemannian}  Let $M$ be a complete Riemannian
manifold and let $\gamma_{(x,v)}(t)$ be the unique geodesic with
initial conditions as follows: \[\left\{\begin{matrix}
\gamma_{(x,v)}(0)=x;\\\dot{\gamma}_{(x,v)}(0)=v.
\end{matrix}\right.\]
\begin{definition}  For a given $t \in \R$, we define a
diffeomorphism of  the tangent bundle $TM$  \[ \phi_t \colon TM
\rightarrow TM, \] as follows \[ \phi_t (x,v)\, :=\,  \left(
\gamma_{(x,v)}(t) , \dot{ \gamma}_{(x,v)}(t) \right). \]
\end{definition}
The family of diffeomorphisms $\phi_{t}$ is in fact a \emph{flow},
that is, it satisfies $\phi_{t+s} = \phi_t \circ \phi_s$. This
last property is an easy consequence of the uniqueness
of the geodesic with respect to the initial conditions. Let $SM$
be the \emph{unit tangent bundle} of $M$, that is, the subset of
$TM$ given by those pairs $(x,v)$ such that $v$ has norm one.
Since geodesics travel with constant speed, we see that
$\phi_{t}$ leaves $SM$ invariant, that is, given $(x,v)\in SM$,
for all $t\in\R$ we have that $\phi_{t}(x,v)\in SM$.

\subsection{Euler-Lagrange flows}\label{S:Euler-Lagrange}
Let $L:TM \rightarrow \R $ be a smooth function and let
$\Omega_{xy}$ be the space \[ \Omega_{xy}\,:=\, \{ u\,:\,[0,1]
\rightarrow M, \mbox{piecewise differentiable and } u(0)=x,
u(1)=y \}.\] The \emph{action} $A$ of $L$ over a path from $x$
to $y$ is the map,  \[ A\colon \Omega_{xy} \rightarrow \R
,\qquad A(u)\,:=\, \int_0^1 L(u(t), \dot{u}(t))\, dt. \]

Let us try to find the critical points or extremals of $A$.
Consider a variation $s \mapsto u_s \in \Omega_{xy}$ with $s \in
( -\varepsilon, \varepsilon )$ such that $\frac{d}{ds}
A(s)|_{s=0} =0$.  If we set
```

$$\int_0^1 \left\{ \frac{\partial L}{\partial x}(u,\dot{u}) - \frac{d}{dt}\frac{\partial L}{\partial v}(u,\dot{u}) \right\} (W)dt = 0.$$

If we assume that this equation is satisfied for all variational vector fields $W(t)$ arising from variations with $u = u_0$, we have

$$\frac{\partial L}{\partial x}(u,\dot{u}) - \frac{d}{dt}\frac{\partial L}{\partial v}(u,\dot{u}) = 0.$$

This is known as the Euler-Lagrange equation.

There is a class of Lagrangians that has received lots of attention in recent years. We shall say that a Lagrangian L is *convex and superlinear* if the following two properties are satisfied.

1. Convexity. We require that $L|_{T_xM} : T_xM \to \mathbb{R}$ has positive definite Hessian for all $x \in M$. This condition is usually known as *Legendre's condition.* In local coordinates this means that

$$\frac{\partial^2 L}{\partial v_i \partial v_j} \text{ is positive definite.}$$

2. Superlinearity. There exists a Riemannian metric such that

$$\lim_{|v|\to+\infty} \frac{L(x,v)}{|v|} = +\infty,$$

uniformly on x.

If M is compact, the extremals of A give rise to a complete flow $\phi_t : TM \to TM$ called the Euler-Lagrange flow of the Lagrangian. A very interesting aspect of the dynamics of the Euler-Lagrange flows is given by those orbits or invariant measures that satisfy some global variational properties. Research on the dynamics of these special orbits and measures goes back to M. Morse and G.A. Hedlund and has reappeared in recent years in the work of J. Mather, trying to generalize to higher dimensions the theory of twist maps on the annulus. See [Mat, Fa] and references therein for an account of this theory.

It is well-known that geodesics can be seen as the solutions of the Euler-Lagrange equation of the following convex and superlinear Lagrangian:

$$L(x,v) := \frac{1}{2} g_x(v,v)$$

where g denotes the Riemannian metric of M.

```
$W(t)\,:=\, \frac{\partial u_s}{\partial s} (t) |_{s=0}$, then a
computation in local coordinates shows that $u$ is a critical
point if and only if \[ \int_0^1 \left\{ \frac{\partial
L}{\partial x} (u, \dot{u}) - \frac{d}{dt} \frac{\partial
L}{\partial v} (u, \dot{u} ) \right\} (W)\, dt = 0 .\] If we
assume that this equation is satisfied for all variational vector
fields $W(t)$ arising from variations with $u= u_0$, we have
\[\frac{\partial L}{\partial x} (u, \dot{u}) - \frac{d}{dt}
\frac{\partial L}{\partial v} (u, \dot{u} ) =0.\]
This is known as the Euler-Lagrange equation.

There is a class of Lagrangians that has received lots of
attention in recent years.  We shall say that a Lagrangian $L$
is \emph{convex and superlinear} if the following two properties
are satisfied.

\begin{enumerate} \item Convexity. We require that $L|_{T_x
M}\colon T_x M \rightarrow \R$ has positive definite Hessian for
all $x\in M$. This condition is usually known as \emph{Legendre's
condition}. In local coordinates this  means that \[
\frac{\partial ^2 L}{\partial v_i \partial v_j}\; \mbox{is
positive definite}.\]

\item Superlinearity. There exists a Riemannian metric such that
\[\lim _{ |v| \rightarrow +\infty} \frac{L(x,v)}{|v|} = +
\infty,\] uniformly on $x$. \end{enumerate}

If $M$ is compact, the extremals of $A$ give rise to a complete
flow $\phi_{t}\colon TM\to TM$ called the Euler-Lagrange flow of
the Lagrangian. A very interesting aspect of the dynamics of the
Euler-Lagrange flows is given by those orbits or invariant
measures that satisfy some global variational properties.
Research on the dynamics of these special orbits and measures
goes back to M. Morse and G.A. Hedlund and has reappeared in
recent years in the work of J. Mather,  trying to generalize to
higher dimensions the theory of twist maps on the annulus. See
\cite{M,Fa} and references therein for an account of this theory.

It is well-known that geodesics can be seen as the solutions of
the Euler-Lagrange equation of the following convex and
superlinear Lagrangian: \[ L(x,v)\,:=\, \frac{1}{2} g_x(v,v),\]
where $g$ denotes the Riemannian metric of $M$
```

1.2 Symplectic and contact manifolds

1.2.1 Symplectic manifolds

Definition 1.2. A 2-form w is said to be *symplectic* if w is:

- closed, $dw = 0$;
- nondegenerate, that is, if $w_p(X, Y) = 0$ for all $Y \in T_pM$ then $X = 0$.

A pair (M, w) of a smooth manifold and a symplectic form is called a *symplectic manifold.*

Remark 1.3. The existence of a symplectic form in a manifold M implies that M is even dimensional.

Definition 1.4. Let (M, w) be a symplectic manifold and $H : M \to \mathbb{R}$ a given C^r function. The vector field X_H determined by the condition

$$w(X_H, Y) = dH(Y) \text{ or equivalently } i_{X_H}w = dH$$

is called the *Hamiltonian vector field* associated with H or the *symplectic gradient* of H. The flow φ_t of the vector field X_H is called the *Hamiltonian flow* of H.

The nondegeneracy of w ensures that X_H exists and that it is a C^{r-1} vector field. In the next lemma we shall see that the Hamiltonian flow of H preserves the sympletic form w. Let us denote by $L_{X_H}w$ the Lie derivative of w with respect to X_H.

Lemma 1.5. $L_{X_H}w = 0$.

Proof. Using Cartan's formula

$$L_{X_H}w = di_{X_H}w + i_{X_H}dw,$$

and the fact that $dw = 0$ and $di_{X_H}w = ddH = 0$, we get $L_{X_H}w = 0$. □

Exercise 1.6. Show that $L_{X_H}w = 0$ if and only if for all $t \in \mathbb{R}$, $\varphi_t^*w = w$, where φ_t is the flow of X_H.

1.2.2 Contact manifolds

Definition 1.7. A 1-form α on a $(2n-1)$-dimensional orientable manifold M is called a *contact form* if the $(2n-1)$-form $\alpha \wedge (d\alpha)^{n-1}$ never vanishes. A pair (M, α) of a smooth odd-dimensional manifold and a contact form is called a *contact manifold.* A *contact flow* is a flow on M that preserves the contact form on M.

```
\section{Symplectic and contact manifolds}\label{S:Sym_con}
\subsection{Symplectic manifolds}\label{S:Symplectic}
\begin{definition}\label{D:symplectic} A $2$-form $w$ is said
to be \emph{symplectic} if $w$ is:
\begin{itemize} \item closed, $dw=0$; \item nondegenerate,
that is,  if $w_{p}(X,Y)=0$, for all
$Y \in T_p M$, then $X=0$. \end{itemize}
A pair $(M,w)$ of a smooth manifold and a symplectic form is
called a \emph{symplectic manifold}.
\end{definition}
\begin{remark} The existence of a symplectic form in a manifold
$M$ implies that $M$ is even dimensional. \end{remark}
\begin{definition}\label{D:Hamiltonian}  Let $(M,w)$ be a
symplectic manifold and $H:M \rightarrow \R$ a given $C^r$
function. The vector field $X_H$ determined by the condition
\[ w(X_H , Y ) = dH(Y) \mbox{ or equivalently } i_{X_H} w = dH
\]  is called the \emph{Hamiltonian vector field} associated
with $H$ or the \emph{symplectic gradient} of $H$. The flow
$\varphi_t$ of the vector field $X_H$ is called the
\emph{Hamiltonian flow} of $H$.
\end{definition}
The nondegeneracy of $w$ ensures that $X_H$ exists and that it
is a $C^{r-1}$ vector field. In the next lemma we shall see
that the Hamiltonian flow of $H$ preserves the sympletic form
$w$. Let us denote by $L_{X_{H}}w$ the Lie derivative of $w$
with respect to $X_{H}$. \begin{lemma} $L_{X_{H}}w=0$.
\end{lemma} \begin{proof} Using Cartan's formula \[ L_{X_H} w =
d i_{X_H} w + i_{X_H} dw, \] and the fact that $dw=0$ and
$di_{X_H}w= ddH =0$,  we get $L_{X_H} w =0$.
\end{proof}
\begin{xca}\label{1-One}
 Show that $L_{X_{H}}w=0$ if and only if for all $t\in\R$,
$\varphi_{t}^{*}w=w$, where $\varphi_{t}$ is the flow of
$X_{H}$. \end{xca} \subsection{Contact
manifolds}\label{S:contact}  \begin{definition}  A $1$-form
$\alpha$ on a $(2n-1)$-dimensional orientable manifold $M$ is
called a \emph{contact form} if the $(2n-1)$-form $\alpha
\wedge (d \alpha )^{n-1}$ never vanishes. A pair $(M, \alpha )$
of a smooth odd-dimensional manifold and a contact form is
called a \emph{contact manifold}.  A \emph{contact flow} is a
flow on $M$ that preserves the contact form on $M$.
\end{definition}
```

References

[An] D.V. Anosov, *Geodesic flows on closed manifolds of negative curvature,* Proc. Steklov Inst. Math. **90** (1967), 23–29.

[Ba1] I. Babenko, *Analytic properties of Poincaré series of a loop space,* (Russian) Mat. Zametki **27** (1980), 751–765.

[Ba2] I. Babenko, *Topological entropy of geodesic flows on simply connected manifolds, and related problems,* (Russian) Izv. Ross. Akad. Nauk. Ser. Mat. **61** (1997), 57–74.

[BBB] W. Ballmann, M. Brin, K. Burns, *On surfaces without conjugate points,* J. Diff. Geom. **25** (1987), 249–273.

[Ba] W. Ballmann, *Lectures on spaces of nonpositive curvature,* with an appendix by Misha Brin. DMV Seminar, 25, Birkhäuser, Basel, 1995.

[BGS] W. Ballmann, M. Gromov, M. Schroeder, *Manifolds of nonpositive curvature,* Progress in Mathematics, 61, Birkhäuser Boston, Cambridge, MA, 1985.

[Ban] V. Bangert, *Minimal geodesics,* Ergod. Th. and Dynam. Sys. **10** (1989), 263–286.

[BB] M. Berger, R. Bott, *Sur les variétés à courbure strictement positive,* Topology **1** (1962), 302–311.

```
\begin{thebibliography}{DGMS}

\bibitem[An]{A}
D.V. Anosov, \emph{Geodesic flows on closed manifolds of
negative curvature}, Proc. Steklov Inst. Math. \textbf{90}
(1967), 23--29.

\bibitem[Ba1]{Ba1}
I. Babenko, \emph{Analytic properties of Poincar\'e
series of a loop space}, (Russian) Mat. Zametki \textbf{27}
(1980), 751--765.

\bibitem[Ba2]{Ba}
I. Babenko, \emph{Topological entropy of geodesic flows
on simply connected manifolds, and related problems}, (Russian)
Izv. Ross. Akad. Nauk. Ser. Mat. \textbf{61} (1997),  57--74.

\bibitem[BBB]{BBB}
W. Ballmann, M. Brin, K.Burns,
\emph{On surfaces without conjugate points},
J. Diff. Geom.  \textbf{25} (1987),  249--273.

\bibitem[Ba]{Ball}
W. Ballmann,
\emph{Lectures on spaces of nonpositive curvature}, with an
appendix by Misha Brin.  DMV Seminar, 25, Birkh\"auser,
Basel, 1995.

\bibitem[BGS]{BGS}
W. Ballmann, M. Gromov, M. Schroeder,
\emph{Manifolds of nonpositive curvature}, Progress in
Mathematics, 61,  Birkh\"auser Boston,  Cambridge, MA, 1985.

\bibitem[Ban]{Ban}
V. Bangert,
\emph{Minimal geodesics},
Ergod. Th. and Dynam. Sys. \textbf{10} (1989), 263--286.

\bibitem[BB]{BB}
M. Berger, R. Bott,
\emph{Sur les vari\'et\'es \`a courbure strictement positive},
Topology \textbf{1} (1962), 302--311.
```

APPENDIX

G

Conversions

If you want to do a conversion, chances are that you have a LaTeX document and you want to convert it to use the `amsart` document class. You can do so in two steps: First, add the amsmath package as described in Section G.2.1, then use your AMS article template—created in Section 8.4—to complete the conversion (see Section G.3.1).

Theoretically, however, there are dozens of possible conversions. We group them into three sections.

Section G.1 discusses how to convert documents to LaTeX. For converting from

1. Plain TeX, see Section G.1.1
2. LaTeX 2.09, see Section G.1.2

You may want to convert to LaTeX utilizing the AMS packages (version 2.0). For converting

1. A LaTeX document, see Section G.2.1
2. An AMS-TeX document, see Section G.2.2
3. A document using version 1.2 of the AMS packages, see Section G.2.3

Finally, in Section G.3, we discuss how to convert a document to use version 2.0 of an AMS document class. To convert from

1. A LaTeX document, see Section G.3.1
2. An AMS-LaTeX 1.1 document, see Section G.3.2

G.1 Converting to LaTeX

You may want to convert to LaTeX from Plain TeX or from LaTeX 2.09.

G.1.1 Converting Plain TeX to LaTeX

To convert a document from Plain TeX,

- Watch out for any commands listed in Table G.1. Replace them with their LaTeX equivalents.
- Copy your personalized template file (see Section 1.8), save it under a new name, and enter the appropriate information for the new document. Then paste your TeX document into the `document` environment of the new file.
- Replace TeX's displayed-math delimiters (`$$`) with `\[` and `\]`.
- Retype all the sectioning titles as discussed in Section 1.9.2, and add any cross-references.
- Retype your bibliography as shown in Section 1.9.4; adding `\cite` commands where necessary.
- Define and invoke any proclamations as described in Section 3.4.
- Convert tables to `tabular` form.

Using TeX code in LaTeX

Nearly all document and page design problems are addressed by LaTeX itself or by a package. Therefore, mixing TeX and LaTeX code is seldom necessary, and requires a deep understanding of the underlying code. Avoid using TeX code in LaTeX unless you have mastered the internals of both languages.

There are a number of reasons why a Plain TeX command may not work as expected in LaTeX:

- LaTeX rewrites TeX's output routines; that is, the way that paragraphs and pages are formatted. Avoid using any TeX command that directly affects output (see Chapter 15 of Donald E. Knuth's *The TeXbook* [34]).
- LaTeX provides a number of environments that make some TeX commands obsolete ; `tabbing` and `center` are two examples.
- A number of TeX commands that change the font size are not defined in LaTeX.
- Some TeX commands change parameters that are also used by LaTeX. For instance, using the `\hangindent` command within a LaTeX list environment will change the shape of the list.

\+	\folio	\pageinsert
\advancepageno	\footline	\pageno
\beginsection	\footstrut	\plainoutput
\bye	\headline	\settabs
\centering	\leqalignno	\sevenbf
\cleartabs	\line	\seveni
\dosupereject	\magnification	\sevensy
\endinsert	\makefootline	\tabalign
\end	\makeheadline	\tabsdone
\eqalignno	\midinsert	\tabset
\eqalign	\nopagenumbers	\tabs
\fivebf	\normalbottom	\teni
\fivei	\oldstyle	\topinsert
\fiverm	\pagebody	\topins
\fivesy	\pagecontents	\vfootnote

Table G.1: TeX commands to avoid using in LaTeX documents.

Table G.1 provides a short list of Plain TeX commands to avoid.

Ⓐ The amsmath package strongly discourages the use of TeX's generalized fraction commands; namely,

```
\above  \abovewithdelims
\atop   \atopwithdelims
\over   \overwithdelims
```

G.1.2 Converting LaTeX 2.09 to LaTeX

In the preamble of your document, you must change the `\documentstyle` command to `\documentclass`. Most of the document style options have become packages that are loaded with the `\usepackage` command. You may change any two-letter font commands (see Section 2.6.9) to their LaTeX equivalents, but doing so is not really necessary (see Section 2.6).

In some cases no conversion is needed at all: LaTeX can typeset many LaTeX 2.09 documents in compatibility mode. If you plan to update your file or plan to share it with others, however, I recommend that you take the time to update it to LaTeX.

LaTeX symbols

The latexsym package defines 11 math symbols that were once part of LaTeX 2.09. To use any of these symbols, you will have to load the latexsym package. The only frequently used symbol in this set is `\Box`, which some writers use as the end-of-proof symbol. You will find these 11 symbols in the tables in Appendix A with Source latexsym.

G.2 Converting to LaTeX with the AMS packages

If you are starting with a Plain TeX or LaTeX 2.09 document, first convert it to LaTeX, as described in Section G.1, then go on to Section G.2.1.

If you are starting with an AMS-TeX document, do the conversion in Section G.2.2.

G.2.1 Using the AMS packages in a LaTeX document

There are only a few adjustments you need to make when using the AMS packages.

To convert a LaTeX document to use the amsmath package, simply add the lines

```
\usepackage{amsmath}
```

after the `\documentclass` line in the preamble of the document. Typically, the LaTeX document will typeset with no change in the typeset result. There is one minor consideration: LaTeX allows page breaks in multiline math environments, whereas the amsmath package prohibits them by default. If you add the line

```
\allowdisplaybreaks[1]
```

in the preamble of your document, the amsmath package will allow page breaks as LaTeX does.

Make use of the many features of the AMS packages in typesetting math. In particular, redesign, as necessary, any multiline formulas using the multiline math environments provided by the amsmath package—you should change any LaTeX `eqnarray` math environments to an appropriate AMS multiline math environments.

G.2.2 Converting from AMS-TeX

Although the amsmath package is essentially AMS-TeX recoded for use with LaTeX, there are a number of differences. These differences seldom cause problems since most mistakes are caught by LaTeX during typesetting.

The major differences are

- AMS-TeX uses pairs of commands of the form

  `\command` and `\endcommand`

  to delimit environments; for instance,

```
\document  and  \enddocument
\proclaim  and  \endproclaim
```

LaTeX uses `\begin{name}` and `\end{name}` to delimit environments.

- Some AMS-TeX commands
  - were dropped because there were LaTeX commands that accomplished the same task.
  - became optional parameters of packages or commands.
  - were renamed because there were already LaTeX commands using those names.
- There are no bibliographic formatting commands in LaTeX.

Here are the steps to take when converting a document from AMS-TeX:

1. Take a personalized template (see Section 1.8); save it under a new name, and type in the appropriate information. Then copy the entire AMS-TeX article from `\document` to `\enddocument` and paste it in the body of your new document.
2. Replace the AMS-TeX displayed-math delimiters (`$$`) by `\[` and `\]`.
3. Look for AMS-TeX commands that start with `\end`. Change command pairs to the corresponding LaTeX environments. In particular, be sure to rewrite each proclamation as an environment.
4. Retype your bibliography. Change the `\cite` commands to reference the labels you specify.
5. Rewrite any user-defined commands. Notice the change in syntax: `\define` and `\redefine` have become `\newcommand` and `\renewcommand`.

If your document is long, first create an appropriate master document for it (see Section 12.3.2 and Appendix F), and then proceed to step 1.

A number of AMS-TeX commands that affect the style of the whole document have become document class or amsmath package options (two were dropped). These commands are listed in Table G.2.

The AMS-TeX commands listed in Table G.3 may also cause some difficulties if you have used them in the document.

G.2.3 *Converting from version 1.2 of the AMS packages*

Converting a document that uses version 1.2 of the amsmath packages to version 2.0 requires almost no changes. Some errors in a version 1.2 document were not caught by version 1.2 of amsmath, but will be caught by version 2.0. For example,

```
\[
  \begin{align*}
    ...
  \end{align*}
\]
```

$\mathcal{A}\mathcal{M}\mathcal{S}$-TEX Command	AMS Package Equivalent
`\CenteredTagsOnSplits`	`centertags` document class option
`\LimitsOnInts`	`intlimits` amsmath option
`\LimitsOnNames`	`namelimits` amsmath option
`\LimitsOnSums`	`sumlimits` amsmath option
`\NoLimitsOnInts`	`nointlimits` amsmath option
`\NoLimitsOnNames`	`nonamelimits` amsmath option
`\NoLimitsOnSums`	`nosumlimits` amsmath option
`\TagsAsMath`	dropped
`\TagsAsText`	dropped
`\TagsOnLeft`	`leqno` document class option
`\TagsOnRight`	`reqno` document class option
`\TopOrBottomTagsOnSplits`	`tbtags` document class option

Table G.2: AMS package equivalents of $\mathcal{A}\mathcal{M}\mathcal{S}$-TEX style commands.

was accepted by version 1.2, but version 2.0 gives the error message

```
! Package amsmath Error: Erroneous nesting of equation structures;
(amsmath)                trying to recover with 'aligned'.
```

In version 1.2 of amsmath you had to use the capitalized versions of the math accent commands (`\Acute`, `\Bar`, `\Breve`, `\Check`, `\Dot`, `\Ddot`, `\Grave`, `\Hat`, `\Tilde`, and `\Vec`), for double accents to work properly. Version 2.0 of amsmath no longer requires you to use the capitalized commands; however, for compatibility, the capitalized versions are still available.

G.3 Converting to an AMS document class

If you have a LaTeX article and the journal you submit it to requires an `amsart` submission, you will have to perform the conversion in Section G.3.1. Finally, I describe how to convert from version 1.1 of $\mathcal{A}\mathcal{M}\mathcal{S}$-LaTeX in Section G.3.2.

G.3.1 Converting from LaTeX

To convert a document to use a version 2.0 AMS document class, first convert it to a LaTeX document using the AMS packages as described in Section G.2.1. Then convert the top matter. For an article, this conversion becomes easy if you utilize the template file you created in Section 8.4 by customizing `amsart.tpl`.

To convert a LaTeX document to use an AMS document class (along with amssymb and latexsym), do the following steps:

AMS-TeX Command	AMS Packages	
	Status	Workaround
`\:`	Conflict	Renamed; use `\colon`
`\adjustfootnotemark`	Dropped	Reset the counter `footnote`
`\and`	Conflict	Renamed; use `\And`
`\boldkey` (math style change)	Dropped	Use `\boldsymbol`
`\botsmash`	Dropped	Use the optional parameter `b` of `\smash`
`\caption`	Changed	Use the `figure` environment and the `\caption` command
`\captionwidth`	Dropped	Use the `figure` environment, the `\caption` command, and the `\captionindent` length command
`\cite`	Changed	Use new syntax
`\displaybreak`	Trap	Place it before `\\`
`\dsize` (math size change)	Dropped	Use `\displaystyle`
`\foldedtext`	Dropped	Use `\parbox`
`\hdotsfor`	Changed	Use new syntax
`\innerhdotsfor`	Dropped	
`\italic` (math style change)	Dropped	Use `\mathit`
`\midspace`	Dropped	Use the `figure` environment
`\nopagebreak` in multiline math environments	Dropped	
`\pretend`...`\haswidth`	Dropped	Pad the label with blanks
`\roman` (math style change)	Conflict	Use `\mathrm`
`\slanted` (math style change)	Dropped	Use `\mathsl`
`\ssize` (math size change)	Dropped	Use `\scriptstyle`
`\sssize` (math size change)	Dropped	Use `\scriptscriptstyle`
`\spacehdotsfor`	Dropped	Use the optional parameter of `\hdotsfor`
`\spaceinnerhdotsfor`	Dropped	Use the optional parameter of `\hdotsfor`
`\spreadlines`	Dropped	
`\thickfrac`	Dropped	Use the `\genfrac` command
`\thickfracwithdelims`	Dropped	Use the `\genfrac` command
`\topsmash`	Dropped	Use the optional parameter `t` of `\smash`
`\topspace`	Dropped	Use the `figure` environment
`\tsize` (math size change)	Dropped	Use `\textstyle`
`\vspace` in multiline math environments	Dropped	Use the optional argument of the `\\` command

Table G.3: AMS-TeX commands to avoid when using the AMS packages.

1. Take your personalized template (see Section 8.4), save it under a new name, and enter the article information. Paste the contents of the `document` environment of your LaTeX article into the `document` environment of your new file.
2. Define and invoke any declarations using the forms described in Section 3.4.
3. Do not use a LaTeX bibliographic style if you use an AMS document class; use an AMS bibliographic style instead.

G.3.2 Converting from AMS-LaTeX, version 1.1

Despite the dramatic changes behind the scenes, you will have to change very little to make an AMS-LaTeX 1.1 document work with an AMS document class. The changes you will have to make include

- The `\documentstyle` command must be changed to `\documentclass` in the preamble.
- Most of the document-style options have become packages, and should be loaded with the `\usepackage` command. See Sections 8.5 and 12.1.3 for information about the options of the AMS document classes.
- The aligned math environments have been redesigned. You should replace any
  - `xalignat` environments with `align`
  - `xxalignat` environments with `flalign`

  The `align` and `flalign` environments do not require an argument to specify the number of columns (see Section 5.5).
- `@` is no longer a special character—typing `@` yields @ (make sure that you replace `@@` by `@` in the `\email` command in the top matter of the document). As a result, the `@-` command had to be renamed (it is now `\nobreakdash`—see Section 2.4.9) and the `@>>>` and `@<<<` arrow commands can only be used in commutative diagrams (elsewhere, use the `\xleftarrow` and `\xrightarrow` commands; see Section 4.10.3).
- There are additional commands for changing font sizes in version 2.0. You may want to change `\small` to `\Small`, `\tiny` to `\Tiny`, and `\large` to `\Large` (see Section 8.1.1).
- The `\bold` command has been renamed `\mathbf` (see Section 4.13.3).
- The commands

  `\newsymbol`, `\frak`, and `\Bbb`

  have been renamed to

  `\DeclareMathSymbol`, `\mathfrak`, and `\mathbb`

  respectively. They are provided by the amsfonts package, which is automatically loaded by amssymb.

- The following eight rarely used commands have been moved to the amsxtra package:

`\accentedsymbol`	`\spdot`	`\sphat`
`\spbreve`	`\spddot`	`\sptilde`
`\spcheck`	`\spdddot`	

  See Section 4.9 for information about these commands. If you need to use any of them, add the line

```
\usepackage{amsxtra}
```

  to the preamble of your document.
- `\fracwithdelims` has been removed. Use the `\genfrac` command (see Section 4.16) to rewrite constructs using the `\fracwithdelims` command.
- `\lcfrac` and `\rcfrac` are now options of the `\cfrac` command: Replace
  - `\lcfrac` with `\cfrac[l]`
  - `\rcfrac` with `\cfrac[r]`

  (see Section 4.16).
- The functionality of the multiline subscript and superscript environments, `Sb` and `Sp`, has been taken over by the `\substack` command (see Section 4.8.1).
- The environments `pf` and `pf*` have been replaced by the `proof` environment.
- The names of most font commands have changed; you may wish to update any font commands that appear in your document. If you only use the CM fonts, however, there is no hurry; the old commands should continue to work.

APPENDIX

Final word

In this final appendix, I will outline some of the material I did not discuss, and suggest some additional reading to learn more about LaTeX, typesetting, and writing.

H.1 What was left out?

The mission statement in the introduction stated that my goal for this book was to provide you with a good foundation in LaTeX and the AMS packages, and that we would not cover programming or visual design. As a result, I have omitted a great deal of material.

H.1.1 LaTeX omissions

LaTeX has some additional features that I have not discussed in this book:

1. The `picture` environment allows you to draw simple pictures with lines and circles.
2. The `array`, `tabular`, and `tabbing` environments have a number of additional features.

3. LaTeX makes the style parameters of a document and of most LaTeX constructs available to the user for modification. Very few of these parameters have been mentioned in this book.
4. Low-level NFSS commands provide finer control over fonts.

The following are some pointers to additional information on these topics:

1. Drawing with the `picture` environment has the advantage of portability. This environment is described in Leslie Lamport's *LaTeX: A Document Preparation System* [39]; many extensions are discussed in Chapter 10 of *The LaTeX Companion* [17]. However, I believe that the best approach is to use a drawing application that can save your illustrations in EPS format so that you can include them in your document using the graphics package (see Section 6.4.3).
2. The `tabbing`, `tabular`, and `array` environments—and their extensions—are described in detail in Leslie Lamport's *LaTeX: A Document Preparation System* [39] and Chapter 5 of *The LaTeX Companion* [17].
3. The style parameters for LaTeX are set by the document class. When a publisher changes the document class loaded by your document, the style parameters are changed to its specifications. If you explicitly change style parameters in your document, a publisher will have trouble getting your source file to conform to their publishing style. If you must change any basic style parameters, be sure to explain what you did with comments.
4. There are two types of commands defined in the NFSS: high-level and low-level commands. The latter are, by and large, meant for style designers and package writers. Nevertheless, anyone who wants to use fonts other than Computer Modern (the default) would do well to read Chapters 7 and 11 of *The LaTeX Companion* [17].

   Low-level NFSS commands are briefly mentioned in Section 2.6.10 and are used in Appendix D.

H.1.2 *TeX omissions*

Almost all discussion of Plain TeX was omitted from this book. TeX is a powerful programming language, allowing you to design any page layout or formula. Remember, however, that to change any design feature, you should be knowledgeable not only about TeX, but also about document design. Also keep in mind that making such changes may make it difficult or impossible for a publisher to make your document conform to its own specifications.

H.2 *Further reading*

Much documentation is included with the LaTeX and the AMS distributions; many third-party packages are also well documented. You will also find a great deal of documentation on CTAN.

As you have no doubt noticed, there are many references to *The LaTeX Companion* [17] in this book; while it is not a beginner's book, it is indispensable for advanced LaTeX users with special needs not served by existing document classes and packages. It is also the best overview of more than a hundred important packages. For package writers and students of NFSS, *The LaTeX Companion* [17] is *the* basic textbook. For graphics work, we now have *The LaTeX Graphics Companion* [18]; and on Web publishing *The LaTeX Web Companion* [19]. Consult these definitive books if your work requires them.

Learning TeX is a bit more complicated than learning LaTeX. You may want to start with Wynter Snow's *TeX for the Beginner* [55]. It introduces many of TeX's basic concepts in a very relaxed style with many examples; the notes on LaTeX make the book especially useful, and the author gives many examples of writing macros. The use of TeX as a programming language is not discussed.

Raymond Seroul and Silvio Levy's *A Beginner's Book of TeX* [54] is another good introduction; this book also includes a chapter on TeX programming. Donald E. Knuth's *The TeXbook* [34] provides an easy introduction to TeX, as long as you avoid the difficult parts marked by dangerous bend signs. Paul W. Abrahams, Karl Berry, and Kathryn A. Hargreaves' *TeX for the Impatient* [1] explains many TeX commands, grouped by topic. This book has a very useful, nonsequential approach. Finally, Victor Eijkhout's *TeX by Topic: A TeXnician's Reference* [16] is an excellent reference book on TeX, mainly for experts. For many tutorial examples, see the articles and columns in *TUGboat* (see Section 13.4).

For advice to authors of mathematical articles and books, see *Mathematics into Type. Updated edition* [58] by Ellen Swanson (updated by Arlene Ann O'Sean and Antoinette Tingley Schleyer); you may find it interesting to see how many of the rules in Swanson's book have been incorporated into LaTeX. The definitive book on style (in North America) is *The Chicago Manual of Style* [12]. Two other views on copy editing are presented in Judith Butcher's *Copy Editing: The Cambridge Handbook* [10] and *Hart's Rules for Compositors and Readers at the University Press, Oxford* by Horace Hart [32]. The special problems of writing about math and computer science are admirably dissected in Lyn Dupré's *BUGS in Writing: A Guide to Debugging Your Prose* [15]. Her advice is indispensable for anyone doing nonfiction writing.

Most people who write math have little or no background in typography, the art of printing with type. But when you become a typesetter, it can be useful to learn a little bit about typography. I would highly recommend Robert Bringhurst's *The Elements of Typographic Style* [9]. See also Ruari McLean's *The Thames and Hudson Manual of Typography* [40] and Alison Black's *Typefaces for Desktop Publishing: A User Guide* [8].

Harley Hahn's *A Student's Guide to Unix* [31] provides an excellent introduction to UNIX; and Kiersten Conner and Ed Krol's *Whole Internet: The Next Generation* [13] is a good first book on the Internet.

Bibliography

[1] Paul W. Abrahams, Karl Berry, and Kathryn A. Hargreaves, *TeX for the Impatient.* Addison-Wesley, Reading, MA, 1990.

[2] Adobe Systems, *PostScript Language Reference Manual.* Third edition. Addison-Wesley, Reading, MA, 1999.

[3] Adobe Systems, *Portable Document Format Reference Manual.* Addison-Wesley, Reading, MA, 1993.

[4] Adobe Systems, *Adobe Acrobat 4.0 Classroom in a Book.* Adobe Press, 1999.

[5] American Mathematical Society, *AMS-LaTeX, Version 1.1—User's Guide.* Providence, RI, 1991.

[6] ———, *AMSFonts, Version* 2.2 *User's Guide.* Providence, RI, 1997.

[7] ———, *User's guide for the* amsmath *package* (*version* 2.0). Providence, RI, 1999.

[8] Alison Black, *Typefaces for Desktop Publishing: A User Guide.* Architecture Design and Technology Press, London, 1990.

[9] Robert Bringhurst, *The Elements of Typographic Style.* Second edition. Point Roberts, WA: Hartley & Marks, 1996.

[10] Judith Butcher, *Copy Editing: The Cambridge Handbook.* Second edition. Cambridge University Press, London, 1981.

[11] Pehong Chen and Michael A. Harrison, *Index preparation and processing.* Software Practice and Experience **19** (9) (1988), 897–915

[12] *The Chicago Manual of Style.* 14th edition. University of Chicago Press, Chicago, 1993.

[13] Kiersten Conner and Ed Krol, *Whole Internet: The Next Generation.* Third edition. O'Reilly & Associates, Sebastopol, CA, 1999.

[14] Michael Doob, *TeX Starting from* 1. Springer-Verlag New York, 1993.

[15] Lyn Dupré, *BUGS in Writing. A Guide to Debugging Your Prose.* Revised edition. Addison-Wesley, Reading, MA, 1998.

[16] Victor Eijkhout, *TEX by Topic: A TEXnician's Reference.* Addison-Wesley, Reading, MA, 1991.

[17] Michel Goossens, Frank Mittelbach, and Alexander Samarin, *The LATEX Companion.* Addison-Wesley, Reading, MA, 1994.

[18] Michel Goossens, Sebastian Rahtz, and Frank Mittelbach, *The LATEX Graphics Companion.* Addison-Wesley, Reading, MA, 1997.

[19] Michel Goossens and Sebastian Rahtz (with Eitan Gurari, Ross Moore, and Robert Sutor), *The LATEX Web Companion: Integrating TEX, HTML and XML.* Addison-Wesley, Reading, MA, 1999.

[20] George Grätzer, *Math into TEX: A Simple Introduction to AMS-LATEX.* Birkhäuser Boston, 1993.

[21] ———, *AMS-LATEX.* Notices Amer. Math. Soc. **40** (1993), 148–150.

[22] ———, *Advances in TEX implementations. I. PostScript fonts.* Notices Amer. Math. Soc. **40** (1993), 834–838.

[23] ———, *Advances in TEX implementations. II. Integrated environments.* Notices Amer. Math. Soc. **41** (1994), 106–111.

[24] ———, *Advances in TEX implementations. III. A new version of LATEX, finally.* Notices Amer. Math. Soc. **41** (1994), 611–615.

[25] ———, *Advances in TEX. IV. Header and footer control in LATEX.* Notices Amer. Math. Soc. **41** (1994), 772–777.

[26] ———, *Advances in TEX. V. Using text fonts in the new standard LATEX.* Notices Amer. Math. Soc. **41** (1994), 927–929.

[27] ———, *Advances in TEX. VI. Using math fonts in the new standard LATEX.* Notices Amer. Math. Soc. **41** (1994), 1164–1165.

[28] ———, *Math into LATEX: An Introduction to LATEX and AMS-LATEX.* Birkhäuser Boston, 1996. Second printing 1998.

[29] ———, *General Lattice Theory.* Second Edition. Birkhäuser Verlag, Basel, 1998. xix+663 pp.

[30] ———, *First Steps in LATEX.* Birkhäuser Boston, Springer-Verlag New York, 1999.

[31] Harley Hahn, *Harley Hahn's Student's Guide to Unix.* Second edition. McGraw-Hill, New York, 1993.

[32] Horace Hart, *Hart's Rules For Compositors and Readers at the University Press, Oxford.* Oxford University Press, Oxford, 1991.

[33] Donald E. Knuth, *The Art of Computer Programming.* Volumes 1–3. Addison-Wesley, Reading, MA, 1968–1998.

[34] Donald E. Knuth, *The TEXbook*. Computers and Typesetting. Vol. A. Addison-Wesley, Reading, MA, 1984, 1990.

[35] ———, *TEX: The Program*. Computers and Typesetting. Vol. B. Addison-Wesley, Reading, MA, 1986.

[36] ———, *The Metafontbook*. Computers and Typesetting. Vol. C. Addison-Wesley, Reading, MA, 1986.

[37] ———, *METAFONT: The Program*. Computers and Typesetting. Vol. D. Addison-Wesley, Reading, MA, 1986.

[38] ———, *Computer Modern Typefaces*. Computers and Typesetting. Vol. E. Addison-Wesley, Reading, MA, 1987.

[39] Leslie Lamport, *LATEX: A Document Preparation System*. Second edition. Addison-Wesley, Reading, MA, 1994.

[40] Ruari McLean, *The Thames and Hudson Manual of Typography*. Thames and Hudson, London, 1980.

[41] Thomas Merz, *Web Publishing with Acrobat PDF*. Springer-Verlag New York, 1998.

[42] Robert Miner and Jeff Schaefer, *Gentle Introduction to MathML 1.0*. `http://www.webeq.com/mathml/gitmml/`

[43] Frank Mittelbach, *An extension of the LATEX theorem environment*. *TUGboat* **10** (1989), 416–426.

[44] Frank Mittelbach and Chris Rowley, *LATEX 2.09 → LATEX3*. *TUGboat*, **13** (1) (1992), 96–101.

[45] ———, *LATEX 2_ε—A new version of LATEX*. TEX and TUG NEWS, **2** (4) (1993), 10–11.

[46] ———, *The LATEX3 project*. Euromath Bulletin, **1** (1994), 117–125.

[47] ———, *LATEX3 in '93*. TEX and TUG NEWS, **3** (1) (1994), 7–11.

[48] Frank Mittelbach and Rainer Schöpf, *The new font family selection—user interface to standard LATEX*. *TUGboat* **11** (1990), 297–305.

[49] Chuck Musciano, Bill Kennedy, Mike Loukides (Editor), *HTML: The Definitive Guide*. Third edition. O'Reilly & Associates, Sebastopol, CA, 1998.

[50] Ted Padova, *Acrobat PDF Bible*. IDG Books, Foster City, CA, 1998.

[51] Oren Patashnik, *BIBTEXing*. Document in the BIBTEX distribution.

[52] ———, *BIBTEX 1.0*. *TUGboat* **15** (1994), 269–273.

[53] Rainer Schöpf, *A new implementation of the LATEX* `verbatim` *and* `verbatim*` *environments*. *TUGboat* **11** (1990), 284–296.

[54] Raymond Seroul and Silvio Levy, *A Beginner's Book of TEX*. Springer-Verlag New York, 1991.

[55] Wynter Snow, *TEX for the Beginner*. Addison-Wesley, Reading, MA, 1992.

[56] W3C's Math Home Page, *Mathematical Markup Language (MathML)*. `http://www.w3.org/Math/`

[57] Michael Spivak, *The Joy of TEX*. Second edition. American Mathematical Society, Providence, RI, 1990.

[58] Ellen Swanson, *Mathematics into Type. Updated edition.* Updated by Arlene Ann O'Sean and Antoinette Tingley Schleyer. American Mathematical Society, Providence, RI, 1999.

[59] Ed Tittel and Natanya Pitts, *HTML4 for Dummies.* Second edition. IDG Books, Foster City, CA, 1999.

[60] Gabriel Valiente Feruglio, *Typesetting commutative diagrams. TUGboat* **15** (1994), 466–484.

Index

The Ⓐ symbol indicates an AMS enhancement to LaTeX; *italic* numbers indicate figures or tables.